To
Janet Sabrie Ley
Our dear daughter
From Mother.

WALLACE CLEMENT SABINE

A Study in Achievement

By WILLIAM DANA ORCUTT

———

Novels

> THE MOTH
> THE SPELL
> THE LEVER
> THE BALANCE
> THE BACHELORS
> ROBERT CAVELIER
> CHANGING PATTERNS
> THE FLOWER OF DESTINY
> DAGGER AND JEWELS:
> > *The Gorgeous Adventures of Benvenuto Cellini*

Books on Books

> THE BOOK IN ITALY
> THE KINGDOM OF BOOKS
> THE MAGIC OF THE BOOK
> MASTER MAKERS OF THE BOOK
> IN QUEST OF THE PERFECT BOOK

Biography and History

> WALLACE CLEMENT SABINE:
> > *A Study in Achievement*
> BURROWS OF MICHIGAN
> > *and the Republican Party*
> GOOD OLD DORCHESTER:
> > *A Narrative History of the Town*

Other Volumes

> THE PRINCESS KALLISTO
> THE WRITER'S DESK BOOK
> THE AUTHOR'S DESK BOOK
> THE DESK REFERENCE BOOK
> THE MADONNA OF SACRIFICE

Wallace Clement Sabine
in 1906 [æt. 38]

WALLACE CLEMENT SABINE

A STUDY IN ACHIEVEMENT

By

WILLIAM DANA ORCUTT

———

PRIVATELY PRINTED BY THE
PLIMPTON PRESS, NORWOOD, MASSACHUSETTS
MCMXXXIII

———

THE PLIMPTON PRESS · NORWOOD · MASSACHUSETTS · U · S · A ·

To HARVARD UNIVERSITY

and

To WALLACE SABINE'S STUDENTS

THIS VOLUME IS DEDICATED

————————

PREFACE

THE LIFE of Wallace Sabine embraces the fundamental history of a new science and the romantic story of its discovery. What Morse did for the Telegraph, what Edison did for the Electric Light, what Alexander Bell did for the Telephone, what Marconi did for the Wireless — Sabine did for the Science of Acoustics, by solving the mystery of the intricacies of Sound which had baffled investigators from the time of ancient Greece. Each made a direct application of Science to human use.

Scientists require no introduction, for the technical side of Sabine's life is forever recorded in mathematical formulae, which the limited number of his scientific colleagues can understand, respect, and admire. " His direct contributions," wrote Dr. Theodore W. Richards of Harvard University, " are destined to carry his influence far into the coming years."

Sabine's name ranks high among the foremost educators of America. " I came under the influence of a great master, Henry Adams," the historian, Edward Channing, records. " Had I studied Physics with Sabine I should have become a physicist — or, at any rate, it would have been an even thing between two great teachers." As an educator, Sabine's fame grows more imposing as the basic principles of life which he imparted to his students are passed on from one generation to another. Instead of merely teaching Science, he taught *men*. Not only at Harvard University, but in the national evolution of education, his constructive work ranks with the highest.

Architects need no introduction to him. His theories are as fundamental today as the lever of Archimedes, and his writings are accepted in their offices as definitive. " He resolved seemingly intangible sounds into elements which he measured," one of his collaborators observed. " With these elements he created a system so perfect that auditoriums are built free from objectionable resonances and echoes; he corrected the poor acoustic properties of others already constructed. . . . What he did was so marvelously accurate and complete that it forms the foundation for all future work."

In the Great War, Sabine applied his genius in Sound to the problems of the Allied Forces with such effect that the German High Command singled him out for special destruction while he was conducting his work at Fort Douaumont. He influenced England, France, and Italy to form a joint commission to consider sound-problems as applied to submarines, airplanes, and inter-communication between the lines. He invented photographic apparatus for airplanes with which he discovered hitherto unknown enemy hangars in the Austrian Alps. After America entered the struggle, Sabine's work as Director of the Department of Technical Information in the Bureau of Aircraft Production in Washington was so effective that one of the high officials remarked, " He is the one man who, claiming to know least, actually knows most about all phases of aircraft problems."

Yet, as the President of one of the country's most important power and light companies once observed, " Sabine was the least known *great* man America has produced."

Sabine himself is the reason for this. Claude M. Fuess defines biography as " the revelation of a personality," and the biographer as " a psychoanalyst, a diagnostician, a seer, and a judge . . . with ability to pierce beneath the protective crust of reserve." Wallace Sabine lived during his entire life behind a " protective crust of reserve " — as a result of early training, by choice, by nature, and because the vital contributions he made to the world were necessarily accomplished under conditions which demanded seclusion or secrecy.

This volume is not a biography in the ordinary sense, for no adequate life of Wallace Sabine can ever be written. The full portrayal demands the data he instinctively concealed behind his " protective crust of reserve," and requires access to the intimate facts which lie buried in the secret archives of the American, British, French, and Italian War Records. It is rather a deferential attempt to pierce that " protective crust of reserve " in order to find beneath it the romantic story of a rare genius who, by his ability, ingenuity, and indomitable will, discovered and conquered the mysteries of Sound; of an inspired teacher who taught life; of a peace-loving citizen who made himself one of the dreaded opponents of the German Juggernaut. Through it run the dramatic elements of superhuman efforts with amazing accomplishments; of stubborn refusal to permit even Nature to interfere with his experiments and achievements; of ineffable tenderness and strength of character; of sublime courage in the face of danger.

W. D. O.

April, 1933

ACKNOWLEDGMENTS

———

In addition to the credits made throughout the text in connection with the quoted matter, special acknowledgment should be made to the following who gave freely of their time and knowledge in supplying valuable material and advice, and, in some instances, reading the manuscript. Without their assistance this volume could not have been written:

To *Mrs.* WALLACE C. SABINE
   Mrs. FREDERIC A. LEY (*Janet Sabine*)
   President A. LAWRENCE LOWELL
   Professor WILBUR H. SIEBERT
   Professor EDWIN H. HALL
   Professor WILLIAM F. OSGOOD
   Professor WILLIAM H. WHEELER
   Doctor HOLLIS GODFREY
   WILLIAM L. W. FIELD
   JEROME D. GREENE
   JOHN GODDARD HART
   CLIFFORD M. SWAN
   EDGAR H. WELLS

Permission to reprint copyrighted material has been graciously extended by the American Academy of Arts and Sciences, the American Association for the Advancement of Science, " The American Architect," the " Journal of the Franklin Institute," the National Academy of Sciences, the American Institute of Architecture, " The Brickbuilder," " The Engineering Record," " The Harvard Architectural Quarterly," " The Harvard Graduates' Magazine," Messrs. G. P. Putnam's Sons, the Harvard University Press, and Methuen and Company.

To all these friends the author extends his grateful thanks.

CONTENTS

Contents

ILLUSTRATIONS

WALLACE CLEMENT SABINE

A Study in Achievement

I. The Boy "Tinto" · 1868–1886

In the autumn of 1884 the American Association for the Advancement of Science was holding a session in Philadelphia. It so happened that the weather was excessively hot, to the great discomfort of speakers and audiences. Professor John Trowbridge, at that time Director of the Jefferson Physical Laboratory at Harvard University, was Chairman of the Section of Physics, and, while presiding over one of the sessions, his attention was attracted by a boy in the back of the room, intently following the proceedings, who made himself conspicuous by his apparent indifference to the exhausting physical conditions from which others so clearly suffered. At the close of the meeting, this young man, accompanied by his mother, modestly approached Professor Trowbridge, and, with restrained eagerness and excitement showing in his face, expressed the pleasure he had experienced during the session, saying that what he had heard had determined him to enter Harvard University. " I had always entertained some doubts," Professor Trowbridge said, in relating this incident, " of the value of large public meetings for the popularization of Science; but in reflecting upon the influence which one can exert upon young men of the character of Wallace Sabine, I have grown to take a more liberal view."

Young Sabine was at that time sixteen years old, and his interest in Science, as expressed to Professor Trowbridge, was as natural to him as that which other boys of his age might have manifested in athletics. His entire early training had fitted him for this moment and for this decision. The home atmosphere into which he had been born, the influences which surrounded him during his earliest youth, and the deep impression made upon him during his years of preparation for Ohio State University under that inspiring teacher of Physics, Professor Thomas Corwin Mendenhall,[1] could not fail to instill in him an abnormally early interest in all matters which had to do with Science.

Whatever arguments may exist regarding heredity and environment, no man ever reflected more directly inherited family characteristics and early surroundings than Wallace Sabine. To understand him one must know his lineage and become intimately acquainted with his parents and his home life. According to the traditions of the family, four distinct racial strains were combined in his blood — Scotch, English, French, and Dutch. "Our boy was born at four o'clock, twenty minutes, on the afternoon of June 13, 1868, in Richwood, Ohio," records his mother in her Diary. "We name him Wallace Clement Ware Sabine, being our mothers' maiden names and our fathers' names. We call him 'Tinto.'"

The earliest ancestor appears to have been William Sabine, or Sabin, of French Huguenot stock, who came to America in 1643 from the south of England, where he had found refuge in his flight from France, and became one of the founders of the town of Rehoboth, near Plymouth, Massachusetts. The records show William to have been a man of substance who stood well in the community. He lies buried in the Old Granary Burying Ground in Boston, having died in 1687, and his will, written two years before his death, is probated in Suffolk County Records, mentioning by name sixteen of his twenty children.

---

[1] Mendenhall had just returned to Ohio State after three years in the University of Tokyo, as Professor of Physics. At different times he held the positions of Superintendent of the Coast and Geodetic Survey, Washington, D. C., President of Rose Polytechnic Institute, Terre Haute, Indiana, and President of the Polytechnic Institute at Worcester, Massachusetts.

From William the line runs down through Benjamin, four Nehemiahs, John Fletcher, and Hylas, to Wallace Clement Ware Sabine. The fourth Nehemiah, early in the nineteenth century, emigrated with his family from New England to a fertile district of central Ohio known as the Darby Plains. Here he became a " pioneer preacher, with a circuit of fifty miles' radius. Leather saddle-bags on his horse carried the Bible and his doctrine of eternal rewards and punishments."

John Fletcher Sabine, one of Nehemiah's eleven children, devoted himself diligently to farming, but found his greatest satisfaction in books. In 1853 he was elected auditor of his county, whereupon he moved his family to Marysville, the county seat, building there a commodious Colonial house, the feature of which, unusual for that locality, was a well selected library. John Fletcher had been brought up on the ponderous religious volumes of the period, but, after reaching man's estate, his disposition was too gentle to perpetuate the stern creed preached by his father. This explained the presence of English Literature and Classics in his library, from which he gleaned the more hopeful message that all men might be saved. He preserved his remarkably retentive memory and his clear, vigorous mentality up to the time of his death at the ripe old age of eighty-nine years. His wife, Euphemia Clement, though a gentle and retiring soul, was a capable woman who thoroughly approved her husband's pacific doctrines. Hylas Sabine, born July 5, 1829, was their eldest son.

On the maternal side, Wallace Sabine came of English Quaker stock. Jacob Reed Ware, his grandfather, was born a month after his own father's death, and the youth was taken to the new State of Ohio by his mother and her family, the Reeds. This little group of pioneers settled at Mechanicsburg, Champaign County, where Jacob grew up, applying himself to farming with such success that in his manhood he acquired no less than six farms.   Like many other Quakers in Ohio, Indiana, and adjoining states, Ware became an ardent abolitionist, and rendered valiant assistance to fugitive slaves who sought freedom in Canada. It was, in fact, due to his influence upon his neighbors that Mechanicsburg became so important a station on one of the main lines of the " underground railway" through Ohio. Speaking of her childhood, Anna Ware, Wallace's mother, used to relate that she would be awakened at night by muffled steps on the piazza, which would be a signal for all members of the household to arise and minister to the needs of the fugitive slaves.

Jacob Ware was no less earnest in his advocacy of the temperance cause, and he did much in promoting the establishment of the common-school system in his State. He was a strong, fearless man, who exerted a powerful influence upon the community in which he lived. " Untiring in body, alert in mind, and strong in purpose," so the records run, " he lived in perfect health with such simple habits that at the age of ninety-four, without disease, he fell asleep."

Jacob Ware married Almira Wallace, herself a woman of force and uprightness, who was in hearty and active sympathy with her husband's outspoken principles. Their first daughter, Anna Ware, who became Wallace's mother, was born September 13, 1835.

As this story of Wallace Sabine progresses, the deep significance of this family history will become apparent. Wherever one of his ancestors appears, the historical record emphasizes the attributes of kindliness, gentleness, untiring energy, fixity of purpose — all traits which appear in him. Quoting from the rare tribute paid Sabine in the " Memoir " [2] written by Professor Edwin H. Hall, his senior colleague in the Department of Physics at Harvard: "The individualism and stern conscience that made Sabine's

[2] National Academy of Sciences, Volume XXI, Thirteenth Memoir, 1924.

ancestors on the one side Quakers in England and on the other side Protestants in France, found expression in him under changed intellectual conditions. He was of the very stuff of which martyrs are made — but with an austerity of morals and capacity for devotion which none of his conspicuously religious forefathers could have surpassed. He held aloof silently and absolutely from all public profession of religious creed, and took small part in religious observances."

Anna Ware married Hylas Sabine on October 8, 1857, in spite of her father's violent opposition to a son-in-law outside the Quaker faith. Except for this difference in religious belief Jacob Ware acknowledged Hylas' full eligibility, but he did not relent in his resentment until the two children born of this union were full grown. Then he sent them money for a trip to Europe.

Anna Ware Sabine received her early education at the high school of Marysville, Ohio, and later at Antioch College, at Yellow Springs, Ohio. Here she spent two years, during both of which she had the rare privilege of rooming and boarding in the home of its famous President, Horace Mann. It was from contact with him that she developed her insatiable passion for learning.

Madame Sabine plays so important a part in this story of her son that she should be early visualized. We shall see how unreservedly she gave of herself to her family, yet in spite of her abnormal conscientiousness in the exercise of her maternal duties, she possessed such surplus energy that she expressed her Quaker traditions by active participation in various forms of social reform. In the early '70s she took part in the women's crusade against the saloon; in 1918 she accepted the passing of the Eighteenth Amendment as a personal triumph. Out of respect to her husband, she renounced the Quaker dress, and usually wore a shawl or cloak or sealskin sacque, varying in accord with the prevailing mode, but she always adhered to her early fondness of adorning her head with a small, becoming bonnet.

Hylas Sabine grew up on his father's farm in Marysville, Ohio, sharing with him the farm labors by day and the choice collection of books by night. Here, in John Fletcher Sabine's library, was formed Hylas' great fondness for English Literature and the Classics, which he, in turn, later imparted to his own son. Until eighteen years of age, Hylas attended the county schools, completing his education at Ohio Wesleyan University. After college, he taught for two years in Kentucky, returning then to Marysville to become his father's successor as County Auditor.

At the time of his marriage, Hylas was editor and publisher of the "Union Press," at Marysville, through the columns of which he so exposed the graft which had entered into the letting of county contracts that he succeeded in bringing about the competitive system of bidding. But the ambitious bride was not long satisfied with the opportunities offered by country journalism for her husband's future, and encouraged him to extend his horizon through professional training. Preferring to study law under eminent teachers rather than in a practitioner's office, and realizing his wife's overwhelming desire to add to her own intellectual stature by taking courses under Professors Gray and Agassiz at Harvard College, the young husband decided to transfer their home from Marysville to Cambridge, Massachusetts. Here Hylas entered the Harvard Law School, and embarked on what they both hoped would be a great legal career, while Anna achieved her ambition and at the same time shattered a Harvard precedent by being the only woman ever to attend Professor Agassiz' lectures:

From Professor George H. Parker

Wallace's mother was a woman of very unusual character. Quiet in manner and slight in person, she seemed one whom a breath might blow away, but no one could know her long without coming to recognize the source of Wallace's strength. Very clear in mind, and simple and direct in all her ways, she was a woman whose decisions seldom required amending. Without show or effort she usually gained her point.

She once told me that as a young woman she found herself in Cambridge for a winter, and wished to gain admittance to the lectures on Natural History given at that time in Harvard College by Professor Louis Agassiz. She betook herself to the Professor and made her request, only to be informed that the lectures were open exclusively to the young men of the College, and could not be attended by a woman. Professor Agassiz had no personal objection to her presence in the class, but he stated to her the invariable college rule. Some words were dropped about a small, unused gallery that surrounded the lecture hall, but nothing very definite was said one way or the other. When the lectures were to begin, Madame Sabine surreptitiously made her way to the hall and up to the gallery. To her surprise, she found there, in an otherwise empty space, a single chair! Here she sat, unseen by those in the audience, but within earshot of the speaker, and not only for that lecture but for all the remaining lectures of the course. Thus she quietly but effectively won her point by means which were often to be seen in Wallace Sabine.

The young couple boarded for a time in the historic old Wadsworth House. Here, in Cambridge, during the next two years, interrupted only by the birth of her first child, Annie (now Mrs. Wilbur H. Siebert), Anna Ware Sabine not only carried on her own studies but followed her husband's notes, and completed with him all the work incidental to his law courses. " It was the desire of her life to have been a practicing lawyer," Mrs. Wallace Sabine says of her,

" and she always rejoiced that I had embraced the profession of Medicine. Mother Sabine's clear, legal mind often upset and confused even eminent men by the direct, pointed questions she asked. There was, however, no combativeness nor dogmatic superiority manifested because of her mental grasp of affairs."

After receiving his LL.B. degree in 1864, Hylas Sabine returned to Union County, Ohio, with his wife and infant daughter. There he established a new town, which was called " Richwood " from the primeval forest surrounding it. He hewed out for himself from the timberland a splendid farm, attracted as neighbors a superior class of settlers, and built the conventional church and schoolhouse. It was at Richwood that Wallace was born and spent his boyhood days, and here Hylas Sabine had visions of becoming the prosperous Squire of a thriving community. But Hylas' handicap was that his vision was never backed by that practical quality which was so marked a characteristic of his wife. In creating this domain he spread out his resources so thin that the depression of 1873 engulfed him, and he emerged with but three hundred and fifty acres left of his original princely forest empire. But he retained the respect and affection of his neighbors, who, in 1876, sent him as a delegate to the Cincinnati Republican Convention which nominated Rutherford B. Hayes for the Presidency of the United States, and a year later elected him a State Senator. In the Senate, Hylas was recognized as a cool, prudent, and wise counselor, well versed in political history and in the statistical records of the State.

Following this first entry into politics, Hylas returned to his farm for two years, devoting himself particularly to the care of his two growing children. Then Governor Charles Foster appointed him State Commissioner of Railroads and Telegraphs — a position he held acceptably for four years. He is said to have been the first railroad commissioner in the country to establish and adequately enforce State supervision of railways through State inspection and compulsory returns. In 1880 he was an alternate delegate to the Republican Convention in Chicago which nominated James A. Garfield for the Presidency.

After 1884, Hylas maintained an office in Columbus, Ohio, but, instead of practicing law, his visions still led him into less productive fields. He devoted himself for several years to working out a plan for a belt line about the city of Columbus — an ambitious scheme which for a time seemed in a fair way to receive the support of the roads involved, but in the end lacked the essential support. Another of his inventions, very late in life, was an automatic, ball-bearing, safety coupler, which possessed such acknowledged merit that in 1901 the family, with great sacrifice, raised $1800 to present it properly at a railroad convention being held at Saratoga Springs, New York.

Wallace Sabine took upon himself the actual presentation of the device at the convention, and here he came against a condition which until then he did not know existed: the railroad experts admitted the value of the invention and were ready to adopt the coupler as standard equipment, but demanded sums far beyond the family resources in exchange for their approval. Sick at heart with his first contact with this phase of human nature, Wallace returned home and sadly related his experience at a Sunday dinner, where his parents were guests. They listened quietly until the end; then Hylas said, "You were quite right, my son. There shall be no graft or dishonesty in connection with anything of ours." When wealthy friends heard of the matter they offered to advance $200,000 as a promotion fund, but as both Hylas and his son stood firmly against using any portion of this in unholy tribute, the project was abandoned.

As a result of the collapse of the belt line proposition, Hylas devoted himself more exclusively to the cultivation of his farm, until physical disability interfered. When that time came, in 1895, he leased his property, and, with his wife, spent the closing years of his life in Cambridge, near his son.

In person, Hylas stood almost six feet high, was well proportioned, with an unusually large head. His memory was exceedingly retentive, and his mind was always active. As a young man he wore his dark, thick hair rather long, combed to one side of his high forehead. His beard, after the fashion of the times, almost covered his tall collar and black stock. He usually wore a black frock coat, figured waistcoat, striped gray trousers, polished boots, and a silk hat. In dress, manner, and speech he was a typical gentleman of the old school, whose favorite maxim was, " Treat every one with respect — especially yourself." His clear, penetrating eyes invited confidence, and his smile always won affection. Up to the time of his death he attracted attention by his courtly bearing and his unwavering courtesy. When his granddaughter, Janet, was but a child, he stooped and restored to her a dropped handkerchief with the respect and dignity due a queen.

The pioneer community at Richwood, in which the young couple lived, naturally contributed nothing to gratify Hylas' great love for Literature and Art, and he improved every opportunity offered by his political associations to supplement this lack. His official duties took him frequently into large cities, and whenever possible he made a point of visiting each art museum even before attending to the business for which he had come. When he was elected State Senator, and became a resident of Columbus, Ohio, during the sessions of the General Assembly, it was remarked that although he included among his friends State officials, professors of the Ohio State University, and the leading professional and business men, he found peculiar pleasure in associating with local artists, frequenting their studios and encouraging them in their work. On occasional visits with

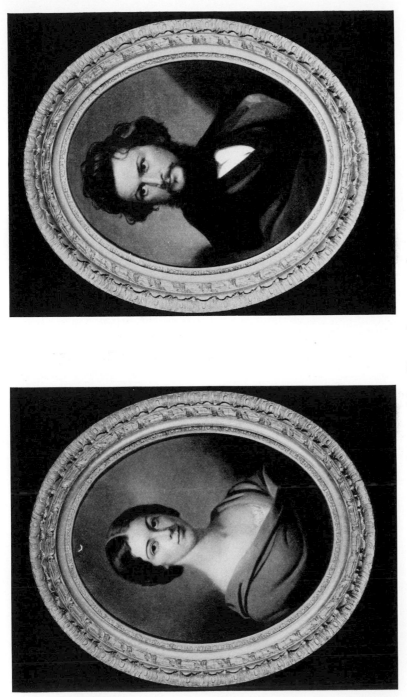

Mr. and Mrs. Hylas Sabine in 1857
from portraits by E. O. Eaton

his family in Cincinnati, Washington, Baltimore, and New York, after he became Railroad Commissioner, he always took them to the art collections in these cities, acting as their personal guide, and developing their appreciation of Art. The nickname " Tinto," bestowed upon his son at birth, was an expression of his admiration for the great painter Tintoretto.

Hylas was himself an artist of no mean ability. He drew and modeled with exquisite skill, and cut amazingly beautiful cameos. During a political assembly he once made a pen-and-ink sketch of President Lincoln, whom he knew personally, which was so admired that Ida Tarbell, Lincoln's biographer, begged the loan of it when writing her famous biography. Hylas stimulated his children to develop the cleverness of their hands. Both inherited their father's talent, and even in their youth drew skilfully and delicately not only from copies but from life. " Tottie," as the daughter was nicknamed, later achieved a high reputation as a painter of miniatures and portraits, while Wallace, applying his artistic skill in a practical way to his chosen profession, won his fame in a field of exact science closely related to esthetic art.

This genealogical outline shows the perfect blending of outstanding inherited characteristics from both lines. One finds in Wallace Sabine the same grim determination which marked those pioneers who undauntedly faced the unknown in carving out their careers; the same health and physical endurance possessed by those who had been partners with Nature; the same unswerving adherence to Truth; the same gentleness that assumed leadership by expression of character rather than by force; the same intellectual capacity that found sermons in stones and poems in running brooks. More directly from his parents he inherited courtliness of manner mingled with practical common sense; a passion for exact learning tempered by the humanizing beauties of

Art and Literature — and to the sum total of this combined inheritance he added that rare attribute of broadminded generosity, which placed the epoch-making results of his life-work freely at the disposal of the world.

Wallace's education began in the home in far more than the ordinary sense. In him his mother saw the opportunity to gratify vicariously the ambition for personal expression in a broader field than the home offered, which had been denied to her. A farmer's life was not to be the portion of her son! For several years after Wallace's birth, Hylas Sabine was submerged in his strenuous efforts to translate the dream of his forest empire into reality, so, during that early, formative period, the mother became Wallace's first teacher, jealously guarding mind and body of her " boy-man " as he developed from babyhood into the child, and from childhood into the youth. Her husband's life was not unfolding in the way she had hoped, even with the new asset she had helped him to secure through his legal studies. Hylas lived above the realities while his wife kept her feet firmly on the ground. Her admiration for the tenacity with which he clung to his ideals never weakened, her affection for the big-hearted, devoted companion never faltered; but she was fully aroused to the fact that material success inevitably makes itself a stranger to such as he. Her ambition, which had been centered in her husband, was now transferred to her son. To him should be given all the old-time courtesies, all the learning and love of culture, all the infinite personal charm of his father, but to this blessed inheritance the mother proposed to add scientific knowledge and the practical sense of how to use it.

So fascinated did she become in her own vision that she kept a Diary (from which the record of Wallace's birth has already been taken), in which she plotted the curve of her son's development up to the time of his marriage. In this priceless heirloom, now in the possession of Mrs. Siebert, are so many appealing evidences of the peculiarly intimate relations between mother and son that I shall quote from it freely, as being far more revealing than the words of any biographer.

When Wallace attained the age of eight, he was sent to a small private school in the village, from which he went on to the public school; but the lessons were still continued at home, and the mother's instruction supplemented the school work far beyond the teachers' ability. At this time Wallace was a well developed, full-faced, healthy lad, with clear eyes which even then were full of questions. While not lacking the innate, boyish love of fun, his expression was serious, and he approached his elders with unusual poise and maturity. There were few playmates in the village, and the number was made even smaller by his mother's discriminating selection. Study, in the Sabine household, was held to be a delightful recreation. To prevent monotony from the daily lessons, the father introduced Wallace to the choice volumes on the library shelves. Years later, when pacing the Addison Walk, in Oxford, England, Wallace remarked to his wife that he owed his education in Literature to his father — that it was from him he first became familiar with Addison, and intimate with Shakespeare. Famous poems were committed to memory, and the utmost care was exercised to guide the boy's reading during his adolescence.

From the Diary   [*June* 13, 1880

Now he is twelve years old — a good and true boy. Every word I think of to describe the nobility of his character seems poor and faded in comparison with the truth. He is quick to perceive and ready to express. In morals he instinctively knows the right, and has almost too tender feelings. He is a gentleman in every respect, although a little boy. He is slender and fair, only reaching to my shoulder. Looks delicate, but has perfect health. He is strong in purpose, cheerful, and *obedient*. During the summer I am teaching him Algebra, and reviewing the primary studies.

[*September,* 1880

He begins the preparatory course at the Ohio State University by special permission of President Orton — as he is two years younger than the age for entering as required by the rules. And now, with many anxious hopes, he starts on the course.

From these records it is not difficult to trace the genesis of Wallace Sabine's reserve which was so marked a characteristic throughout his life. Even at the tender age of twelve, when most boys in his vicinity would be thinking of games or of swimming in the " old swimming hole," Wallace had attained an intellectual maturity which made such pastimes seem childish and unattractive. Even the recreations, planned by the devoted mother to give him relaxation, were not those ordinarily included in a youth's galaxy of sports:

From the Diary   [*September,* 1881

During the school vacation Tinto has had complete rest, going out over the State sometimes with the bridge inspectors. He also took some half-dozen lessons in oil painting from Mr. Silas Martin. In the fall he attended the Cincinnati Exhibition.

[*September,* 1882

During the summer vacation he went partly over the State with the bridge inspectors, and by invitation he went with Professors Mendenhall and Anderson to attend the Teachers' Institute in Morgan County.

[*September* 2, 1884

We all, with Professor McFarland and family and Professor Robinson and family, took a trip, starting down the Scioto Valley Railroad, over the mountains by the Chesa-

peake and Ohio Railroad, to Old Point Comfort, Virginia.
Spent a day and night, then by steamboat to Baltimore,
and by cars to Philadelphia. For several days we listened to
the learned men of America and other countries, especially
of England, who were members of the Scientific Association.
Then for a few days we attended the Electrical Exposition
held in Philadelphia.

This entry refers to the meeting of the American Association for the Advancement of Science, at which occurred
the incident with the relation of which this chapter opens.
Had it not been for his mother's deep interest in the sciences, Wallace might not have found such early opportunity to disclose his aptitude for Physics. Hylas Sabine's high
ideals as applied to education tended toward the classical
rather than the scientific, and, while not opposing the sympathetic interest Mother Sabine showed toward her son's
obvious preference, he insisted that Latin and Greek should
be studied side by side with the scientific subjects, even at
the expense of Modern Languages.

Fifty years ago comparatively few public high schools in
Ohio were able to prepare their pupils for admission to
college, and for this reason a preparatory course was maintained at the State University.

From Professor Thomas Corwin Mendenhall

The instruction was under the direction of, and, in some
instances, was given by members of the college Faculty. It
was to this preparatory course that young Sabine was admitted. In contrast with the present, it was the day of small
things, but neither students nor professors of that period
will ever forget the inspirational value of that close association — fellowship, in fact — of teacher and pupil, which under modern conditions seems no longer possible.

Inheriting a love for exact learning (his mother
" coached " him in Analytical Geometry and Calculus dur-

ing vacation time), Wallace, it is not surprising to learn, gave early evidence of excellence in the science in which he afterward became renowned. It was a bit of good fortune that just then I had Newton M. Anderson as an assistant in the Physics Department, a young man who had taken his B.S. degree at the University only a year or two earlier; who, much as he loved his subject, loved boys still more, and who later became the founder of two of the best known private schools for boys in the country, at Asheville, North Carolina. At thirteen years, young Sabine was a quiet, serious, handsome boy, with much dignity of manner, but still a boy. And I know that he always valued his intimacy at this time with this inspiring teacher and lover of boys. We hear not infrequently of inspiring teachers, but I have had the good luck to find many inspiring pupils. Of these, Wallace Sabine was a conspicuous example. In the company of such, one may feel the joy and echo the cry of old Roger Ascham: " I love to learn and dearly love to teach."

From the Diary   *[September,* 1881

He has begun the second year, and is now taking military drill, from which he was excused the first year. So, to put on the military uniform, he has taken off the " little boy's round coat " which he had worn up to this time, and in which he had become so familiar to us,[3] for he has never worn a " man's coat." I cannot help a regret, although he looks trim and nice in the blue uniform.

[June 20, 1882

Second year finished, everything right, nothing to regret. He has grown remarkably tall. Although he has been eager in all his studies, he has shown more enthusiasm in the study of Physics, under Professor Mendenhall.

---

[3] Up to that time Wallace had been dressed in a belted blouse which buttoned down the front, turned-down collar, with knee breeches and long stockings.

[*September*, 1882

He now enters the freshman class at the age of fourteen, a tall, beardless boy, a handsome boy — in others' eyes. He is as tall as I.

[*May* 25, 1884

He is now almost sixteen years old, and today he has put on his first citizen's suit of clothes. . . . Up to this time I have made them all.

An interesting sidelight, as showing the direction young Sabine's mind was taking, is given in a memorandum made by a former clerk in the office of Wallace's father in Columbus, now a Professor *emeritus* in the University of Michigan:

From Professor Horace L. Wilgus

I have a very distinct recollection of Wallace's great pleasure in studying the figures made in loose sand on vibrating discs of various shapes and sizes, emitting different sounds and notes. He, at the same time, was greatly skilled in constructing pendulum devices for tracing Lissajous curves for various sounds. I think he must have become, at that early age, an expert in such things, judging from the beauty of the curves he obtained, that I saw in the office.

At the time Wallace entered Ohio State University that institution was still in its infancy, including in its catalogue scarcely more than two hundred students. The boy's courses during the next four years included Classics, Mathematics, English Literature, the Art of Discourse, Anglo-Saxon, Chemistry, Physics, Botany, Zoölogy, Geology, Psychology, Philosophy, Political Economy, and Military Science and Tactics. He received no instruction in German or French, and very little in History. His instructors in the various subjects were in general excellent teachers, and Wallace responded instinctively. His Latin Professor gives this picture of him at that time:

From Professor Samuel Carroll Derby

He was an ideal student, prompt and constant in attendance; always fully prepared upon the day's topic, and alertly interested in its discussion. He showed an intelligence unusual in its grasp and keenness, and an unflagging industry. He evinced in a marked degree that rare and delightful trait — intellectual curiosity. He gave to his chosen work, in those early years, the same devoted attention that marked his service as professor, dean, and scientist. In his intercourse with his comrades and instructors he displayed even then the considerate courtesy characteristic of his later years. His mental qualities were unusual, his moral quality was even more rare.

Professor Mendenhall played an important part throughout Sabine's life, first as teacher and mentor, and later as devoted friend. It was to him that Sabine first turned when President Eliot asked him to undertake the correction of the acoustical faults of the Fogg Art Museum, remembering that, in the early years at Ohio State University, Mendenhall had made some studies and experiments regarding a similar condition of the auditorium of the then newly erected City Hall in Columbus. It was Mendenhall who instructed Wallace in Physics, his favorite subject, and the combination of the inspired teacher and the enthusiastic pupil produced results which otherwise would have been impossible. As recorded in his mother's Diary, one of the great adventures which Wallace had in college was when he accompanied Professor Mendenhall to the session of the Teachers' Institute held in Morgan County. Other experiences which thrilled were long tramps on holidays with Gerard Fouke, the archaeologist, through whom the boy became familiar with the Indian mounds in Ohio, and frequent geological trips with Edward Orton, then President of the College.

But Wallace's main recreation was still found in study. "During his vacation between his junior and senior years," his mother jots down in her Diary, "Tinto studies Analytical Geometry and Calculus, which do not come in his regular B.A. course. Begins to study as soon as school closes in June, and finished on the last day of August." Professor Mendenhall supplies the modest omission of the fact that she herself was his instructor.

From the Diary [*June*, 1885

End of junior year. Tinto is now showing remarkable maturity of thought. The studies of this year have been pursued with ease, and with success also, judging by the words of President Scott, who remarked that he had kept up all his studies more evenly than any other student. This year he also has given some thought to other things besides his studies. Besides attending to the work required by the Alcyone Literary Society, which he joined at the beginning of the year, he joined with other students in establishing a Chapter of a Greek letter society.

[*December*, 1885

About the middle of the term the Class appeared in their senior " silk high hats," without which, however, my seventeen-year-old boy stands six feet high!

The Phi Alpha Chapter was admitted into the Beta Theta Pi Fraternity, and that became another red-letter day, as Tinto thinks. He is so ingenuously happy that I am on the point between laughing and crying — crying to think of the thorns inevitably lying farther along in his path, and yet rejoicing that he has not yet reached them; and more — that he does not even suspect they are there.

[*June* 23, 1886

Course at Ohio State University ends today. Yesterday was " Class Day." Tinto was Class Prophet. The Prophecy was written in verse of different meters, the thread of the story being prose upon which was strung the separate futures of the members of the Class. The conceit was novel, the effect pleasing, and his Class well satisfied. Today he delivered his graduating oration, " The Power of Public Opinion." Received his degree of Bachelor of Arts, with Tottie, who took the Master of Arts degree.

Our work at the State University is now done. Such perfect health has he, and such regular habits, that through his whole course of six years, preparatory and college, he has never missed a recitation. He is loved for his genial, hearty way, while he is respected for his healthy opinions and feelings. His mind is pure, his heart is right; and when I add " purse empty " I give the cause, perhaps, of *all* that goes before. Ten days ago he was eighteen years old.

[*September,* 1886

We are ready to go to Cambridge, that the two children, before setting out in life, may be still better equipped.

Thus we find Wallace Sabine standing at the threshold of the new life that was to open up for him. Never had there been any question that he would be a physicist since his mind was developed at an abnormally early age to a point where a decision was possible. Never had he wavered in his determination to complete his life preparation at Harvard since he heard and met Professor Trowbridge at Philadelphia.

From Professor Thomas Corwin Mendenhall

He was at an age at which young men who have passed through the regularly prescribed preparatory years are entering college. But, in spite of his youth, there was no doubt in his own mind regarding the next step; no vacillating uncertainty as to " what he had better do," as is so often the case with young men just out of college, and no putting off

the decision for a year or two, as some might have advised
and many might have expected in one of his years. One of
the most interesting and important qualities of his mind,
and one which had large influence in determining his success in life, was a rare capacity for making a quick " integral " of the various aspects of a situation, and reaching a
conclusion swiftly. Few men decided important questions
more promptly than he, or more safely, and he always
seemed " easily and immediately sure of himself " and of
the decision which he had reached.

Mother Sabine had achieved the first great step in gratifying her insatiable ambition for her son, and her heart beat
high with satisfaction. Wallace, her man-grown boy, faced
opportunities which her eighteen years of thoughtful, unswerving guidance fitted him admirably to embrace. The
sacrifices — and there had been many — were forgotten in
the proud contentment of that moment. That there were
other and greater triumphs to follow she doubted not, but
she felt that he still needed her companionship and advice.
Hylas Sabine, after the unfortunate failures at Columbus,
had found temporary employment with Major George Ruh-
len, for whom he had done many favors, among the Black-
foot Indians, so there was no reason why his wife should
not transfer her residence to Cambridge for a period at
least long enough to settle the two children — Wallace at
Harvard, and Annie at the Massachusetts Institute of Technology. But had the sacrifice of separating themselves been
far greater, the parents would not have hesitated. The children had long since become their obsession, and every question was settled by considering its bearing on their future.
The biographer cannot avoid the inevitable inquiry as to
the permanent effect upon the life of Wallace Sabine of the
unusual maternalism under which he was brought up. That
he lost much of the happiness of youth, during that period

when youth craves and is entitled to joy and laughter, cannot be denied. In his relations with his own children he reflected this sense of personal loss in the constant emphasis he placed upon the importance of relaxation. " Play, Janet, play," he writes his little daughter with an appeal that cannot be misunderstood. " High marks are to be desired, but never at the cost of health or happiness." He insisted that his children become proficient in every form of social and athletic diversion; he entered into their childish games with the avidity of a partially starved nature.

It may be that his youthful companionship with older people rather than of his own age produced the reserve which became so striking a characteristic. Perhaps the ill-natured comments made upon his home-made " little boy's clothing " by jealous older classmates in the University caused him to draw still farther within himself. He frequently, in later life, expressed his regret that he had been denied the study of Modern Languages, which forced him to take up French, German, and Italian after he had reached maturity, even though by the time he gave his Sorbonne Lectures he was a proficient linguist.

Yet there were definite compensations. Without that constant drilling of his mother, could he have attained the heights he reached? He was certainly never conscious that he was being forced, for he found in the strict intellectual routine a joy second only to that given his mother by his instinctive and happy response. As a result of it, he established a family relationship so rare that no later friendship could ever replace or approach it, and beyond which there could be no desire. Wallace Sabine would have declared with the full vehemence of his intense nature that he would not have altered the course of his early life by a single jot or tittle, yet, by that curious paradox which is common in all parents, he did not permit his own children to be subjected to the same training.

As he stands there, proudly beside his devoted mother, before the Harvard gates which are about to open to him, I see a calm, tense, dignified, happy boy, fully conscious that this is her moment as well as his, eager to embrace the opportunities his parents' sacrifice and devotion have made possible, as the fullest expression of his own gratitude and affection.

II. LAYING THE FOUNDATIONS · 1886–1894

O N THE opening of the fall term of Harvard University in 1886, Wallace Sabine presented himself as a candidate for graduate study, to specialize in Physics. At that period bachelors' degrees from State universities were not considered sufficiently conclusive to secure admission to the graduate courses in the older Eastern universities without further evidence as to the preparedness of the candidate. Wallace Sabine asked no favors when he submitted himself for examination. The calm assurance, the keen expectancy, the exact knowledge of this boy of eighteen, completely belied his youthful appearance, and made a deep impression upon his examiners.

With his eligibility triumphantly established, young Sabine began work in his favorite subject under the direction of the same John Trowbridge whom he had approached two years before at the meeting of the American Association for the Advancement of Science, in Philadelphia. Trowbridge recalled the youthful enthusiast with interest, gave him a hearty welcome, and, as their association became closer, gradually and completely took him into his heart. The other courses Wallace elected during that first year placed him under the guidance of Professor Benjamin Osgood Peirce (whom, twenty years later, he was to succeed as Hollis Professor of Mathematics and Natural Philosophy), and also under Professor Edwin H. Hall, who had brought to Harvard the ideals and inspiration instilled in him at Johns Hopkins by the famous Henry Augustus Rowland. In Mathematics, young Sabine's instructors were Professors James Mills Peirce and William E. Byerly.

The family boarded that first year at 6 Story Street, Cambridge, where a new world began to unfold for this boy, fresh from his Western environment. The culture which had always surrounded him in his home made the contrast less striking, but he was overwhelmed by the wealth of opportunity which he now saw on every side. Trips with his father to various great cities had made him familiar with their personalities, but he had known them as a transient visitor. Now he was an integral part of a great metropolis and of a great university. At Ohio State he had absorbed the maximum of what it had to offer; he had been a prize student, held in high esteem and envied by his less industrious or less competent fellow-students. At Harvard he found a treasure-house of knowledge so rich that the span of man's life was insufficient to extract from it more than a tithe of what was freely placed at his disposal. He found other students as well drilled as himself, and comrades whose wider experience with life enlarged his own horizon. It was a tremendous experience, which excited him to greater effort and encouraged him to look for greater personal satisfaction than he had ever before imagined could come to any man.

The social side of life at Harvard did not especially appeal to Wallace. With the zeal for learning which had been inculcated in him from his earliest days, he begrudged the time over-indulgence in this would have taken from the all-too-limited hours during which the freely offered intellectual treasures might be acquired. Yet he by no means remained isolated. He brought with him to Cambridge letters which made him a welcome visitor in such homes as those of Dr. Justin Winsor, Professors Albert Bushnell Hart, John Williams White, and George Herbert Palmer. He took his meals at a club table in Memorial Hall made up of fellow-members of the Eta Chapter of the Beta Theta Pi fraternity. He joined the Mathematical and Physical Club, at Professor Trowbridge's suggestion. Through all this he made the important discovery that social contact with men brought together by a common interest could teach him something beyond the lectures of his professors, his experiments in the laboratory, or the contents of his scientific volumes.

There was another dominating influence which kept Wallace's mind concentrated upon his work. He never lost sight of the price his parents were still paying that he might have his chance in life. He never forgot that his father's increasing infirmities threatened even the meagre income which supported them. He knew that the future stability of the family structure rested squarely upon his shoulders, and he redoubled his efforts to hasten the moment when he might be prepared to accept the welcome responsibility. The initial step in this direction was achieved at the end of the first year, when he was awarded a Morgan Fellowship.

The income from this Fellowship simplified the financial problem for the next two years. To supplement it, Wallace found employment, during the vacation period, in the Bell Telephone Laboratories, where his abilities attracted sufficient attention to warrant that company in offering him a permanent position at a salary starting at $1200. a year. This was the first tangible evidence Wallace received that his work was assuming practical value, and it gave him a new confidence. His immediate reaction was that the moment had arrived for him to assume his position as the bread-winning head of the family; but his courageous parents refused even to consider the offer. Their masterpiece was as yet unfinished, and, until Wallace's education was fully rounded out, nothing could divert them from their predetermined course.

At the beginning of his second year at Harvard the family

moved to 10 Dana Street, Cambridge, where they remained
for two years. This was a boarding house located " on the
Hill," the ground sloping sharply down to what is now
Massachusetts Avenue. Besides the Sabines, the boarders
included several advanced students of the University, among
them Wallace's friend and roommate, Wilbur H. Siebert,
now Research Professor of History at Ohio State University,
who married Annie Sabine six years later. This group of
young people, including the daughter and a niece of the
owner of the house, afforded pleasant relaxation to the
younger members of the Sabine family. After dinner there
were games or music, with dancing on Saturday evenings.
Dancing [1] was a form of amusement which never appealed
to Wallace, but when it came to bob-sledding down Dana
Hill, he entered into the sport with the same enthusiasm
that he devoted to his studies. When young Siebert pur-
chased a banjo, Wallace bought a guitar, and the two friends
combined their efforts to add to the gaiety of the occasions.
Quiet and reserved as he seemed to those who knew him
little, to his intimates he was gay, witty, whimsical, and
amusing — an altogther delightful companion. Siebert thus
recalls that period when they roomed together:

From Professor Wilbur H. Siebert
    For days at a time Wallace would be deeply absorbed in
the study of a problem. Then, not infrequently in the
middle of the night, he would waken from sleep, light the
gas or student lamp, seize a pencil, draw the diagrams for
a piece of apparatus that had been puzzling him, and write
out the equations that were the key to his problem. With
his mind thus relieved, he would put out the light, return

---

[1] A few years later, Wallace decided that to know how to dance was an essential
part of his education, so he presented himself to Miss Post, a popular teacher in Boston.
At the end of the first lesson, Miss Post remarked facetiously: "You may be light on
your own feet, Mr. Sabine, but you are heavy on mine." Greatly chagrined, Wallace
never returned for another lesson.

to bed, and be asleep again almost instantly. This was his usual method of solving his most difficult problems.

The second year at Harvard brought him into more intimate contact with Professor Trowbridge, who had been quietly watching the development of his erstwhile intellectually inquisitive acquaintance at Philadelphia. The older man was charmed by the young man's personality as it unfolded beneath the warmth of his sympathetic encouragement, and he became deeply impressed by the brilliancy of mind and adaptability of nature. Little by little Trowbridge drew him more closely into his own experiments. He called upon Wallace for assistance in his spectrum study at the Laboratory; together they worked out experiments in electricity, in electric lighting, in photography, and kindred subjects, in all of which Trowbridge was amazed at young Sabine's knowledge, ingenuity, and versatility. From this growing confidence came a constantly increasing reliance upon his assistance, expressed, even during this early association, by asking Wallace to substitute for him as a speaker before the Mathematical and Physical Club, and to collaborate with him in published scientific papers.

Let us turn to Madame Sabine's Diary for further records of this eventful year:

From the Diary   [*June,* 1888

On the day before Commencement, the greatest surprise and pleasure comes to us. A note from Professor J. M. Peirce, saying that the authorities of Harvard College have decided to award Tinto at this Commencement the degree of Master of Arts. It had not been applied for. Then a letter came from father saying he wished to give the two children a summer in Europe — a long dreamed of but unexpected pleasure.

So this year, 1888, brings to us many things in the first six months of it: Tottie receives the degree of Bachelor of

Science from the Massachusetts Institute of Technology; Tinto unexpectedly has the degree of Master of Arts awarded him by Harvard College — and both are now given the pleasure of a summer in the Old World. He has now reached his twentieth birthday.

June 30 — the middle day of the year 1888. And now we separate for the first time — the children to go together. This beautiful Saturday afternoon I saw them standing together on board the " Cephalonia," slowly gliding out to sea. Their *standing together* was an anchor to my feelings, though the slowly widening water-way between us was — forever, may be.

Grandfather Ware's belated relenting in his resentment over his daughter's desertion of the Quaker faith could not have taken a more acceptable form. The mother's Diary gives a faint echo of the feelings in her heart; let us discover how the father expressed the same emotion, from a letter placed in Wallace's hands on sailing, " to be opened when at sea ":

From Hylas Sabine   [*Cleveland, Ohio, June 26,* 1888

MY VERY DEAR SON: For the first time in your life you have now bid your parents " good bye," and have stepped out alone to meet the responsibilities of life. You are full of hope and anticipations. I want you to carry with you, in this your first departure from us, some thoughts that I feel it my duty to impress upon you, a parting injunction.

So far you have had with you in all your affairs a noble-hearted, self-sacrificing mother, who has always been vigilant that every thought and impulse in your developing mind should be such (as would be) best calculated to exalt and qualify you for the affairs of life. Her work has been complete, and there is really nothing left for me to do or say. Yet I want to say something I have not heretofore said to you. I want to participate more fully in the good work of your mother than I have.

There is nothing I wish to correct in your life — I am happy beyond measure in the gentleness of your nature, in the thought of your intellect, and in the kindly tractability you have blessed us with in all the past. You step out from us leaving no wound behind; all is serenity and peace and high hope.

I am satisfied that your mother's devoted life, her Christian patience, her great and abiding faith in a surrounding presence of a Divine Providence, have made such impressions upon your youthful mind that no possible combination of circumstances in your future life will impair their value. You have been blest with a mother whose value can be measured only by an Infinite Mind. There is no need of my attempting to add to the value of the admonitions her life affords. Yet I want to say something, to take part in some way — that I may be counted a small factor, at least, in your most sacred thoughts.

There is a relationship more sacred than that of parent and child (the tenderness of this relation — how dear to my heart at this moment!) . — It is that which you bear to your Divine Maker. I want to say, my dear boy, that the noblest thoughts known to mankind can arise only in the mind of him who bears daily in his inmost thought a profound reverence for the Infinitely Great and ever-present Providence that is near us at all times. I pray that you may constantly bear this reverence in your heart. There is nothing more ennobling, nothing more manly.

I have prayed daily that God would direct your feet in the paths of innocence, lift up your mind into a high order of intelligence, that you may be happy and useful in all the affairs of life, and now, when you are beyond the guidance and care of your mother, I ask that you always bear this Providence in mind. . . .

Wonderful as this tribute is from father to son, it is even more revealing in its frank acknowledgment of the greater part the mother had played in the boy's development, and of his own yearning " to be counted even a small factor " in his son's life. There is a touch of pathos in his words, " Her work has been complete, and there is really nothing left for me to do or say. Yet I want to participate more fully in the good work of your mother than I have."

Father Sabine need have had no misgivings as to the niche he filled in Wallace's life. The gentle courtliness, the instinctive consideration for others, the high idealism which he had exemplified rather than taught, were recognized in source, and, as the years went on, were fully returned to him in kind, enriched by his son's personal interpretation.

And in this letter I read another underlying thought, of peculiar significance because so carefully concealed — that Hylas Sabine feared Wallace to be slipping away from the religious faith of his fathers. So he was, and as the boy matured he found himself more and more separated from the Methodist-Episcopal creed on which he had been brought up, and from all other man-made creeds. Professor Hall says of him, " He held aloof silently and absolutely from all public profession of religious creed, and took small part in religious observances "; Professor William Morton Wheeler recalls a conversation he had with him in Paris which left the impression that Wallace was an agnostic; Professor Francis Greenwood Peabody expressed surprise, when Sabine served with him on the committee of Phillips Brooks House, that " the sanest judgment and clearest vision concerning the spiritual interests of the University were contributed by the one member who did not definitely represent a specific religious communion or social code."

Again, Hylas Sabine need have had no apprehensions concerning his son's " reverence for the Infinitely Great and ever-present Providence." Abraham's God was the same as

Peter's, but He appeared in a different form because Peter belonged to a later generation. Nor should Wallace's friends have misunderstood his religious attitude. Sabine was an intensely religious man. Like others before him, who, through their work with the forces of Nature come into closer contact than the majority with the tangible manifestations of God's infinite power, he saw less reason to visualize the Divinity as a personal being, and became less indulgent toward man's impotent discussions of ways and means. " No one can be an investigator in Science," he once said, " without believing in God; but no preacher can rightly interpret God through sermons which contradict scientific facts." While not a church-goer, he frequently attended the Harvard Chapel exercises. As his children grew up, he himself took them to Sunday School. In living his own life he recognized with fervent reverence the existence of a Something, call it what you will, which represented a power greater than man, and he worshiped it. He asked only that he be permitted to worship this power in his own way, and by the same token he extended the same privilege to others. His basic religion came to him from the example set him by his parents; in his expression of it he departed only in his personal interpretation.

From the Diary   [*Christmas Day — the last of* 1888

All — Hylas, children, and self — are together again at 10 Dana Street, Cambridge. The last half of the year has been full for all — for me full of fears, which have, however, turned out most beautiful successes; full of anxious anticipations for Hylas, yet to be realized.

The children have visited most of the principal cities of Europe, as far south as Florence. Fresh from school, alert and interested, but entirely without experience, they started alone. The art galleries, cathedrals, and peculiar characteristics of each city, together with the leading universities, were the points of interest. They had a close, intelligent, well-ordered plan of travel. Returned on the " Scythia," arriving on the 10th of October.

Tinto went immediately to work in the Jefferson Physical Laboratory, again with Professor Trowbridge, and the result of their work has been published in the " American Journal of Science." Title — " On the Use of Steam in Spectrum Analysis." Their former articles, published in the " Proceedings " of the American Academy, were " Wave Lengths of Metallic Spectra in the Ultra Violet," and " Selective Absorption of Metals for Ultra-Violet Light." Their articles have been copied in the " Scientific American," " London Philosophical Magazine," and the German " Breblasser." One evening every week Tinto has been teaching Mathematics to three men who are employed in the engine works.

The entire Sabine family went to Marysville, Ohio, for the summer vacation of 1889, and when Wallace and Annie returned to Cambridge in the fall Mother Sabine remained behind to be with her husband. Again the Diary picks up the narrative:

From the Diary   [*September,* 1889

Tinto now returns to Cambridge, and he and Tottie are together. They, with Mr. Siebert, find a home at 53 Trowbridge Street. Tinto has been appointed Assistant to Professor Trowbridge in the Jefferson Physical Laboratory, teaching several hours each day. He receives $500. Besides this, he pursues his work in Physics, as the result of which he published, with Professor Trowbridge, a paper on " Electrical Oscillations in Air."

[*June,* 1890

On the close of College he was asked to look over and mark the examination papers in Physics of those applying for admission, and received $84. for it. He was appointed to take charge of the Summer School of Physics, lasting during the month of July, and was given $400.

From these entries we learn how rapidly and tangibly the early idol of the young scientist was expressing his confidence and affection:

By Professor Edwin H. Hall

Rather early in his Harvard residence Sabine was taken by Professor Trowbridge as partner in a photographic study of the oscillating electric discharge, and he showed a remarkable aptitude for work of this kind, requiring high experimental skill; yet he never became a candidate for the Ph.D.[2] Absorption in the work of teaching prevented him for several years from engaging deeply in further work of research. He spent his energy and his talents in building up courses of laboratory work, designing and making apparatus for instruction, and in every way practicing with devotion the profession of a teacher.

From Professor John Trowbridge

It is the experience of most heads of departments that there is a disposition among younger men to make evident the superior initiative of youth. There is a strong tendency for those in authority to dominate and to repress individuality. Airy, the Astronomer Royal, dominated for a lifetime astronomical work in England, and held back, by the influence of his position, the progress of his science. Sir Humphry Davy did not look with favor on his young assistant, Michael Faraday. The history of almost every scientific institution will contribute similar facts. It is my own belief that the strength of laboratories lies in the cultivation of understudies.

---

[2] Sabine's wife once asked him why he never offered himself as a candidate for the degree of Ph.D. "Because," he answered, laughing, "when the proper time came for me to do so, I should have been my own examiner!"

I was peculiarly fortunate, during my holding of the Directorship of the Jefferson Physical Laboratory, in being associated with a remarkable body of professors who supported me in every way without thought of self-advancement, for no one sought his own ends to the exclusion of those of his colleagues. Among them, no one was more self-forgetful than Sabine.

We worked together, particularly upon the subject of electrical oscillations, and to him was largely due the perfection of apparatus which led the way to a recognition of the importance of electrical tuning in wireless telegraphy. He entered enthusiastically into all plans to make the Jefferson Physical Laboratory a centre of research, and to him is due the plan of publishing each year the results of the investigations of the Laboratory in an attractive form. This scientific series is unique in the history of laboratories.

I gave up, finally, two of my largest electives to Sabine, at his own solicitation, in order that the Director should devote his time largely to research. This solicitation was extremely complimentary; and at the same time it showed a breadth of view which augured well for his future administration of the scientific branch of the University.

From the Diary [*August,* 1890

It happened on Tinto's twenty-second birthday that President Eliot said to me, " Mrs. Sabine, we are much pleased with your son's work, and we have appointed him Instructor in the College." Oh! the satisfaction of that moment! My poor little mother-heart is *too* full. This, then, is the result of the long, steady, persistent effort. Can it be so soon! Here I must indulge myself in retrospection. At eight years of age he entered the public school. At twelve, the preparatory school of Ohio State University. At fourteen he entered the same University, freshman class. At eighteen he graduated. At eighteen he entered the Graduate Department of Harvard. At twenty he was awarded, unsolicited, the Master's Degree by Harvard. At twenty-one he was appointed Assistant. At twenty-two years of age, he is made Instructor. This could not have come without ability. Ability could not have succeeded without diligence. And both would not have won, at least would now give me no pleasure, were he not the dearest, kindest, gentlest, most loving and obedient and self-renouncing, and altogether the sweetest boy in all the world. I can still see the *earnest* little boy of two years, in his white-linen slips, and now the tall boy of twenty-two — and all between is a precious memory, *not one regret* in all the years. But best of all, he is unconscious of his own worth, and only knows that we love him.

As soon as the Summer School closed, he hurried to us in Marysville, but in a few days went on to Indianapolis to read his paper before the Association. The rest of the summer was spent in rest, mixed with a good deal of study preparing for the winter's work.

[*September,* 1890

The two children return together, alone, to Cambridge, and take rooms at 53 and 55 Trowbridge Street.

As a part of his college duties, young Sabine conducted the laboratory examinations in Physics of applicants for admission. He had never forgotten how much it had meant to him, in the Ohio State University days, to have the sympathetic and understanding help of Newton Anderson, an instructor not much older than himself. Now the opportunity was offered him to give the same understanding of youth to youth in meeting these preparatory-school boys who approached their entrance examinations in fear and trembling. " Encouragement," Sabine used frequently to say, " is the best teacher ":

From George W. Creelman

A rather scared boy climbed the back stairs to the top floor of the Jefferson Physical Laboratory one June day in 1891. Once inside the large and well-lighted room, a very young man came forward quietly to meet me. I thought he might be one of the students, or some young helper or secretary. He was tall, slender, and rather silent. His suit was of some dark pepper-and-salt material, and he gave me the impression that nothing about him, inside or out, could ever be out of place, irregular, or unkempt.[3]

From F. A. Eustis

I was entirely unknown to Mr. Sabine — one of a large number of boys who had come to Cambridge to be examined in Physics. We waited our turn to be given apparatus and a problem to perform, and naturally felt alarm lest we should make some error and not pass our examinations. By good fortune, I came under Professor Sabine's attention. When my turn came, I was astonished to have him begin by apologizing for the condition of the apparatus which he was handing me with which to perform. He took his handkerchief from his pocket and wiped off the balances before handing them to me.

This was a small detail, but it made a lasting impression. It was entirely characteristic of the man as I came to know him later. It was a typical example of his universal consideration of others, and of his politeness and charm even in the most minute details. I am satisfied that there are few men who have taught at Harvard who would have troubled themselves to wipe a piece of apparatus with their pocket handkerchief before handing it to a candidate for an admission examination!

---

[3] James H. Ropes refers to this characteristic of Sabine when he mentions, in a letter, "the singular elegance of his person, which was, in fact, the expression of a rare elegance of mind."

From Oscar F. Shepard

Coming with insufficient preparation from a distant country school, I was bungling my experiments gloriously, and becoming more confused with each moment. Professor Sabine noticed my predicament, interrupted the experiment to talk with me, and to inquire about my school course. In a few moments I had confidence restored, and was able to proceed with a fair degree of success. It was not the incident which was important; it was the feeling that this man understood my difficulties and sympathized with me — and in so doing, gave me the confidence I needed.

In 1892 Sabine's appointment as Instructor at Harvard was made permanent, and he thus became a member of the Faculty. The personality of the young instructor made an impression on his older colleagues when he appeared at his first faculty meeting:

From Barrett Wendell

Sabine was then very young, and, after you had looked at him across the room two or three times, you came to see that, in a quiet way of its own, his face had great beauty of expression, as well as gentle regularity of features. So I asked Frank Bolles if he knew who that handsome boy was. He answered that Sabine was not a boy but a man, and a man who was content to do whatever work he was called on to do, no matter who got the credit for it. " We shall hear from him," he ended.

In February, 1893, Wallace published his only book, " A Student's Manual of a Laboratory Course in Physical Measurements." This was a small volume of ninety pages and fifty diagrams, in which he crystallized the work outlined for junior students at Harvard. It contained an outline of seventy experiments in Mechanics, Sound, Heat, Light, Magnetism, and Electricity, arranged with special regard to a systematic and progressive development of the subject. The description of each experiment was accompanied by a brief statement of the physical principles and definitions involved, and a proof of necessary formulae. That the manual might be of more general service, a set of apparatus was designed by the author which was especially adapted to the course.

Walter Le Conte Stevens, Professor of Physics in Washington and Lee University, found this little volume an introduction to Sabine, and to a friendship that developed from their mutual respect for each other:

From Professor Stevens

In this book the youthful author manifested conspicuously his power of good arrangement and clear expression; his ability to anticipate the student's difficulties and to guide him where guidance was needful, but without causing the loss of self-dependence. Sabine's book was a model of its kind, and served to introduce its author to the confidence of his fellow-teachers in Physics throughout our country.

During the years his mother was away from Cambridge, Wallace made a practice of spending what remained of the summer vacations, after the Summer School ended, in Marysville, Ohio. Mother Sabine was sorely torn between her desire to be with her husband in his failing health and her enjoyment of personally coöperating in her son's career. Usually, after the summer reunion, Wallace returned to Cambridge with eager anticipation of the coming year's work, but in the fall of 1894 this joy was somewhat tempered by his appointment as proctor in Conant Hall. Mentorship over the students was always exceedingly unpleasant to him, and he accepted the irksome duty with genuine regret. Out of this experience occurred a coincidence which made a deep impression on the Sabine family.

By a curious irony of fate, Wallace was called upon, during that single year as proctor, to report to the college office, after generous warnings, eight young men for flagrant disorderly conduct, knowing well that his action meant expulsion for all — yet the offense was such that he could not compromise. Years later, after Sabine's marriage, his wife was accosted on a trans-Atlantic steamer by an attractive woman, who inquired if by chance Professor Sabine of Harvard was her husband. Upon receiving an affirmative reply, she exclaimed with much feeling, " There is no man to whom my family feels under deeper obligation." Then she referred to the incident related above, saying that she was the sister of one of the students implicated, and that from that night to the present moment he had remained an ardent " dry." When he returned home in disgrace, her brother had rehearsed the details of the sordid affair, ending with a reference to the genuine sorrow manifested by the youthful proctor. " We owe it to him to make good," the boy had declared solemnly; " he suffered more than we did." This experience of Mrs. Sabine's supplemented a visit her husband had received years before from this same man, then a well-known and influential citizen, who called upon him at the Laboratory with a special request that he permit a younger brother, just entering Harvard, to be placed under him as advisee.

Sabine's versatility was frequently a vehicle to introduce him to professors in departments other than his own:

From Professor George H. Parker

Some time in 1894 I had gone to the Jefferson Physical Laboratory to consult Professor B. O. Peirce about an acoustical outfit I needed for experimental work on the hearing of fishes. His remark was " Oh! I am an old fogy about such matters. You should see young Sabine. He is a wizard on Sound." I sought Sabine out, and found that

Professor Peirce's remark about the youthful instructor was fully justified. Sabine quickly entered into my problem, grasped at once the biological as well as the physical intricacies of the situation, and soon had laid out a program of procedure that served my needs.

During a subsequent summer's vacation, when I was working at the Woods Hole Laboratory of the United States Bureau of Fisheries, he spent much time watching my tests on the responses of fishes, and commented on and criticized the apparatus that I had constructed under his guidance. Later, when I was at work on the same subject in Cambridge, he showed his keen interest in the matter by coming to the Zoölogical Laboratory, testing my outfit, and eventually transferring me to a larger piece of electrical apparatus of his own, which enabled me to telephone tones of known pitch from a distant part of the cellar to the water of a large aquarium, and thus test fish-hearing as it had never been done before. In all this work Sabine was as alert to the biology as to the physics of the problem.

In later years, when my interests had shifted to the reactions of animals to light, Sabine was most painstaking and thorough in his help in the construction of optical devices for the testing of organisms. He produced the most satisfactory light-grader and light-reducer I have ever seen, and he helped me construct a radiomicrometer of great delicacy, with which some of my students and I reached reliable results in the comparison of colored lights.

In June, 1895, Sabine was made Assistant Professor. "With the appointment," Madame Sabine records, "came the words of President Eliot, more valuable than the position itself, ' I know that the Corporation have a good opinion of his attainments, capacity, and character.'"

That fall Hylas Sabine leased his farm, and the parents came East to establish a permanent home with Wallace at

40 Shepard Street, Cambridge, where they lived together until his marriage. The reunion was well-timed, for a crisis was at hand for the young scientist, the importance of which could not have been fully appreciated even by this far-seeing mother, but of which she would have forever regretted not to have been a part:

From the Diary [*Fall of* 1896

Tinto is asked to study the acoustic qualities of the Fogg Lecture Room, and determine, if possible, an improvement. In order to school his ear to an accurate perception of sound, and the duration of residual sound, he prepared apparatus, and spent night after night, from eleven o'clock till four, when everything was quiet, in the underground room at the Jefferson Physical Laboratory, making numberless experiments. This took so many nights, when no time could be spared for sleep in the daytime, that others besides myself became anxious. The President protested, and asked him to come to his summer home and rest.

The responsibilities of an assistant professorship had been calmly assumed by this mature twenty-seven-year-old youth, and to these was now added the apparently impossible suggestion of solving a mystery which had defied investigators since the world began. Looking backwards, with the knowledge that Wallace Sabine did solve the mystery, it seems incredible that, although the results of what is now termed Acoustical Science and Engineering were realized and appreciated by as early a civilization as that of the ancient Greeks, no attempts should have been made through the succeeding centuries to discover the governing fundamentals. Of all the phenomena included in this science, echo was undoubtedly the best known, perhaps because Echo had become personified and given a place in Mythology. In that simple entry in her Diary, the devoted mother connotated for an echo which was to be heard around the world.

III. THE TEACHER · 1895–1905

SABINE had been teaching at Harvard for six years when he received the appointment of Assistant Professor, during which period he had devoted himself almost exclusively to personal study and teaching. The scientific papers in which he had collaborated with Professor Trowbridge and his text-book represented his only contributions of original research to the scientific world. " This was partly because he set a most severe standard for what a research paper should be," Professor Hall explains; " it should describe some piece of work so well done that no one would ever have to investigate this particular matter again. To this standard he held true, with the result that his published papers are remarkably few and remarkably significant." These served, however, as Professor Stevens remarked, to introduce their author " to the confidence of his fellow-teachers in Physics throughout our country."

Teaching was to Sabine the noblest opportunity for service the world offered. Throughout his life, even after extraordinary recognition had come to him from his research work in Architectural Acoustics, he always designated himself as " teacher " in personal reference, on his passports, and whenever the occasion arose. To be addressed as " Professor " or " Doctor " was particularly distasteful to him. Titles were empty honors in Sabine's eyes, and no worldly decoration could surpass the all-embracing appellation he elected.

Once, when on shipboard with his family, curiosity developed among his fellow-passengers as to his profession.

Mrs. Sabine, during a rest period for the children in their stateroom after luncheon, through the open window overheard two men discussing her husband. They remarked that Sabine, instead of seeking to enlarge his acquaintance on board ship, seemed to prefer the companionship of his wife and daughters, yet was unusually affable and communicative when actually approached. " Judging from his consummate knowledge of paintings and painters," one man said, " I think he must be an art dealer, probably on his way to Europe to buy pictures. I, myself, am a dealer, and I think I may find Mr. Sabine a competitor for some of the things I am after."

The other man, a banker, insisted that Sabine was a financial expert, explaining that, during a conversation with him, he had shown himself not only familiar with present financial problems, but particularly intelligent and far-sighted in his views concerning the future. At that moment, Sabine's younger daughter appeared on deck, and the banker suggested, " Why not ask the child? "

Acting on this impulse, he said, " Little girl, what is your father's business? "

The nine-year-old Ruth drew herself up proudly, and answered, " My papa is a teacher; and he asks us always to love and 'spect our teachers."

Sabine's love for teaching is explained by his exaggerated human interest in life. His major contribution was his direct application of Science to human use. Just as research forces an investigator back into himself and his own resources, so does teaching keep him alert because of contact with his students. " He always seemed more interested in me than in my work," an undergraduate remarked, thus unconsciously defining Sabine's instinctive approach to his profession. In all his relations with life, human personality appealed to him far beyond individual accomplishment. Where the two failed to coördinate in one of his students,

Sabine felt himself afforded a precious opportunity to contribute to their proper merging. Yet he believed research and teaching to be " mutually dependent." An investigator, Sabine would have told you, should never have preconceived ideas as to results, keeping his mind open to be led step by step, to Truth as the final result; while the teacher's function is to convey that truth to his pupil, made clearer by his own interpretation.

The depth of his feeling on this subject is shown in a letter he wrote to one of the Trustees of the Carnegie Institution of Washington, with respect to the course of development that Institution might hold. President Woodward says of this: " When the history of the Carnegie Institution comes to be written, Professor Sabine's letter will be cited as one of the earliest expressions of views concerning this much-discussed topic ":

To Major Henry L. Higginson from W. C. S.
[*January* 24, 1902

. . . My principal hope is that the Institute may not serve to separate the research and the educational functions of scientific men. The two are mutually dependent, not merely broadly, as will be readily admitted, but in the individual. The instructor who does not engage in research work not only loses a great privilege, which it is to be hoped will always remain a perquisite of his profession, but soon teaches Science as isolated facts rather than as groups of problems, solved in part, but not solved in all their varied relationships. If he be engaged in research work, the spirit of it inevitably enters into his teaching.

On the other hand, an investigator who does not teach serves a diminished constituency. Next to its direct results, the value of scientific work lies in its stimulating influence on every activity, not of the individual but of the country at large, and this can be best attained through its connection with the universities. The Institute will fail in part of its purpose if it concentrates the research work in one place, withdrawing it from the universities, or dwarfing by its great facilities local efforts.

I should like to suggest the counter-plan of making grants for work done, as it were, *in situ,* which might take the form either of grants (liberal, for the best results) for apparatus and similar expenses, or, if it is deemed desirable to pay salaries, to pay a portion of the regular salary for a year or term of years, the amount of instruction to be diminished proportionately, the total salary not to exceed the regular salary. These grants should be made only for work of considerable magnitude. The greatest fault of scientific work in this country in my own subject, Physics, is that it is, with very few exceptions, such as Rowland's spectrum work and Michelson's work on the interferometer, scattering and concerned with trivialities. Such grants might be restricted generally to investigations of promise already under way.

Jerome D. Greene, who for several years was Secretary to President Eliot, and thus knew Sabine from many sides, considers his greatest service to have been that of teacher. His estimate refers particularly to Sabine's personal application of the principles elaborated in the Higginson letter:

From Jerome D. Greene
His passionate devotion to Science was closely bound up with his love for teaching. It would be hard to find a better example of that inter-relationship between the two functions, each contributing to the success of the other. In both, his mental and moral integrity was the main factor; and his influence on pupils and colleagues could be described as preëminently spiritual, if not religious.

The courses in the Harvard curriculum which came directly under Sabine were Physics C (experimental Physics,

Mechanics, Sound, Light, Magnetism, and Electricity, primarily for undergraduates), Physics 2 (Light and Heat, Thermodynamics and Physical Optics, for graduates and undergraduates), Physics 5 (Light, for graduates and undergraduates), Physics 20d (Light and Heat, research), and Physics 20f (Light and Heat, research); but it was the work with his students in Physics C that interested him most. This was the so-called " popular course " in Physics, yet, at the time Sabine assumed charge, it attracted an attendance of only sixty-nine men.

In his annual report for 1899–1900, President Eliot made this comment: " The neglect of the subject of Physics by the students of the College and of the Graduate School still continues, and is one of the most curious phenomena in the University today. . . . In this respect there is a great contrast between the Department of Physics and the Department of Chemistry, the resort to the chemistry courses being much larger. The advanced courses in Physics require a good knowledge of Mathematics, and this requirement may restrict the numbers choosing them; but the elementary courses do not require any Advanced Mathematics. The applications of Physics in modern industries are certainly as extensive as the applications of Chemistry, and the subject is even more many-sided than Chemistry. There is a strong demand for competent teachers of Physics, as well as for engineers who have received thorough training in Heat, Light, and Electricity. This limited resort to the course in Physics is not at all peculiar to Harvard University; it seems to be a widespread phenomenon. There are some indications that the number of students attending these courses is gradually increasing; but that increase ought to be large and rapid."

The explanation of President Eliot's " curious phenomenon " came with dramatic promptness after Sabine took charge of Physics C, and introduced the human note through his teaching. In three years the attendance jumped from 69 to 236. In his report of 1902–03 to the President, Professor Trowbridge says: " The marked success of this elective is due to Professor Sabine, who has devoted himself to the perfection of apparatus and to the enlargement of laboratory accommodations. Much of the space once devoted to the Physical Cabinet is now largely used in laboratory work. This change is highly desirable, for the pieces of apparatus are before the student while he is engaged in testing the physical laws which they illustrate, and old apparatus, which is apt to be lifeless in its influence to all except the antiquarian, becomes alive and speaking to the working student."

A year later Trowbridge adds: " Physics C now occupies three large laboratories. . . . It is encouraging to note that students in comparatively large numbers take a course which requires regular weekly work, and which cannot be crammed. The success of this elective is due to the constant effort of Professor Sabine to increase its instrumental appliances [1] and to raise its intellectual level."

" Many years ago," once remarked Edward Channing, late McLean Professor of Ancient and Modern History at Harvard. " I happened to be on a committee of which President Eliot was Chairman, and I, being the youngest member, was Secretary. In preparing the report, some question arose, and Mr. Eliot desired me to go to Mr. Sabine and get his opinion on the matter. I think he was then an assistant professor, or possibly an instructor. I remember going to the door of the Jefferson Laboratory, and, after some meanderings in wrong directions, I stumbled into a room where Sabine was addressing some research students. I remember being singularly attracted to him at once — his

---

[1] Sabine designed and supervised the manufacture of all his apparatus, and introduced so many improvements and additions that he was besieged for patterns and models. He permitted any one to copy them, and frequently he would give some piece of apparatus away to a teacher who could not afford to have it made.

slight figure and intelligent face and extraordinarily incisive and simple discourse. I am an historical student because I came under the influence of a great master in my junior year in college — the late Henry Adams. I am very sure that, if I had studied Physics with Sabine, I should have become a physicist, or, at any rate, it would have been an even thing between two great teachers."

This comment by Professor Channing is the more impressive because Sabine's appearance and personality concealed the force behind the modest bearing and the unassuming attitude toward his students:

By Professor Edwin H. Hall

During his early years at Harvard the slightness of Sabine's figure, the delicacy of his face, the deferential courtesy of his manner, may have raised in the minds of some the question whether he was fitted for the not always easy task of teaching and controlling a large class of possibly boisterous undergraduates. But this solicitude was quite gratuitous. He was the son of a woman who, at seventy years or more, described her own way of crossing the proverbially dangerous streets of Paris thus: " I have no difficulty. I wait till the street is fairly clear, and then I walk across, looking neither to the right nor to the left." So Sabine, telling how to deal with an incipient lecture-room disturbance, said, " It is perfectly easy. All you have to do is to survey the audience and look every man in the eye." I suppose, however, that he was rarely obliged to use even this measure of discipline, for young men were drawn to him. He spoke in a low, though clear tone, and they kept still in order not to lose his words; they clustered about him after his lectures, partly to hear more, and partly, I suspect, for the mere pleasure of being near him. They took his advice about their studies and their life-work, and they could not have done better.

It is not too much to say that, for the fifteen years preceding his taking the duties of deanship, he was the most effective member of the Harvard Department of Physics in giving inspiration and guidance to individual students of promise. This was due in part to his comparative youth, though no one of the Department was repellently old; in part to his sympathetic willingness to spend much time in giving help, though others were not lacking in this quality. It was perhaps due mainly to the fact that, while he was no more deeply versed than others in the profundities of Physics and Mathematics, he had a peculiarly clear vision for the right kind of experimental problem and for the best way of attacking it, and his students instinctively, it may be, perceived this.

A fuller explanation of the great popularity of Physics C, and of the grip which the instructor gained upon his students, is found in the unusual methods Sabine adopted to excite their imagination and arouse their interest:

From W. L. W. Field [2]

Physics C was a course in physical measurements. It introduced the students to instruments for precise measurements, and the problems were all in the nature of measurements and determinations of different quantities. It was a relatively fundamental course, and demanded close attention. Nominally the same course is still given, although I can't imagine its being the same without Sabine. The members met once a week for an entire afternoon from half past one to whenever the work was finished, which was usually at least four hours later, and sometimes more.

Each session used to begin with a brief lecture, in which Professor Sabine would explain the instruments used, comment on the problem to be tackled, and emphasize the inherent errors in the method. I have never known any other

---

[2] Now Headmaster of Milton Academy.

scientific man more clearly and consistently to remind his students that, whatever method they used, they were going to find errors in it. It was through his insistence on that point that many of us got a clearer idea of his ideal of Truth that stood out in all our minds as the salient thing about the man.

We assembled in the lecture room at the eastern end of the Jefferson Physical Laboratory, on the second floor. Sabine used to come in through a little door in the south-eastern corner of the room, always exactly on time, and we, too, formed the habit of promptness, which was unusual for a college class.

Professor Sabine had a long laboratory table with gas rings, test tubes, etc., on it, behind which he would stand to lecture. As he came through that little door he had a way of half averting his gaze, walking with a quick step but with great dignity, yet with a shy and diffident manner. He would walk to the lecture table and rest his hands on it for a moment, his head bent, as if deep in thought. Then he would raise his eyes and look us all squarely in the face. We knew then that it was time to get to work.

He would begin, " May I call the roll, gentlemen? " And then he would give each man the prefix " Mister," even though he had forty or fifty names to call. He was most methodical. He knew every student by name. Each man present would answer, " Here," and when the roll had been called, Sabine would put his list and pencil down and pick up his little book, " A Laboratory Textbook in Physics." The students used to say, " He's one of the great men here, but he never has written a book bigger than that. His work is in his teaching." He would then introduce the topic.

Let us assume that the lecture was on the micrometer gauge. He would say, " Gentlemen, the exercise today is on the micrometer gauge. I hold in my hands a micrometer gauge." He would then say a few words about the exercise, perhaps something like this: " The applications of this instrument are manifold, but I may illustrate a few of them." And he would quickly do so. He inculcated respect for the instrument before he set us to work with it. And then he would say, " The problem this afternoon is to measure seven steel bicycle bearing-balls, and to calculate the total volume of the balls. Now, gentlemen, in this calculation, you will find that you are confronted with the absolute inevitability of errors," and he would go on to explain how we couldn't escape the errors, and would illustrate on the blackboard how errors could be eliminated by taking the measurements in several different ways. He would explain that the manufacturer of the steel balls couldn't escape the inevitability of error, and that therefore, in his guarantee, the manufacturer would safeguard himself by a statement of such an inevitability. Sabine used to explain why, if we took a number of measurements in different ways, many of these errors might be eliminated.

Having outlined what we were to do, he lost no time in closing his lecture with the words, " I thank you," and a little bow. In some men it would have seemed affected, but in him it seemed graceful and inherent. Then everybody went right to work.

After we settled down, he would have a few words with the assistant, Mr. Hillery, who always had the apparatus ready for us, and who, having given it out and checked his list of names, would come around and see how we were getting on. Mr. Sabine in the meantime would have left the room. After Hillery had made the round of the room two or three times, and it would be perhaps half past three, Mr. Sabine would come in again, and he would first speak to the assistant to get an idea if any particular student was in difficulty. Then, having gained Hillery's impression of the situation, he would go around himself. I never observed that he had any routine method, but, in a most deferential way, he would stand right beside you while you were computing something, and wait until he saw that you had reached a stopping place. Then you were moved to tell him of your difficulties, if you had any.

No one realized more than he that the afternoon was long and wearing. Sometimes he would say, "It's rather fatiguing, isn't it? Suppose we go and look out of the window a moment." I remember one time there was a baseball game in progress on Holmes Field, when we looked out of the window. We became very interested in the game — no one more than Mr. Sabine. Some people thought he wasn't interested in such things. We let the work slide, and sat in the window for fifteen minutes or so. Possibly some of the students kept on with their work, but, if they did, it was of their own accord. It is significant that I can't remember just how he got us back to the work.

At the end of the first experiment, he would be in the room making his mid-afternoon round, and would say, "Now, gentlemen, if you will assemble in your seats again we will take up the next experiment." At such times there was always a little less formality than when one introduction would serve for the whole afternoon, and sometimes we used to ask him questions. His answers, while invariably patient and thorough, never permitted any waste of time, and sometimes, when a man asked a question that really couldn't be answered promptly on the spot, he would say, "Well, Mr. So-and-so, that is rather involved. If you will drop in and see me (at some mentioned time), I will try to answer it for you; but I mustn't take the time of the class."

From Doctor Theodore Lyman

Undergraduates are sometimes not very discriminating, but I am glad to remember that when I first came under the influence of Professor Sabine, in his course in Physical Optics, I immediately began to appreciate the qualities of the man and the teacher, and that those feelings of admiration and affection which grew steadily to the end, had their beginnings in the first few weeks of the course.

From Simon J. Lubin

Out of all my Harvard experiences, that which I have always valued highest is my association with Professor Sabine. The dearest recollections of that period are involved in my reflection upon the moments spent with him in the Laboratory, when he was kind enough to go with me into a quiet corner, and there discuss the problems in which I was interested. I first met him when he was designated as my advisor,[3] in 1900. At our very first meeting I felt that my decision to go to college, after a working experience of five years, was a wise one, if for no other reason than that it put me in touch with a man like Professor Sabine.

For a long time my interest was in social and human affairs. Possibly at that stage my thoughts were tinged with a degree of sentimentalism. Therefore it was a wonderful experience to be brought in contact with a scientifically trained mind, superimposed upon a heart that could appreciate the deeper things in which I was interested. If out of my social experiences I was able to bring forth anything of a practical nature in these later years, I attribute it more than anything else to the many discussions we had in the Physical Laboratory after the practical scientific work of the day was over.

From William E. McElfresh

I well remember one incident that illustrates the way in which Professor Sabine would refuse to spare himself when an opportunity to help another was presented. I was en-

---

[3] Sabine took the relation of advisor to advisee with deep seriousness. He kept in constant touch with the work of his men in all their courses, arranging for outside tutoring or personally " coaching " them in subjects even so far removed from his own as German.

gaged in a piece of research work in which I finally found it necessary to undertake a series of observations that would extend, without break, over a period of perhaps forty hours. When I told him of my plans, he at once volunteered to relieve me during some of the night hours. I suggested that if he could carry the work from perhaps seven in the evening until midnight, I could easily manage the rest. He at once replied, " No; you are unable to get sound sleep except during your regular hours, while I can make up lost sleep at any time." And my old note-book shows, by the handwriting in which the entries were made, that he took up the work at midnight and carried it until eight in the morning. An hour or two later he was giving a lecture in his course on Light. All this was done to help in a comparatively unimportant piece of work, for which he would receive no recognition beyond the thanks of the individual — a piece of work that was not even being conducted under his direction. As he helped me, he helped others, and all the while he was conducting his teaching day by day, and was devoting night after night to his researches on Sound.

Extract from Alexander Forbes' College Diary
[Conversation with Professor W. C. Sabine, 1902
The great aim of Physics is to learn the nature of matter, first of ether, then of matter; he believed that this understanding would come in about forty years.[4] When that was known we could begin to understand the nature of life. Meanwhile, all any one could do was to make his contribution toward the understanding of the nature of matter, and that in most cases these contributions came from investigations not directed at that understanding.

From these simple narrations it is easy to understand why his students idolized him, and why, at the close of each col-

---

[4] Sabine's prediction is coming true in much less than the number of years he allowed.

lege session, it was a common sight to discover a group of them gathered about him, seemingly unwilling to leave, how lasting this affection proved, and how deeply Sabine's personality influenced their later lives.

Perhaps an explanation of Sabine's grip upon his students is self-revealed in this paragraph quoted from a letter to his mother (March 27, 1913) : " I am sick at heart tonight. —— did not do well today in his doctorate examination. I care more for —— than for any graduate student whom I have had, and it hurts to see him so all broken up, as he has been since he heard the result. Such things are so cruel. Why! why! why! It is not worth while. I would rather fail myself than examine a student and have him fail."

During all this period Sabine was carrying on his research work in Architectural Acoustics side by side with his college work and other college responsibilities that were laid upon him, the years 1895–1898 being occupied with the application of his investigations to the poor acoustical conditions at the Fogg Art Museum — an experience to which a later chapter is devoted. His mother records some of the extra responsibilities:

From the Diary   [*September*, 1897
Tinto is appointed on the Administrative Board of Harvard College.

[*November*, 1897
On Sunday morning President Eliot called to say that he " wanted Professor Sabine to call on him at one o'clock." Tinto went. The President wanted help in his correspondence for a year. This request, giving as it does such an intimate association with the President, is so amazing that Tinto scarcely knows what to do, but dares not question the President's judgment, his own duty being to obey.

Besides his regular college work, this work with the Presi-

dent was kept up till the end of the school year. The association with the President every day, and the knowledge
gained of the working of the College, were of great interest and value. He was invited to spend a week at the
President's home at Bar Harbor at the end of his Summer
School.

Eliot's selection of Sabine as his unofficial Secretary was
neither an accident nor the casual result of need for clerical
assistance. The rare success of the President's administration was due more to his uncanny understanding of men
than to any other single characteristic. Few students or
members of the Faculty realized how accurately their value
to themselves and to the College was being assessed when
they were called into conference on questions frequently
raised for no other purpose than to confirm preconceived
appraisals.

Sabine had early attracted his attention: " My first sight
of Wallace Sabine," Eliot records, " was in 1888, when, at
twenty years of age, he took the degree of Master of Arts at
Harvard. His face then, as ever after, was extraordinarily
expressive and attractive. It declared a gentle but firm
character which included high-mindedness, quick insight,
perfect mental and moral directness, and an impregnable
loyalty to truth, honor, and duty. Physics was his subject,
and he seemed to have chosen the career of a teacher and
investigator. Naturally I was eager to get him into the serv-
ive of the University; but the Physical Department was very
poor in salaries and appropriations, so that new appointments and promotions were rare."

During the nine years which followed, Sabine had lived
up to the President's early estimate. Eliot had watched the
work of the young scientist after his appointment as Assistant in the Laboratory in 1889; he knew of Professor
Trowbridge's unbounded admiration for Sabine's research

work; he had noted the remarkable versatility Sabine demonstrated in attacking the apparently hopeless problem of remedying the wretched acoustical conditions at the Fogg Art Museum. The time had come when he wished to study this personality at closer range. The new relations continued for two years — until, as the President himself remarked, " Sabine has become too valuable a man to be diverted from his obvious calling."

What did Eliot consider Sabine's " obvious calling " to be? If it lay along the line of Acoustics, this constructive fostering of an embryonic science seemed likely to lead its youthful discoverer away from Harvard; and the President had shown in countless ways his strong desire to keep him there. Here again Eliot demonstrated the correctness of his appraisal: while he encouraged Sabine in his research, he relied implicitly upon his innate love of teaching to hold him true to academic traditions.

As early as 1891 the Smithsonian Institution had offered Sabine the lure of a substantially higher salary if he would come to the Smithsonian Astro-Physical Observatory. During his academic career he was sounded out as the possible head of three great educational institutions — each to be declined with the same indifference to monetary considerations or social prestige. One of these was the Presidency of Harvard University. In spite of his insistence that the position did not attract him, his friends made his candidacy as President Eliot's successor a vigorous and spirited campaign.

Only once did young Sabine waver, and that was when he momentarily and regretfully believed that the President wished him to accept the headship of the Bureau of Weights and Measures in Washington. Before approaching the young assistant professor, Superintendent Henry S. Pritchett announced his purpose to President Eliot, who placed no obstacles in his way. This apparent approval of

the suggestion disturbed Sabine, and, before making reply
to Pritchett, the following letters were exchanged:

To President Charles W. Eliot from W. C. S.
                    [*Cambridge, Mass., June* 17, 1899
There is but one point in connection with the proposition made by Professor Pritchett in regard to which I wish
to inquire, and that is whether I am to understand you to
suggest that I accept the position. Otherwise I believe I
should not value it as I do my present one.

From President Charles W. Eliot to W. C. S.
                    [*Cambridge, Mass., June* 19, 1899
I by no means suggested that you accept the proposition
which Superintendent Pritchett made to you; on the contrary, I told him that I did not believe you would accept
because you knew that you had a clear road here. I hope
he did not say that I advocated your accepting the position.

In his secretarial capacity, Sabine was encouraged to
make himself familiar with the intimate and confidential
affairs which had to do with Harvard University, and he
could not fail to become conversant with Eliot's position on
every academic question. The President skilfully drew from
his young assistant personal opinions which often surprised
him, but which he learned to respect. Eliot once told a
friend that Sabine was the first to point out to him that the
competition between the Massachusetts Institute of Technology and the Lawrence Scientific School was a minor
consideration compared with that between the East and
the West, — naming especially the University of Illinois,
— because of the advantages held by the western institutions from their nearness to natural raw materials with
which to work.

Some of Eliot's letters to Sabine in his secretarial capacity
show the varied subjects in which the President of a great

university has to become interested, and are illustrative of
the relations existing between the two men:

From President Charles W. Eliot to W. C. S.
           [*North-East Harbor, Me., July 27,* 1898
    I am much obliged to you for taking the trouble to write
out the table of light-houses in Northern Europe, which
came to hand this morning. I do not know whether I can
use the facts, because of the lack of a means of comparing
those of Great Britain and Northern France with our own.
Will you kindly send me the number of railroad employees
killed and wounded on the railroads of the United States
in 1897? The figures are usually given in the annual report
of the Interstate Railroad Commission. I remember getting
them for a previous year, classified into trainmen. What I
want is the total for the whole country in one year, with
such classification as the authorities give.

           [*North-East Harbor, Me., August* 1, 1898
    Mrs. Eliot and I should like very much to have you spend
a week with us after the Summer School is over, quite at
your convenience as regards the time. . . . I am afraid that
it has been very hot in Cambridge. I have a new boat this
year, which I like well — better than my last year's boat.
You can go sailing in her every day, and, if you like, you
can occasionally pick up a race with another boat and have
some chance of winning.

           [*North-East Harbor, Me., August* 17, 1898
    Will you please send me an account of smokeless powder?
I should like to know from what materials it is made and
by what process, and, if possible, what chemical discoveries
are involved in the process or in the manufacture of the
materials. This inquiry has to do with my address for next
week.

As an illustration of the thoroughness with which the young Secretary responded to these requests, Sabine, in this instance, secured from James Ford Rhodes, the historian, a letter of introduction to Major Zalinsky, the inventor of smokeless powder, and in his report covered the history from its introduction at the time of the Civil War down to the moment of the inquiry.

From President Charles W. Eliot to W. C. S.
                [*North-East Harbor, Me., August 24,* 1898
Will you let me have on Friday, in Cambridge, a rough estimate of the length of the sea-coast of the United States, Atlantic and Pacific, with a separate estimate of Alaska? It should not include long indentations, or the complete circumference of the islands. I have received your figures for the annual cost of the British Museum. Am I right in thinking that those are the expenses of a single year, namely, of what we should call in the University the year '96–97?

Mrs. Eliot and I are counting on your soon coming to our house for a week.

An entry in Madame Sabine's Diary closes with a memorandum which the sum total of the burdens her son was carrying might easily have forecast. She could have added that during this same year he supplied articles covering the subjects of Acoustics, Reflector, Resonance, Sound, Sounding Board, and Whispering Galleries for " Sturgis' Dictionary of Architecture and Building."

From the Diary
He finished the Summer School, then prepared the Laboratory for the meeting of the A. A. A. Society, and helped carry through " Harvard Day." Was untiring in his efforts throughout the day, and then, with Tottie and me, joyfully listened to the President's speech in the evening. Thus was the busy year's work successfully rounded out and

finished, and the next morning at seven o'clock he suc-
cumbed to his *first* sickness — an attack of appendicitis,
August 27, 1898, just thirty years old, and two months, and
fourteen days.

With seemingly characteristic scientific precision, Sabine
selected the brief interval between the completion of his
work at the Fogg Art Museum and the opening of the college term to indulge in this first illness he had ever experienced, which very nearly proved fatal. His disregard
of pain was almost fanatical, and his ignorance of the significance of physical symptoms made him ignore warning
signals, thus seriously increasing the danger.

The attack came suddenly, with the result that the colored
janitor at 10 Exeter Street, Boston, was badly frightened,
one morning, shortly before eight o'clock, by the sudden
appearance of a very sick man, doubled up with pain, who
asked to see Dr. Jane D. Kelly. It so happened that Doctor
Kelly had left on her bicycle only a few moments before
Sabine's call to attend a patient in Brookline, so the stricken
man left the office, and with difficulty finally reached his
home in Cambridge, in a collapsed condition, having fainted
from pain while crossing Cambridge Common. At the house
he found his sister, Mrs. Siebert, who was spending the
summer East, and she, after making him comfortable, hastened to Doctor Kelly's office, where she awaited the doctor's return. Together they rushed back to Cambridge,
fearing a ruptured appendix, and found the patient in
great pain, which was immediately relieved by ice bags and
opiates.

Doctor Kelly then endeavored to locate a competent
surgeon, but as it was Saturday afternoon she was unable
to reach any one. The younger surgeons were at that time
away from Boston in the Cuban War, and Dr. Arthur Tracy
Cabot and Dr. Maurice Richardson were out of town over

the week end. At last, with the assistance of Dr. Clarence Blake, the noted aurist, Doctor Kelly succeeded in locating Dr. John Monroe, who promised to remain on call, and to rush to Cambridge at a moment's notice in case an emergency operation was required before Doctor Cabot's return. Thus relieved, Doctor Kelly loaded down a hackney coach with surgical supplies, and returned to stand guard over her patient. Fortunately, Sabine's condition improved, and Doctor Kelly was able to administer such treatment as the patient required until Doctor Cabot's return. When the moment came, and Sabine could be safely moved to the Eliot Hospital, in Boston, Doctor Kelly summoned Doctor Cabot, and the operation was successfully performed. " The danger was great, but Doctor Kelly's knowledge and care were also great," Madame Sabine enters in her Diary. " The wound healed *immediately*. Former health and good habits carried him in this way through an emergency."

When Doctor Blake saw Doctor Kelly's personal anxiety over the case, he said to her, " Young lady, it will never do for you to get so wrought up over a patient. Remember, each case must be considered as impersonal."

" Not this one," Doctor Kelly replied with much feeling; " for it happens that this patient and I are engaged to be married! "

It was thus that Doctor Blake knew, two years in advance of their other friends, of the romance which had quietly entered into Sabine's life.

This attack prevented Sabine from paying the projected visit to the Eliots at North-East Harbor, to which he had looked forward so eagerly:

From President Charles W. Eliot to W. C. S.
            [*North-East Harbor, Me., August* 31, 1898
Mrs. Eliot and I are very sorry to hear that you have had to undergo an operation for appendicitis. It is generally

considered nowadays a very safe operation; but still it means confinement and discomfort, and the loss of your intended vacation.

I want to thank you for all the aid you gave me in preparing the address I gave before the A. A. A. S. When I came to write it, it turned out differently from what I had expected, as is often the case; but, if you heard it, you saw that the assistance you gave me was indispensable to its construction.

This letter, however, did not fully express the President's concern. On the day following, he hastened from North-East Harbor to Cambridge to satisfy himself regarding the condition of the patient. Madame Sabine saw him approaching the house, and hurried to the door to greet him. Before he was fairly through the gate, and scarcely allowing himself time for his usual courtly salutation, he demanded abruptly, in his deep, sonorous voice, " Who operated? " On receiving the information, his genial smile replaced the anxiety which had shown clearly in his face. " Good! " he exclaimed. " Cabot is the very man I would have chosen."

As soon as Sabine was out of immediate danger, he treated his adventure lightly, and announced his intention of making a record recovery. After two weeks in the hospital, and one week at home, he again took up his strenuous college work and continued his acoustical investigations, " blithely and smilingly, and with spring step," to use his mother's words.

So, in spite of these warnings, Sabine resumed his extraordinary labors — seemingly already beyond the strength of any human being to accomplish; yet, as the opportunity for service continued to broaden, he welcomed additional burdens with apparent indifference to the weight of his load. He carried on his courses without interruption; he accepted more than his share of committee appointments;

he conducted his absorbing research work in Acoustics, adopting ingenious but strength-taxing methods of securing his data. His secretarial work with the President continued through 1898, to his personal delight, even though at a tremendous sacrifice to himself. Eliot was coming more and more to depend upon the clearness of his vision and the loyalty of his frankness.

These amusing letters which passed between the two are found in Sabine's files:

From President Charles E. Eliot to W. C. S.
                   [*Cambridge, Mass., December, 24, 1898*
Today I received $200. from the " Atlantic " for that article which you helped me to write. I have pleasure in sharing the fee with you.

To President Charles W. Eliot, from W. C. S. (returning the check)   [*Cambridge, Mass., December 25, 1898*
I thoroughly appreciate your kindness, but my clerical work was paid for last summer — fully, and I cannot agree to your kind interpretation of the situation, pleasant as it may be. I thank you heartily, however, for the pleasure your note has given me.

It was difficult for both Eliot and Sabine to meet the obvious necessity of terminating their mutually enjoyable relations, but the President knew that to continue would be unfair to the younger man and a menace to his health. " Wallace never said much about his affection for me," Eliot once said, " but he often looked it and acted it out. I realized it from the early days of our intercourse."

Even after Sabine was released from his position by the appointment of Jerome D. Greene as Eliot's official Secretary, the President continued to consult him upon important university subjects as they arose:

From President Charles W. Eliot to W. C. S.

[*April* 2, 1903

I should like your opinion on this question: Is it expedient to raise the tuition fee in the Graduate School, Harvard College, and the Scientific School, from $150 to $200? This is a question on which opinions differ, and I should like to know the arguments by which you support your own opinion — whatever it is.

To which request Sabine replied at length. This answer is such a typical expression of his constant consideration of the student's point of view that it is quoted in full:

To President Charles W. Eliot from W. C. S.

[*Cambridge, Mass., April* 6, 1903

The situation of the College as to tuition fees, as well as in other respects, seems to me to depend on the relation which it is to bear to the other departments. From the position which the University has taken in requiring a college course for admission to the professional schools there comes the increased obligation to keep the opportunity for this within the reach of every mentally capable boy. The reduction of the course to three years is along this line, but an increase in the tuition fees is a step, though comparatively small, in the other direction. The college course has become more and more a necessity. Harvard University has led in making it so, and, in certain ways, in making its acquisition possible. Scholarships can be relied on to relieve the situation for the financially cramped student after he has been here a year, but not during the first year, and still less can this influence be felt and future relief anticipated by the student before coming. The College is already widely known as the " rich man's college " — an impression to which an increase in tuition fees would be interpreted as giving official recognition. Whether this would increase or decrease the number of students is hard to say.

The same considerations do not hold in regard to the Scientific School, which offers a form of education everywhere regarded as more expensive and not infrequently requiring a tuition fee larger than that of the corresponding academic course. However, my ideal for the Scientific School has long been that it should be a three-years Graduate Engineering or Technological School, becoming so not by a gradual and therefore inconspicuous growth, but by a fiat that would attract attention and give it unique standing, especially if this could accompany the availability of some large endowment. Under such conditions the tuition fee naturally would be larger than it is now, the school corresponding more nearly to the Medical School in the nature of its work and in the quality of men in attendance. Perhaps the hope for this warps my judgment of the present situation.

Probably a majority of the students in the Graduate School find it difficult to meet their expenses even now. The Committee on Fellowships is rarely able to make recommendations for appointment during the first year of residence, and I fear that an increase in tuition fees would be a most serious matter.

Against all of these considerations stands the need of an increase in unrestricted income, which of course I can but partly appreciate, and which the public does not appreciate at all.

The record of this decade in Wallace Sabine's life may be closed by mentioning two distinct honors which came to him. One was his election to the American Academy of Arts and Sciences, to which he alluded casually in a letter to his parents, in announcing to them that he had taken up rowing as an exercise. It is to be regretted that this most necessary relaxation from his labors was not of longer duration:

To his Parents, from W. C. S.   [*April* 4, 1899

The long sweep of the oars, the rhythmic clank of the oarlocks on the out-rigging, the swish of the sliding seat, is music. Or, if the day is quiet, I take a canoe and go up the river —and there is nothing equal to a canoe. Then, afterwards, I go into the shower bath — first just as hot as I can stand it and then just as cold. . . . I would not give this up for anything. If I come out of this year having done anything in my work, it will be due to this. Please rejoice that I have joined the boat-club. It will do me more good than being a member of the American Academy.

The second honor was his election to the Phi Beta Kappa Society, on March 13, 1905. Sabine was one of the first graduates of Ohio State University to be chosen after the establishment of the Ohio Epsilon Chapter, and his pleasure was enhanced by the fact that his sister, Mrs. Siebert, was elected a member at the same time.

IV. The Revelations of Friendship

I<small>F A MAN'S</small> friends were all alike, there would be no need of having more than one. Each fills a separate and unique place in his life, and the measure of what is worth while in any human record is the sum total of these friendships. The converse of this statement is equally true: a man contributes a different element of himself to each of his friends. Certain attributes are obvious to all, yet each friend interprets each characteristic in his own individual way. With Sabine's instinctive retirement behind his " protective crust of reserve," it becomes even more important to gain insight from any momentary lifting of the curtain, when raised through the touching of some hidden spring by those with whom he came in contact.

The seeming paradox is that, while having few intimate friends, Sabine's personality so attracted others that they felt themselves to be intimate until analysis demonstrated the fugitive and intangible basis on which their friendship had become established:

From Dr. John Dane
I often wondered how I could become so fond of a man of whom I saw so little. In a world where so many things are said conventionally, and no one thinks for a moment of being understood to mean exactly what his words would imply, it was always as startling as it was delightful to look straight into Sabine's open eyes and know that for him there was nothing conventional — that he meant each word he spoke to be taken literally. Like all men of the finest nature,

he always over-rated whatever any one was able to do for him; and his whole-hearted expression of gratitude was often quite disconcerting. He magnified everything that one did by his own greatness, and yet he was the most in- ' tellectually honest man I ever met. It was the same undeviating, unshakable mental strength, united with a gentleness and diffidence and consideration that seemed to know no limits. I became so fond of him that I always envied others who were privileged to see him constantly, while I had but few and short opportunities of coming under his influence and spell.

From Barrett Wendell

When I try to recall my memories of Sabine, I am astonished to find them at once so distinct and yet so intangible. Throughout my friendship with him, he was always completely master of himself, and of whatever he was doing, thoroughly and sympathetically friendly, and yet at once unobtrusively absorbed in his work, seemingly unaware of its positive importance, and gently modest.

From C. L. Jackson

We did not meet intentionally for a talk more than five times, yet I have a very strong and vivid impression of Sabine. There are three things which struck me especially in regard to him: first, his unusually charming personality; second, his wonderful singleness and tenacity of purpose; and last, his New England conscience, perhaps the most highly developed I have ever met, and to me especially remarkable as he was not born in New England.

This conscientiousness, while comparable with that attributed to New Englanders, was partly ethical and partly inherited idealism from his father. Early in his relations with Eliot, the President records that Sabine questioned the right of an author to receive royalties from his books, on

the ground that an intellectual discovery should no more
be placed upon a commercial basis than a discovery in
Medicine. In the exploitation of his own investigations in
Sound, Sabine was quixotic in exemplifying the ideals he
advanced. If a publisher sent him a complimentary volume,
hoping to receive some comment which could be used in
promotion, instead of merely returning the book, Sabine
made a point of sending in the purchase price, feeling that
this action freed him from " even the least obligation to
write an acknowledgment or appreciation."

Among his friends, and to the world at large, Sabine was
looked upon as a " silent man," but this reticence became
recognized as a matter of temperament rather than as an
expression of a desire to be let alone. " He was silent," one
of his students observes, " as biographers tell us Washington was silent. He always had plenty to say, but was quite
willing that others should speak the obvious things. When
he saw that matters were being decided as he wished, he
was content to be silent, and seemed not unduly interested;
but when he had to write or speak, he did it well. But silence
seemed his decided natural preference. He never used one
word to conceal his thought."

In conversation, Sabine frequently seemed unduly deliberate, but this was the result of a striking characteristic.
In conferences with students, fellow scientists, or business
men, he first sought to discover the mental approach each
took to the question at issue, so that in his reply he could
meet the discussion from the other man's angle. When he
once began to speak, his ideas were expressed with unusual
facility, directness, and conclusiveness.

The occasion of Sabine's reserve has already become
apparent. Brought up from childhood to regard thought as
the most precious jewel entrusted to man's keeping, his
well-stored mind was ever ready to respond to conversational
intercourse on worth-while subjects, but was indifferent to

the trivial. " Sabine's first remark," one of his colleagues tells us, " referred never to the state of my health or the condition of my family, and upon no account to the weather, but almost invariably to the subject of research. It was usually a question — ' How is your research progressing? ' or ' What are you doing now in the way of investigation? ' And he would listen attentively to anything that I could tell him about biological activities, and discuss them with great appreciation."

From Professor Ephraim Emerton

We always fell at once into some serious conversation about things that were worth while. They were things that concerned neither his " shop " nor mine, but always larger interests of education, or of public life. I fancied that he disliked to talk about his own special work, but perhaps it was only his consideration for my boundless ignorance in his field. On those other, larger subjects, he had views clear-cut and resting upon deep moral convictions. What he said, whether I agreed with it or not, was always pervaded by the nobility of thought which was the reflection of his essential nobility of character.

From Barrett Wendell

I was staying with Lowell Blake, who induced Sabine to come one night to dine with us. In five minutes I discovered that, merely socially, he was among the most agreeable and accomplished men I had ever met. Whether he knew it or not, he was a great master of conversation, at once affable so that you talked your best to him, and more than capable of holding his own. What he said was too quiet to be brilliant — he would never take the floor and set off fireworks; but he had the knack of putting in, at just the right moment, just the right word — startlingly intelligent, completely sympathetic, and implicitly though not superficially witty. Hardly any other man of our time had so fully this social gift. When he was present, talk would never lag.

Barrett Wendell also put into words the disappointment felt by many of Sabine's friends by what seemed to be an aversion to taking part in social gatherings. " I tried my best," Wendell said, " to make him join our old Wednesday Evening Club — about the last place in Boston where men still rant and talk, as they have done there since 1777. He could not be persuaded. His work, he said, demanded his evenings as well as his days. And the familiar, habitual intimacy, which not only I but the whole club desired, never came to be."

It was natural that his attitude should be misunderstood. No man loved human contact more than Wallace Sabine, but with his schedule of work absorbing so abnormal a portion of his nights as well as his days, it was inevitable that the use of such limited time as might be termed leisure moments should be devoted to his family relations, which were unusually close and tender — perhaps the more so because circumstances forced them to be intensive. It was characteristic that he made no explanation.

A notable exception would seem to be Sabine's membership in the Tuesday Evening Club; but this, even though social in nature, was in a way closely associated with his academic responsibilities. The club was made up of a group of the younger men whom President Eliot gathered about him in University administrative work, who dined together periodically to talk over Harvard affairs. " I can see clearly in retrospect Sabine's face in that group about the table where we dined at the Union Club," Dr. Henry R. Christian once said. " I can recall his eager interest in all the discussions of University affairs, and his calm manner and rather gentle, soft voice, behind which evidently was gathered that force which carried conviction to others when once he himself had formed a clear conception of the course that should be pursued. Here, in this group, his sterling worth was recognized by all; heed was at once given to his counsels, and his advice was sought eagerly by all in connection with their individual problems of administration and work. Keenly appreciative of the problems and interests of others, far seeing in vision, quick to sense the lighter side of the situation, sympathetic and appreciative, he was ever a welcomed member of that dinner group."

Friends frequently spoke of the smoothness which characterized Sabine's handling of his overloaded routine. In his classrooms, few students even suspected his night vigils. One of them unconsciously confirms this in telling of impromptu calls upon his instructor when returning to Cambridge. " It never made any difference when I dropped in. He was always glad to see me. He never seemed busy, never had something pressing which he ' must finish and be with you in a minute.' He would sit down and chat away until dark. Even then he never seemed to want me to go. And all this in spite of the fact that he was more active than any other man in the University. I am morally certain he had to work overtime to make up for my calls."

Sabine's surprising store of accurate knowledge on apparently every known subject came from his insatiable " intellectual curiosity," as Professor Derby called it. Whenever he moved about he mingled intimately with workers in all stations of life, and no one of these would ever recognize him under the appellation of the " silent man." Just as the art dealer and the banker on board ship found him intimately conversant with two far varying subjects, so would they have taken him for a steel expert or an expert on international conditions had the conversation turned in a different direction! The details of the one he might have gleaned from workmen at the Watertown Arsenal, with whom he mingled while returning from his own night work in the Jefferson Laboratory; the other from the German truck gardeners, whom, in the early morning hours, he helped to pole their produce into Berlin on the branches of the River Spree. Once, during a vacation period, he spent several days as a workman in an American factory, to test the effect of piece-work. By the fifth day he had outdistanced all his fellow-workmen, but distinctly felt the flagging of his energies, which confirmed his contention of the deadening results of monotony in labor.

Frequently, friends of Sabine, who knew each other, were wholly ignorant of their common friendship for him. Doctor Cabot, who was called in by Doctor Jane Kelly when Sabine met his first physical crisis, never saw him until he came to operate. When he continued to come with what seemed unnecessary frequency, the young attending physician became concerned lest he had discovered some alarming symptoms that had escaped her watchful eye. Doctor Cabot noticed her anxiety, and laughingly explained that his calls were not professional, but to gratify his pleasure in the personal contact. The Doctor was at that time a Fellow of Harvard University, and during his visits he drew from his patient opinions on every phase of college life. " Cabot is the only man," Sabine once remarked, " who made of me a babbling brook." The friendship which began on the operating table, while never intimate, proved a valued possession in the lives of both men.

The Sabine family were perhaps as intimate with the George H. Palmers as with any friends, yet one of Sabine's closest associates in his college work expressed absolute incredulity when some one thus referred to their relations. Mrs. Palmer used to telephone Mrs. Sabine that her husband had " stood it as long as he could without seeing Mr. Sabine," and would invite them to dine at the Palmer home in Cambridge, or to spend the week end at Boxford. Teaching widely differing subjects, and viewing life from the standpoint of different generations, Palmer and Sabine rarely agreed on any subject. Mrs. Palmer once said laughingly that she believed they " always sat in Faculty meetings holding hands and voting opposite! " As Professor Palmer himself expressed it, " I, having been drawn to him on many important occasions, came away with a sense of permanent love."

Sabine's interest in the work of others was not simply a graceful gesture, but rather a constructive expression of genuine human sympathy. Undoubtedly that insatiable " intellectual curiosity " also entered in. He possessed extraordinary ability to disassociate himself from his own problems and concentrate upon those of others not infrequently far outside his own field:

From H. Van Buren Magonigle

During the course of our consultations, my admiration for Mr. Sabine's breadth of view and catholicity of interest grew apace. I found him entirely without prejudice, without a *parti pris* on any aspect of our problems; he was interested solely in a solution which should be the result and reconciliation of the internal forces — the imposed conditions. He entered so sympathetically into my natural preoccupation with the shape and proportion not only of the room itself but of the building as a whole, that it was as though I myself had suddenly become endowed with his insight and experience and resource, as though a new lobe of my own brain were functioning.

From Dr. Hollis Godfrey

The real beginning of my work with Sabine was the occasion of my going to him, one day, and saying that I did not see why Science should not be applied in consumption — the work the consumer did — just as much as it could be applied in the work of production. Before that I had known him only in a general way. He said, " That's absolutely true, and nobody ever thought of it before; but you've got a very long job ahead of you to get that thing out. Let's see what you will have to know in order to do it."

He sat down and outlined the tools that a man would have to have to do the work. His capacity to see a problem and to know instantly whether it was true or untrue, and then to see what would have to be done to complete that job, was one of his greatest capacities. No one else had ever taken that attack, so far as we knew, and that immensely interested him as an advance in Science. The result was that for the next six years I went back to him again and again to check on that advance consistently. He advised me what to read; he advised me what to study. And that continued to the time when he came down to Drexel after I went there as President, and suggested the organization of the Scientific Division.

I took down one sentence which he gave me at the beginning: " There is no problem, except that of human motive, which cannot be solved by use of the law of the conservation of energy." To this he added later: " No barriers exist when human motive is right." He always refused ever to be conquered, either from the viewpoint of Science or of Man. That was the key of Sabine's character.

Sabine was constantly deprecating his ability to be of service in various connections because of his lack of familiarity with the subject — then he would throw himself vigorously into the work and prove himself of the utmost value to it. LeBaron R. Briggs once said: " Wherever Sabine was placed, he proved his strength. When as a Dean he was forced into the Committee on the Regulation of Athletic Sports, he objected on the ground that he did not go to college games, and knew nothing about them; when, not long afterward, he was released from the Committee because needed elsewhere, every member except himself knew that even in the regulation of athletic sports, he had become invaluable."

When Phillips Brooks House was established to promote the religious and philanthropic activities of Harvard students, a committee of the Faculty was appointed to administer the work of the House, and to determine the direction and conditions of its service. It was a difficult undertaking, for there were many differences of opinion as to the functions of such a building, and the Committee represented many shades of religious conviction and of social judgments. The debates were animated and the decisions contested:

From Professor Francis G. Peabody

It was a constant surprise to find that the sanest judgment and clearest vision concerning the spiritual interests of the University were contributed by the one member of our Committee who did not definitely represent a specific religious communion or social code. Sabine's conclusions were simply the result of applying the scientific mind to these sectarian or social problems. He clarified each situation; his conclusions were always sustained; and the successful conduct of Phillips Brooks House, through all these years, is very largely due to the habits of the laboratory and of experimental science.

Professor Parker referred to Madame Sabine as a woman who, " without show or effort, usually gained her point," and called attention to this inherited trait in her son. Other friends of Sabine were impressed by this characteristic. " In the Faculty," James H. Ropes observes, " he was not especially effective in debate, but privately he was one of the most persuasive men that ever lived." Moorfield Storey once said, " When Sabine met a Committee of the Overseers, of which I was a member, and which was strongly committed to a certain proposition, he presented the case so clearly, so temperately, and in every way so convincing a manner, that we were all converted, and we carried away from the meeting a very sincere respect and admiration for him." To this Professor Edward Kennard Rand adds, " Our friendship was increased, not lessened, by the fact that we differed on certain points of educational policy. He had a rare gift of maintaining his own point of view with firmness, while treating his adversary with courtesy, sympathy, and a fine sense of humor."

Another trait, conspicuous in his ancestors, was Sabine's extraordinary association of faces with names, yet, curiously, he often complained of his inability to visualize the physical appearance of even the members of his own family. As long as it fell upon him personally to call the roll of his class in Physics C, the coördination never failed him, and he constantly astonished former students by recognizing them at once, years afterwards, and calling them correctly by name. It was one of his keen regrets that, in order to save time in this class, the roll call had to be delegated to a monitor. When Chinese students were sent to America, shortly after the Boxer Rebellion, to be distributed among various educational institutions, the entire group of nineteen came to Cambridge, and Sabine was on the reception committee. After they had all been presented, he mixed with them informally, and caused amazement by accosting different members of the group each by his correct name, correctly pronounced. When one of the party exclaimed in regard to this unusual feat, another of the Chinese, less impressed, remarked, " After all, it is not so difficult for Mr. Sabine as it would be for one of us, were the situation reversed, for American men all look alike! "

Sabine taught his children, when looking at a photograph, always to close one eye, as the camera, in taking the picture, is limited to a single optic. By the same token, a composite photograph of a man must be less revealing than a composite pen-portrait drawn by such of Sabine's friends who have already been quoted. This summary, given below, of such expressions as they used — for the descriptive comments are drawn from the words of men who do not speak lightly — should show Wallace Sabine physically, mentally, and spiritually as he really was. Yet this composite picture, if painted by any biographer, would appear so extravagant that he would scarcely venture to use it. As it stands, it is simply the joining together of the exact expressions taken from statements of over twenty friends who knew him best:

" In person, Sabine was a tall man, of slight and wiry build, with erect carriage. His face was extraordinarily attractive, declaring a gentle but firm character, which included high-mindedness; a refusal ever to be conquered by Science or Man; quick insight; perfect mental and moral directness; impregnable loyalty to truth, honor, and duty; wonderful singleness and tenacity of purpose; intellectual honesty; unusual consideration for others; highly developed consciousness; far-seeing vision; inherited idealism; and exaggerated generosity.

" The singular elegance of his person was the expression of a rare elegance of mind; he was always calm and completely master of himself, yet gently modest, and self-deprecating, as if unaware of the positive importance of his work. By instinct, he was reserved and silent, yet a great master of conversation — too quiet to be brilliant, but implicitly witty; never controversial but startlingly intelligent and completely sympathetic; basing his comments on a store of accurate knowledge on all subjects, and showing a breadth of view and a catholicity of interest — with a soft voice behind which was a force that carried conviction."

V. THE SCIENTIST AT HOME

WHEN one considers the abnormal demands made upon Sabine's time, and the limited number of hours in each day during which he could indulge himself in relaxation, it seems incredible that this volume should contain a chapter on home life — yet no husband and father ever found greater joy and satisfaction in his family, or gave more completely of himself in tender and understanding companionship. The fact that his hours at home were limited made them the more precious. Beginning with his work on the Fogg Art Museum in 1895, which is covered in the following chapter, he had accustomed himself to the unusual division of day and night; during his courtship his wife-to-be became familiar with his enforced manner of living, and later understandingly adjusted their new home to his necessities; their children were born into this custom of family routine, and, knowing no other, naturally adapted themselves to it. The " three little girls," as Sabine affectionately christened his wife and daughters, instinctively protected him during the rest periods he snatched at home, and reveled in his happy companionship during the limited hours when he could give it to them. " Although his devotion to his scientific work often interfered with or restricted his family life," President Eliot records, " his intercourse first with his parents and then with his wife and daughters was of the sweetest and tenderest sort."

As we shall see, the nature of Sabine's research work made it impossible for him to pursue his investigations during the daytime, even had other college demands not interfered. From 1895 to 1900, while he lived with his mother in Cambridge, she reserved the quietest room in the house in which he might sleep during the evening. After his marriage, it became his habit to take the 11:45 P.M. car from Boston to Cambridge. He worked in the Constant Temperature Room [1] from twelve to four A.M. in summer, and from twelve to five in winter. Experiments then had to cease because of the rumble of noise at Porter Station in North Cambridge, due to the shifting of freight cars. Often he slept in a hammock at the Laboratory until time to go home for a bath and breakfast. In the earlier period of his experiments, for three solid years he worked every other night, rain or shine, heat or cold. In later years he tried to limit a problem to three weeks, which would necessitate at least twenty-one nights in succession. He was always back at the Laboratory at nine o'clock the next morning.

When, after his marriage, he could get an evening at home free from committee meetings and other college affairs that tax a teacher out of hours, his wife would see that the house was quiet, and he retired as soon as possible after dinner. " Nature granted him compensation," she comments; " from nine to twelve he could crowd in more refreshing sleep than any other person I have ever heard of in all my medical experience. So soundly did he sleep that if he were aroused to answer a telephone call he could not grope his way out of the room; but let one of the children cry, and he was at her side before any one else could reach her."

Sabine first met Jane Downes Kelly in Cambridge during the summer of 1892, while he was conducting the Department of Physics in the Harvard Summer School, and she was connected with Dr. Dudley A. Sargent's Department of Physical Education. Jane Kelly possessed a personality as unusual as his own, which undoubtedly proved

---

[1] See page 109.

the first point of contact. She was born in Bristol, Rhode Island, of sound New England stock, her parents possessing ability and culture. Her father, Francis V. Kelly, was of an inventive turn of mind, being associated with the firm which later became Browne and Sharpe, in Providence, Rhode Island. The firm name might have been Browne and Kelly except for the desire of the inventor to found a business upon different lines. Her mother, Eliza T. Willoughby, — directly descended from Elder Brewster, of Mayflower fame, — was a woman of keen wit and charm. The courage with which she accepted her husband's invalidism, resulting from injuries received in the Civil War, prevented his incapacity from being a complete tragedy.

Their daughter showed an early desire for advanced education. While at Smith College she prepared herself to teach Chemistry and Physics, but later decided to study Medicine at the Woman's Medical School of the Northwestern University in Chicago, where she completed the four-year course in three years. It was in a booth of the Anthropological Building at the World's Fair in Chicago in 1893 that she and Wallace Sabine met for the second time.

Miss Kelly resumed her work in Doctor Sargent's Department during the summer of 1894, and, through being in Cambridge, she and Sabine occasionally met. Little by little their friendship developed, and when she left Boston, that fall, to take a postgraduate course at the Johns Hopkins Medical School, the young scientist was one of the group that saw her off at the station. On her return, in 1895, she again became connected with Doctor Sargent's School — an association which continued for twenty years. She also gave a course each year in the Harvard Summer School.

On January 1, 1896, Doctor Kelly, as she should now be called, opened her office in Boston. That city had taken kindly to women physicians from the time they first entered the profession, and the new recruit to the ranks found a prompt recognition of her skill in Medicine and Surgery from her men colleagues as well as from an increasing number of patients.

During these four years her friendship with Sabine steadily ripened, yet their courtship was most unusual. Her work opened up a new world as it revealed to him the close relationship existing between her science and his. Their meetings were devoted usually to discussions of scientific and preventive Medicine, and the exchange of ideas upon subjects which were treated in the current medical journals. In return, he gave to her a new insight into his own research work which proved equally fascinating. When Roentgen's great discovery of the X-ray was cabled to the American press, a leading New York paper telegraphed an account of the experiment to the Jefferson Laboratory asking for an opinion as to its genuineness. After Professor Hall's test had proved it to be accurate, Sabine rushed out to Brookline, a suburb of Boston, where Doctor Kelly was visiting friends, to share with her, first of all, the astounding news of this new aid to her profession. Her hand was one of the very earliest objects photographed by the X-ray in America.

The fact that Jane Kelly's personality and interests seemed so completely to coincide with his own made their engagement, in June, 1898, a natural step. Immediate marriage was out of the question, so it was mutually decided to keep their secret to themselves. Dr. Clarence Blake, who became Doctor Kelly's involuntary confessor at the time of Sabine's appendicitis [2] crisis, was the only friend who knew of the engagement until two years later. Each settled down contentedly to a continuation of his own scientific work, now enriched by the complete understanding of a sympathetic companionship.

[2] See page 64.

JANE DOWNES KELLY AND WALLACE SABINE
at the time of their engagement, in 1898

Because of their proximity there were few letters exchanged, but I am permitted to reproduce one which might properly be taken as a text for this chapter:

To Jane D. Kelly from W. C. S.

[*Cambridge, Mass., July* 18, 1898

MY DEAR GIRL: Your beautiful note came this morning. I am very glad that you are happy. The only prayer I have ever made is that you always may be.

> *Ce que ma main donne, ma main ne l'a plus;*
> *Ce que mon coeur donne, mon coeur l'a encore.*

They were married August 22, 1900. Madame Sabine thus records the event in her Diary: " This summer of 1900 is the most important date of any in Tinto's life, I have good reason to believe it will prove to be the happiest, and I quite as earnestly hope it will be the happiest event in the life of Jennie D. Kelly. She is noble, sincere, and of a beautiful spirit, and deserves the best — he is the dearest and truest boy ever given to an anxious mother. I go back now to my own dear little boy of two years, in white linen dress, little white socks, and slippers. He is always with me, has been with me for thirty years, ever the same, and will stay now with me in his purity till the end, and will go over with me.

Their honeymoon was spent in the New Brunswick woods — the first real vacation Sabine had ever enjoyed! It so happened that a student of Sabine's was at the camp at the same time, tutoring the son of their host, and he made a chronicle of the event:

From George W. Creelman

In 1900 I was spending the summer in camp in the New Brunswick woods, with my friends, the Hopkins'. There was a commodious club-house there at our disposal, and numerous smaller quarters scattered around through the woods. Imagine my surprise one day when Colonel Hopkins announced that Professor Sabine of Harvard had just married a friend of the family. This was real news to me, but nothing to what followed. He and his bride were to be in camp and spend their honeymoon there in the woods. It was great fun for us, and all of us youngsters were tremendously excited. And the next day they came, and stayed for some two weeks with us.

It was a wonderful time and a splendid company. None of us will ever forget those days. Fishing, tramping, canoeing, bathing, and general visiting filled our days and nights. Mr. Sabine had as good a time as any of us, but in his own way. He was always looking out for some one else. If time hung heavy on a rainy day, he invented some game, or started some interesting conversation. Sometimes he told stories to little Louise Hopkins, and we all stopped writing letters to listen. One afternoon we all started out for a walk down along the shore of the lake. Professor Sabine started out with us, but soon turned back under some excuse or other. It developed later that he had gone back because one of the guide's dogs — a mongrel pup — had cried at being left behind, and the Harvard professor returned to comfort him, afraid he was not having a very good time!

The young bride was prepared to relinquish her professional career upon her marriage, but her husband, realizing the personal sacrifice involved in thus giving up her service to humanity, insisted that she continue. He was proud of her work and gloried in the honors that came to her. Even after the children were born, he sympathized with her desire to keep on with her practice, frequently exclaiming, " How do families get along when the mothers are not physicians? "

It was into this unusual family that two daughters were

born — Janet [3] on October 23, 1903, and Ruth [4] on July 8, 1906. From this time on the parents devoted themselves exclusively to two great causes — their professions and their children. Sabine was a member of the Century Association in New York, and the St. Botolph and the Thursday Evening Clubs in Boston, but he rarely made use of his memberships. Some of his friends from time to time expressed surprise that, although seemingly indifferent to social life, he fitted so naturally into any social gathering of which he became a part. Barrett Wendell once said, " He seems to me never duly to have indulged his social faculty, and thus to have denied himself experiences which might have been not only a pleasure but a stimulating recreation." LeBaron R. Briggs expressed the same thought when he remarked, " Though uncompromising and almost ascetic, Sabine could not have camped out for a month in a group of sporting men without winning their affection."

It would never have occurred to Sabine to suggest that, with such unusual restrictions placed upon his leisure, he surely had the right to elect the satisfying refreshment of worship at his family shrine. To accomplish this, he held his home sacred to his family and friends, rigidly adhering to his practice of meeting students and those connected with business affairs at his Cambridge office; but with equal fidelity to their professions, both father and mother denied themselves many social pleasures they would otherwise have enjoyed. Even the customary luncheon Mrs. President Eliot usually gave each Faculty bride had to be declined because of Doctor Sabine's office hours from one to three.

During their early married life, the Sabines often found relaxation in canoeing on the Charles River, or taking long walks on a Sunday, when Mrs. Sabine was free from hospital engagements. Frequently postgraduate students, whom Sabine wished to know better, were asked to join them, the

---

[3] Now Mrs. Frederic A. Ley.   [4] Died October 23, 1922.

little party returning home for an early dinner. Later, when the children were old enough to be companionable, the parents preferred to spend their Sundays at home. Sabine followed the development of the children with deep and fervent affection, and his fatherly pride rejoiced in their prompt response to the thoughtful, tender care each parent gave. He taught them particularly to share his pride in their mother's professional work.

One Sunday morning, when Janet had just begun to sit up in her baby carriage, Sabine proudly wheeled her out into the Fenway. Presently he was joined by a little raga- muffin, perhaps ten years old, who was leading a mongrel cur by a much-frayed rope. The urchin joined Sabine, and, after walking some distance with him, remarked, " Say, mister, if you'll let me push your baby carriage, I'll let you lead my dog."

Sabine looked askance at the dog, but his sense of humor was aroused, and the exchange was made. For some minutes passers-by were amused at the incongruous combination of the dignified Harvard professor and the ragged urchin en- gaged in animated conversation. When the moment came to part, the boy seemed loath to separate. He begged to in- spect the contents of the carriage, and then was seized by a violent struggle of uncertainty. He glanced hesitatingly from the baby to the dog. At last he arrived at a conclusion: " Say, mister," he exclaimed, " I'll tell you what I'll do. I'll swap you even — my dog for your baby! "

The children adapted themselves to the unusual home conditions with surprising versatility. Even while they were quite small, and their mother was playing with them, a tele- phone call would make it necessary for " Doctor Sabine " to go to the hospital or to see a patient. Simply telling the children that " Mama must go " was accepted without a murmur; but the devoted housekeeper, Celia McAvoy, had to steal out of the house to avoid weeping and wailing!

When little Janet was not quite three years old, Mrs. Sabine took her to the bathing beach at Woods Hole, to get her ready to go into the water with her uncle, when a loud pounding came upon the bathhouse door, and a voice asked if Doctor Sabine were there — adding that a serious accident had befallen a woman who had slipped on the wet board-walk, landed on a rock, and was unconscious. Mrs. Sabine had to leave the further care of Janet to an obliging stranger. When the child later arrived at the scene of the accident, and witnessed a crowd about her mother, she remarked casually, " That is what I have my mama for — to take care of sick people." The children were so accustomed to having Mrs. Sabine set a broken arm, and tend to them in illness, that Janet came rushing home one day and said, " What do you think! Jean Cotton fell down and cut her head, and her *father* sewed her up! "

Sabine's cleverness with his hands was such that broken toys were automatically taken to him by the children to be mended. A doll, beloved by Ruth, had been so shattered that it seemed impossible to make it whole again, but the devoted father patiently set to work and repaired it to her satisfaction. When the " operation " was completed, Sabine turned to his wife and said, " I have a harder time than you do. You cut and sew up humans, and the good Lord does the rest; but the Lord doesn't help me a bit in patching up dolls! "

The early military training at Ohio State University was responsible for Sabine's erect carriage, and he attributed to it, and to his abstaining from coffee and tobacco, his power of endurance and unusual good health. Walking, canoeing, and fencing were the forms of exercise he enjoyed most, but the strain upon his time left little opportunity for thus indulging himself. He did not approve of competitive sports, but insisted that his children become proficient in dancing, skating, swimming, horseback riding, sailing, and skiing. His pride in their skill was always manifest.[5]

In view of his mother's strict views on smoking and drinking, Sabine's attitude might easily be accepted as due to inheritance and training; but there were two other practical explanations. The success of his delicate experiments depended absolutely upon his mental keenness of observation and the steadiness of his nerves, and anything which tended to impair these was set aside as finally and unequivocably as he would have discarded an imperfect instrument. His experiments in Biology had demonstrated the harmful effect of alcohol upon brain and tissue; as a member of the Harvard Athletic Committee he found alcohol and tobacco prohibited to athletes in training. To become Master of Sound he must at all times be master of himself.

The second explanation is that he was abnormally sensitive to certain smells, and the odor of tobacco was one of them. Committee meetings, where others smoked, were a severe trial to him, and, no matter at what hour of the day or night he returned home, after such experiences, he not only bathed and washed his hair to remove the objectionable fumes, but even hung his clothing up on a line to air. Yet no one outside the family knew of this inherent dislike. He made no fetish of his abstemiousness, nor did he interfere with others who found pleasure in indulgences which were repugnant to him.

Sabine devoted much thought to securing a well-balanced education for his children. In planning this, he placed such emphasis upon the importance of recreation and play as to confirm the conviction that he regretted the lack of it in his own early life. He was proud of the high marks his daughters gained in their school-work, but by the time he became a parent he had realized the paramount importance of health and happiness, and had learned how much educa-

---

[5] See page 255.

tion there was to be gained outside of books. In a letter to the two children, when they were respectively fourteen and eleven years old, he wrote, " Remember that health and a buoyant, joyous spirit, happiness and an interest in people and things, are quite as much to be striven after and treasured as excellence in your studies. Well educated but at the same time happy and sympathetic children are what we want. This might easily be misinterpreted, but I have no fear that you will do so." President Eliot heartily sympathized with this attitude. " Remember," he once said, " they are the offspring of two highly organized parents, and they must be held back rather than pushed."

As on all subjects, Sabine held definite convictions concerning the education of youth. He always felt that the requirements for admission to college should permit candidates to enter at sixteen years of age, but he realized that this was difficult under the public-school system, where the class must be held down to the pace of the slower pupils, rather than allowing the more intelligent to assimilate knowledge as fast as their mental capacity warranted. Under these existing conditions he deprecated having boys enter college too young. Another echo of his own early school experiences is found in his reply to a friend's rather complacent remark that his son was entering college at sixteen. " Too bad," he said. " I feel sorry for him, because the older boys won't want him around." Who can doubt that his thoughts turned back to the ill-natured comments made by his jealous older classmates at Ohio State University years before?

Reading aloud was a favorite family pastime, affording the medium through which the children became familiar with English Literature. " We trained mother for that," little Ruth once proudly announced. Sabine would often return home during the reading, and would spell his wife. Then, at intervals, the reading would be interrupted by discussing the various characters and events. Ivanhoe and Sir Lancelot thus became living members of the Sabine household. Practical use was made of the reading hours, for the children learned to darn their stockings while listening to the thrilling tales. Ruth preferred to draw pictures, but, when once brought down to earth, her work was so exquisitely perfect that an arrangement was eventually made whereby Mrs. Sabine darned her stockings and Ruth repaired the table linen! Janet was also so clever with her fingers that her father once remarked, " I am afraid the child is going to develop her hands at the expense of her mind." What pride he would have felt had he lived to see this same Janet pass her *bachot* entrance to the Sorbonne *mentionée*, — a unique record for an American-trained child, — and later graduate from Radcliffe College *cum laude* in three and a half years. Little Ruth produced some extraordinarily mature literary work [6] before her untimely death when only sixteen years of age.

Sabine always believed that in his own early education over-emphasis had been laid on Latin and Greek at the expense of modern languages, and he was determined that his children should benefit by his mistake. From their youngest days the girls learned German and French conversation and writing from native governesses. There was no formal studying, but they came to speak the languages naturally from constantly hearing them. This was what Sabine called " acquiring the language habit." He had felt the lack of ability to speak German, and thus learned the practical necessity of supplementing the mother tongue at a time when such assimilation was most natural. Once, when Mrs. Sabine reproved the children for spelling better in French than in English, Janet answered, " Do you realize how very little English I have ever written? I write as well as speak my French, but I only speak my English."

---

[6] See "Fugitive Papers," privately published in 1924.

Nearly every summer Sabine arranged for his family to be in Europe. This plan forced Mrs. Sabine to take a rest from her professional practice, and gave her an opportunity to visit foreign clinics. The fact that the children found a whole nation speaking French or German made these languages living instead of school exercises, and friendships formed with foreign playmates increased their understanding of peoples of varying tastes and impulses.

At the suggestion of James Ford Rhodes, Sabine placed the French " Rose Edition " of juvenile literature in the hands of his children. These extraordinarily high-class volumes were the outcome of a sudden awakening on the part of the French people to the fact that they were nationally deficient in proper stories for the young, and, in supplying this lack, they produced the best collection in existence. Thus absorbing their childhood literature in the French language, the Sabine girls, when later at school in France, found themselves much better read than the French children themselves.

Reference has been made to Sabine's attitude toward the dead languages:

From Professor George C. Whipple

I once asked Sabine what he thought about Greek and Latin. He replied, " I studied Latin for seven years, and I curse the day." I told him that I thought he was a living refutation of his own opinion. He had a wonderfully rich vocabulary, and his choice of words was one of the reasons for his clear explanations. At the time we talked about the subject, he was devoting several hours a day, during a hot summer, to the translation of a Latin book which described the Coliseum of Rome and other amphitheatres from the standpoint of their acoustics.

Sabine's remark, quoted above, gives an incorrect idea of his real attitude toward Greek and Latin. What he objected to was that they were taught as dead languages instead of living. He once jokingly accused his wife of being responsible for this because one of her ancestors, John Carey, is reputed to have taught the first Latin class in the Plymouth Colony, and thus started the wrong method! When the study of Latin was first suggested to Janet, she expressed surprise that she should be asked to learn an " unspoken " language, so Sabine undertook to experiment by teaching her after his own theory of making it live.[7] " We took up the study of Latin," Janet relates, " during the time when my father was giving his Sorbonne Lectures in Paris. He would seat himself in an easy chair, and, after I had perched myself on his knees, he would place a box of candy in my lap. Then we read short stories in Latin, he pronouncing the words and helping me to get their meaning by sound and coördination. He gave me no syntax, no grammar. We approached the subject exactly as I had learned German and French. When I returned to school in America, I found myself at a sad disadvantage with my classmates who had learned Latin by the usual method, but when I was given Terence to translate into French in my baccalaureate examination at the Sorbonne, I realized that I had learned much from my father which other students had missed."

From Herbert W. Rand

I once had a conversation with Sabine regarding the study of the Classic languages. We agreed heartily as to the bad teaching of the Classics, but differed as to the possibilities of such improvement as could make them again a powerful agent in liberal education. He thought the Modern Languages could be made a superior instrument of culture; I did not, but I was greatly interested in his reasoning on the subject. He had thought it out to the last argument, and

[7] See page 303.

I felt in discussing the question with him that there could
be no fairer or more thorough presentation of the case than
was his.

Sabine held an original approach to the study of Shakespeare. The archaic English, he maintained, retarded the
dramatic action and made the speech of the actors sound
unreal. He therefore recommended that the Plays be first
read in German. He gave his daughters their earliest knowledge of the great operas through phonograph records, making them familiar with the scores before actually listening
to the performances. It was natural that he should consider
music a requisite of education. His abnormally acute ear,
trained by his delicate work in Sound, and his knowledge
of Harmonics, enabled him to guide their lessons. Frequently, when he returned home, exhausted by his long
vigils, he would be found listening to the practicing of one
of the girls, instead of seeking his much needed rest. To
him, the childish notes were the most beautiful music in
the world. The Symphony Concerts and Grand Opera
formed a favorite form of relaxation, but the theatre failed
to interest him.

The clearness with which Sabine conducted his teaching in the classroom was reflected in the ease with which
his own children became familiar with subjects which
proved difficult for others. On Sundays, for instance, he
would sometimes make a game of drawing the skyline of
the houses opposite, as a result of which the girls learned
perspective without realizing it, and were surprised by the
crude attempts their schoolmates made to imitate them.
He delighted to impart to them his own rare skill in
sketching.

The question of discipline in the Sabine household
rarely arose. The children seemed from earliest youth to
recognize that their parents were too deeply engrossed in

their professional work to be disturbed by the usual childish misdemeanors. " Must " and " must not " were words not included in Sabine's vocabulary, for his wishes were always expressed as requests. The same courtesy which was conspicuous in his dealing with the outside world governed every act in his own home. His low but carrying voice was always vibrant with an affection which attracted absolute devotion. Mrs. Sabine never heard him raise his voice, or lose his temper but once — when a Paris cabman spoke rudely to her, and on that occasion he was profuse in his apologies to her. He was the living expression of his frequently quoted motto, " Never hurry, never worry."

Other epigrams recalled by Janet are:

" Clear thinking is equivalent to knowing what is right."

" Always try to put yourself in the other man's shoes."

" If you must do something unconventional, at least do it as a lady."

Sabine was always scrupulously careful that no distinction should ever be made between the two girls, even though nearly three years separated them in age. During that terrible summer of 1918 in Washington, while the family were at Woods Hole, even in the midst of his pressing war service, he had this in his mind:

To Mrs. Sabine from W. C. S.

[Washington, D. C., August 24, 1918

DEAREST JENNIE: This is a note just to you. I don't want to hurt Janet, and I don't want Ruth to feel that she has been having a grievance. This is beautifully far from her thoughts now.

But please see that Ruth has an equal opportunity to learn to sail the boat. She is just as capable as any one, and if she is not harassed by abrupt instructions, will think clearly and attentively. It is very hard to be the youngest in the family.

The annual trip abroad of mother and daughters, each summer vacation, resulted in correspondence which reveals the closeness of the home ties and the unusually intimate, understanding relations between parents and children. Usually Sabine was able to join them for a part of the time, but even when separated he followed them with affectionate knowledge. If he wrote one child on a certain day, he was quite likely to write the other, too, lest one be disappointed:

To Janet from W. C. S. [*Cambridge, Mass., June* 10, 1910
. . . What do you think my mind's eye saw all this time. Chester? Warwick? Kenilworth? Oxford? No. Three dear little girls — always three dear little girls, the happiest party in Europe, my sweethearts.

To Ruth from W. C. S. [*Cambridge, Mass., June* 10, 1910
. . . By this time you have seen a castle — Warwick Castle, the finest of them all. You have seen it from the bridge, I hope, and then walked in by the road cut in the rock, across the drawbridge, past Guy's Tower and into the Court. I do not doubt you saw peacocks walking around, and that some of them spread their beautiful tails for you. You saw the pictures and the armour of iron, and perhaps you walked out into the grounds to the head of the castle and saw the " Portland Vase." For two days I thought of you in Oxford — beautiful Oxford. And now I know that you are riding down the Thames on one of the little boats, which, after the large ship I left you on, will seem so small.

To Janet from W. C. S. [*Boston, Mass., June* 12, 1910
SWEETHEART MINE: I did not want mama to be bothered by looking for mail on your rapid trip from Liverpool to Weimar, so I did not make arrangements for any until you finally got settled down at Fraülein Kluge's. This letter will therefore be waiting for you when you get to Weimar. When you get it, just shut your eyes and imagine that I

am holding you close, very close in my arms, and that we are having a loving time together.

This is mama's summer, and we want her to have the happiest kind of rest. I have to depend on you and Ruth to give it to her. You are my dear little responsible girls, and I know that I do not need to tell you what to do to make mama happy and free.

As for yourself, Janet, play! play! play! The summer is meant for play and healthy exercise. One thing that has pleased me very much this year has been your standing straight. Now add strength and health.

To Ruth from W. C. S.   [*Boston, Mass., July* 8, 1910

MY DEAREST RUTH: Four years ago today a very dear little girl with blue eyes came to join Janet in making mama and papa the happiest of people. This dear baby we promptly named " Ruth," knowing that she would be a sweet, simple, steadfast girl and woman.

When we leaned over the basket in which she lay, and put a finger near her hand, she clasped it tightly, and we prayed that the little girl, as she grew up, would always hold fast to us, keep close to us, and share with us her every thought. Dear Ruth, you do not yet know, sometime you will, how much we loved you, and how much we struggled with you through every baby ache and pain.

During these four years you have been all we dared anticipate or hope, all of sweet happiness, all of responsive love, all and more, far more.

To Janet, from W. C. S.   [*Boston, Mass., July* 8, 1910

. . . I wonder if you can recollect — you were almost three years old then — how, four years ago today, little Ruth came to live with us; how she looked in the basket in the front room at 481 Beacon Street; how her little hand clasped round your finger; how you hovered over her; how gently you cared for her and for mama? During these four years you have been a sweet older sister. You have shared with Ruth in your play and in your lessons, and Ruth in return has loved and longed for you. More we could not ask.

Your birthday will come in October, and we shall all be together again in each other's arms. Will not that be a happy time? Mama, Janet, Ruth. I shall have you all.

As Sabine came to be called more and more into consultation because of his acoustical relations with architects, he was compelled to be away from home to an even greater extent, yet his mind was ever centered on it:

To Mrs. Sabine from W. C. S.
                    [*New York, N. Y., February* 5, 1912
   . . . I went up to St. Thomas's Church this afternoon, and passed the wealth of the world as I did so. Would you know my thoughts? With the greatest wealth we could not give our two little girls a happier life than we give them now, or do more to insure a happy future. There is no pleasure which we would give them which we do not give them now. There is much that I should like to do for you. There is nothing that inherited wealth could bring *me*, and much that it could take away. I want to do for my three little girls *myself*. It may be selfish, but it is my privilege. I want to surround you with a beautiful home, with pictures and rugs, but I want to do it myself. I want to feel that it is my own effort, and a measure of my own competence. Of course it will not be much, but will it not be sweeter?

To his Mother from W. C. S.
                    [*Boston, Mass., March* 24, 1912
   . . . This evening, as we tucked Ruth in bed, she said, " Mama, I know what fairies are — they are just the loves we think." She gets things about right!

To Mrs. Sabine from W. C. S.
                    [*Naples, Italy, August* 25, 1912
   . . . I wish you could but know how much pride and

happiness I take in your perpetual youth and beauty. I
know that the children feel as I do. Don't you, Janet? Don't
you, Ruth? Isn't mama the sweetest companion, and the
most beautiful mother in the world?

Sabine's marriage in no way interfered with the closeness
of his relations with his parents, who were then living in
Cambridge. To his father he gave an affection and protection which made the declining years as beautiful as had
been the earlier ones, when he had been the dependent. His
mother was his *confidante* always, particularly in his continuing scientific work. To her he wrote (July 24, 1911)
" I have learned and realized year by year of you and father
so much that is unparallelled of love and gentleness, of
culture, of strength, and of reserve. I knew and I did not
know."

The relations between the Hylas Sabines and their son's
family were the closest, and the fact that the older couple
spent their last years at Cambridge resulted in a continuing
communion. Madame Sabine's estimate of her daughter-in-
law has already been quoted from her Diary; Mrs. Sabine's
reciprocation is given in her comment, " To me, Mother
Sabine has had no equal nor any approach in any brilliant
woman I have met anywhere over the world." Of her father-
in-law, Mrs. Sabine says, " Having had the most intimate
companionship with my own invalid father in reading and
studying, especially his training in Shakespeare, it was a
delight to have another father so devoted as Father Sabine
was. He opened my eyes to a proper appreciation of Art.
During the early years of my married life, and until his
enfeebled condition prevented, he would come in from
Cambridge and take me to some art exhibition, where his
explanations would make the pictures almost speak. I have
never visited a great art gallery of the Old World without
wishing he were with me."

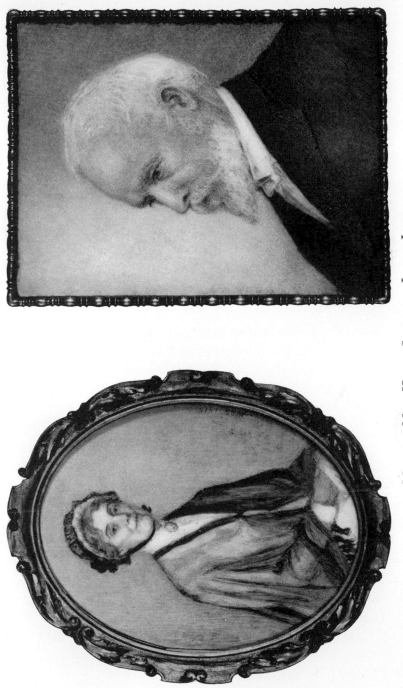

Mr. and Mrs. Hylas Sabine in Later Life
from miniatures by their daughter, Mrs. Wilbur H. Siebert

VI. THE DISCOVERY OF A NEW SCIENCE · 1895–1900

THE FOGG ART MUSEUM at Harvard University was opened to the public in 1895. Special efforts had been taken, during its construction, to secure exceptionally good acoustical conditions in the lecture hall, yet, at the first test, the room proved an outstanding monument to the acknowledged inability of architects to provide against this disaster. The Reverend Henry Ward Beecher once asked Richard Morris Hunt how much he knew about Acoustics. " As much as any one," Hunt answered evasively. " And how much is that? " Beecher persisted. The architect smiled: " Not a damned thing," he acknowledged. Beecher nodded his head thoughtfully as he replied, " I think you are right."

The use of the Fogg Museum Lecture Room had to be abandoned. In desperation, President Eliot turned to Sabine, at that time a youth of twenty-seven, who had just been raised from the position of laboratory instructor to that of assistant professor in the Department of Physics. Sabine had already demonstrated in his research work on problems of Light great keenness of insight, infinite patience in overcoming difficulties, absolute thoroughness, and fearless independence in establishing his own methods. Eliot felt that if any one could remedy the defect in the Fogg Lecture Room, this quiet, popular, and resourceful assistant professor would be the man. Knowing, as he did, that the problem of Architectural Acoustics had defied scientific investigators from the beginning of time, the President's most optimistic hope was that the difficulty might be partially corrected.

It was pure coincidence that Sabine should always have been interested in the subject of Sound. Professor Wilgus has told us [1] that at fourteen years of age the boy found " great pleasure is studying the figures made in loose sand on vibrating discs of various shapes and sizes, emitting different sounds and notes." Even at that time he " was greatly skilled in constructing pendulum devices for tracing Lissajous curves for various sounds." Beyond this, during his early years at Ohio State, young Sabine had watched the experiments Professor Mendenhall made in attempting to correct poor acoustical conditions in the City Hall in Columbus, Ohio.[2] While, therefore, every one discouraged him, and he accepted the assignment with grave misgivings, the adventure appealed to him far beyond an ordinary scientific investigation. Even Mendenhall warned him that he was " undertaking a problem that fairly bristles with difficulties, the extreme complexity of which seems to indicate that a complete solution is hopeless "; and his colleagues in the Department of Physics looked upon his new assignment as a grim joke.

Scepticism was always an incentive to Sabine. While his research work was proving more and more intriguing, this warrant from the college authorities to extend his horizon gave him a vision far wider than the actual commission. President Eliot sought the correction of a defect in a single auditorium; this ambitious youth set himself the task of forcing Science to yield to him a basic answer to a centuries-old riddle which still remained unsolved.

Sabine realized that whatever he accomplished in this new field must come from his own initiative, so he courageously fortified himself against the diverting incredulity of his sympathetic associates. First he made a careful examination of the Fogg Lecture Room, and jotted down the following facts: " The rate of the absorption is so small that

---

[1] See page 19.   [2] See page 20.

a word spoken in an ordinary tone of voice is audible for five-and-a-half seconds afterwards, and during this time even a very deliberate speaker utters twelve or fifteen succeeding syllables. Thus the successive enunciations blend into a loud sound, through which and above which it is necessary to hear and distinguish the orderly progression of the speech. Across the room this cannot be done; even near the speaker it can be done only with an effort wearisome in the extreme if long maintained. With an audience filling the room the conditions are not so bad, but still not tolerable."

Sabine began his task by consulting all available authorities with practically no satisfactory results. " No one can appreciate the condition of Architectural Acoustics — the Science of Sound as applied to buildings," he records, " who has not, with a pressing case at hand, sought through the scattered literature for some safe guidance." [3] It was quite useless to study any author whose work dated earlier than the nineteenth century. During this period theoretical Acoustics had been somewhat advanced by such writers as Chladni, Biot, Savart, Wertheim, Lissajous, Wheatstone, Herschel, Pouiller, Helmholtz, and Rayleigh; but none of these authorities gave any definite facts as applied to Architectural Acoustics. Several French and English architects, between 1840 and 1890, had written on the application of Acoustics to Architecture; but their conclusions were of no practical value. " It is not hard," observes Professor Walter Le Conte Stevens, " to describe auditoriums that have been found satisfactory and to express conjectures about those that are failures, but description and prescription unfortunately have no necessary connecting bond.[4]

To secure this knowledge was precisely the task Sabine set himself to accomplish. " Though he was dealing with a new structure, he was attacking a practical problem as old as the institution of public buildings. It had never been solved in

---

[3] American Architect, 1900.　　　　[4] See Sabine's comments, page 107.

any thoroughgoing manner. He did solve it — not by virtue of any extraordinary resources given by modern Science, but in such a way as to show that it might have been solved by a man like him centuries before." [5]

For three years he continued his experiments before taking the public into his confidence. The loudness of the source of Sound, its best position with regard to the hearer and the reflecting walls, the complexities due to interference of sound waves, to reverberation, echo, and variable absorption — all these elements came minutely under his painstaking observation. To discover which of these were negligible, and to provide remedies for those that were basically serious, formed a problem that might well seem bewildering. Especially difficult was the task in a city where the ordinary noises of the day are such that much of the acoustic investigator's work had to be done during the quiet of night, between midnight and dawn.

As these early experiments at the Fogg Art Museum represent the first known instance of a rational and successful treatment of the difficulties of Architectural Acoustics, they are recorded here at some length — so far as possible in Sabine's own words. A man's character is shown by his methods of work as well as by his actual accomplishments. In the pages which follow will be found an amazing story of patience and exactitude, of ingenuity and understanding, of indefatigable application and endurance — especially surprising in a youth not yet thirty years of age.

After his preliminary groping in the existing literature, and his study of every known optical device for measuring the intensity of sound, he discarded all established methods. Then he proceeded to consider such generalizations as were applicable, and to write down, for his own guidance, facts upon which he proposed to base his experiments:

_____
[5] Minutes of the Harvard Faculty.

" The most definite and often repeated statements are that the dimensions of a room should be in the ratio 2:3:5, or, according to some writers, 1:1:2, and others, 2:3:4. It is probable that the basis of these suggestions is the ratio of the harmonic intervals in music, but the connection is untraced and remote. Moreover, such advice is rather difficult to apply: should we measure the length to the back or to the front of the galleries, to the back or the front of the stage recess? Few rooms have a flat roof. Where should the height be measured? One writer, who had seen the Mormon Temple, recommended that all auditoriums be elliptical. Sanders Theatre, by far the best auditorium in Cambridge, is semicircular in general shape, but with a recess that makes it almost anything; on the other hand, the lecture room in the Fogg Art Museum is also semicircular — indeed, was modeled after Sanders Theatre — and it was the worst. But Sanders Theatre is in wood and the Fogg Lecture Room is plaster on tile; one seizes on this only to be immediately reminded that Sayles Hall in Providence is largely lined with wood and is bad. Curiously enough, each suggestion is advanced as if it alone were sufficient. As examples of remedies may be cited the placing of vases about the room for the sake of resonance, wrongly supposed to have been the object of the vases in Greek theatres, and the stretching of wires, even now a frequent though useless device.

" The problem is necessarily complex, and each room presents many conditions, each of which contributes to the result in a greater or less degree according to circumstances. To take justly into account these varied conditions, the solution of the problem should be quantitative, not merely qualitative; and to reach its highest usefulness it should be such that its application can precede, not follow, the construction of the building." [6]

---

[6] American Architect, 1900.

Note this early prediction, at which even the most famous architects scoffed. Every one knew that theoretically
this should be possible, but it never had been done, so the
confidence of this youthful scientist was attributed to the
optimism of inexperience. Sabine was the only one who
knew that he was on the right track. His work thus far confirmed his original belief that the problem of the Fogg Art
Museum need be only an incident. The experiments, while
directed specifically toward remedying the unfortunate
conditions there, had already carried him beyond his objective.

Together with the elaborate mathematical data he
gathered, Sabine recorded conclusions which gradually ac-
cumulated to form a scientific basis on which the whole
subject of Architectural Acoustics might rest. The way his
mind approached the subject is shown by these records of
general application:

" Starting with the simplest conceivable auditorium —
a level and open plain, with the ground bare and hard, a
single person for an audience — it is clear that the sound
spreads in a hemispherical wave diminishing in intensity
as it increases in size, proportionally. If, instead of being
bare, the ground is occupied by a large audience, the sound
diminishes in intensity even more rapidly, being now absorbed. The upper part of the sound wave escapes unaf-
fected, but the lower edge — the only part that is of service
to an audience on a plain — is rapidly lost.

" The first and most obvious improvement is to raise the
speaker above the level of the audience; the second is to
raise the seats at the rear; and the third is to place a wall
behind the speaker. The result is most attractively illustrated in the Greek theatre. These changes being made, still
all the sound rising at any considerable angle is lost through
the opening above, and only part of the speaker's efforts

serve the audience. When to this auditorium a roof is added, the average intensity of sound throughout the room is greatly increased, especially that of sustained tones; and the intensity of sound at the front and rear is more nearly equalized. If, in addition, galleries be constructed in order to elevate the distant part of the audience and bring it nearer to the front, we have the general form of the modern auditorium. The problem of calculating the loudness at different parts of such an auditorium is, obviously, complex, but it is perfectly determinate, and as soon as the reflecting and absorbing power of the audience and of the various wall surfaces are known, it can be solved approximately. . . ." [7]

For his experiments, Sabine made use of a sub-sub-basement room in the Jefferson Physical Laboratory. " Down a narrow stairway," writes C. B. Palmer in the recent article [8] on " Caves and Cubicles of Modern Black Magic," " is the shrine of all acoustical engineers — the original acoustic laboratory of Professor Sabine. Thick walled and low ceilinged, it is ranked at one end with organ pipes. At the other end is a contraption looking every bit like a therapeutic steam cabinet. In it the observer sat and tried his organ notes and building materials."

When Sabine first took possession, this was known as the " Constant Temperature Room." It was in the centre of one wing of the building, entirely under ground, even below the level of the basement of the building, with separate foundations and double walls, each wall being very thick and of brick in cement. Without windows, its walls, floor, and ceiling all of solid masonry — were smooth and unbroken. The single door to the room was plain and flush with the wall.

From its location and construction this room would have seemed to ensure absolute quiet, but Sabine found that the delicate instruments which he used in his investigations were

---

[7] American Architect, 1900.   [8] Boston Evening Transcript, March 30, 1932.

affected by the tremors of the ground caused by the passage of heavy cars five hundred feet away, in spite of the care taken to support these instruments on piers independent of the walls and floors of the building. To correct this, he had the door sheathed over, leaving the only entrance through a small aperture at the top, over which a heavy slab of stone was placed by an assistant, to be removed, from time to time, for the admission of air. Here the investigator worked night after night between the hours of twelve and five A.M., and here, on one occasion, he came near finding an untimely end, through an oversight which left the slab of stone unremoved for what proved almost too long a period. After this, electric signals were installed. So delicate were Sabine's instruments that the buzzing of a stray mosquito in the Constant Temperature Room produced a noise like a dynamo, and forced the work to be suspended.

Sabine's chief assistant in all his experiments was John Connors, whose death in 1932 removed an historic Harvard figure. " He came to us as a lad fresh from Ireland," Professor Hall says in a well-deserved tribute. " He was new to all the ways of a scientific institution, and was employed at first in the unpretentious position of assistant janitor. After a few years he became janitor-in-chief of the Jefferson Laboratory, and, in the best sense of the word, he magnified his office. He was resourceful, tireless, trustworthy, clear-headed, warm-hearted, and humorous. He and Professor Sabine were of about the same age, and the relations of the two were very close. When Sabine died, ' John ' knew more about his acoustic experiments and his plans for future work than did any member of the teaching staff."

The " Transcript " quotation refers to " racks of organ pipes " in the experimentation room. Professor Hall has recorded the actual operation of these pipes: " A standard horn or organ pipe was blown by means of certain air pressure till the room was as full of sound as this source could make it. The action of the horn was then stopped by the push of a button which simultaneously recorded itself on the cylinder of a chronograph; a good observer placed somewhere in the room listened intently but with unassisted ear, till the reverberation became inaudible, and at this instant pushed another button and thus made another mark on the chronograph cylinder. The interval of time between the two records on the chronograph — that is, the duration of audible reverberation after the sound supply was cut off — could be measured to about 0.01 second."

The selection of the organ pipe was a distinct departure from precedent. In choosing a source of sound, Sabine said, " It has usually been assumed that a source of fixed amplitude was also a source of fixed intensity, *e.g.,* a vibrating diaphragm or a tuning fork electrically maintained. On the contrary, this is just the sort of source whose emitting power varies with the position in which it is placed in the room. On the other hand, an organ pipe is able, within certain limits, to adjust itself automatically to the reaction due to the interference system. We may say, simply, that the best standard source of sound is one in which the greatest percentage of emitted energy takes the form of sound." [9] As Professor Hall exclaims: " Extremely simple in theory, but hard enough in practice; successfully carried out because the man born to do this thing and bound to do it, to break through the armor of difficulties hiding the secret of Acoustics, had been found and had found his place."

As a result of Sabine's observations came three general conclusions, which will be surprising to the layman, as applying to rooms of fairly regular shape:

1. *The duration of audibility of the residual sound is nearly the same in all parts of an auditorium.*

2. *The duration of audibility is nearly independent of the position of the source (the horn).*

---

[9] Collected Papers on Acoustics, page 279.

3. The efficiency of an absorbent in reducing the duration of a residual sound is, under ordinary circumstances, nearly independent of its position.

Again Professor Hall clarifies these conclusions. " All this comes from the fact that a sound-wave emitted by the source is reflected back and forth across an ordinary room many times a second and in many directions, so that, when a horn has been sounding for a few seconds, and has then stopped suddenly, all parts of the air in the room are about equally full of sound energy."

Having noted these general conclusions, Sabine was ready to make the specific application: " Broadly considered, there are two, and only two, variables in a room — shape including size, and materials including furnishings. In designing an auditorium an architect can give consideration to both; in repair work for bad acoustical conditions it is generally impracticable to change the shape, and only variations in materials and furnishings are allowable." [10]

This was the line he adopted in attacking the Fogg Art Museum problem. He was already aware that, other things being equal, the rate at which the reverberation would disappear was proportional to the rate at which the sound was absorbed. The first work, therefore, was to determine the relative absorbing power of various substances, and he began his experiments. One can but wonder if Sabine's attention to this question of absorption could have been first attracted by the description given by Dickens, in " Martin Chuzzlewit," of the old buildings near Todger's boarding house: " But now these mansions, only used for storehouses, were dark and dull, and, being filled with wool and cotton and the like, — such heavy merchandise as stifles sound and stops the throat of echo, — had an air of palpable deadness about them."

[10] American Architect, 1900.

All the cushions from the seats in Sanders Theatre were brought over and stored in the lobby of the Fogg Museum. Sabine thus describes this earliest experiment: " Little by little the cushions were brought into the room, and each time the duration of audibility was measured. When all the seats (436 in number) were covered, the sound was audible for 2.03 seconds. Then the aisles were covered, and then the platform. Still there were more cushions — almost half as many more. These were brought into the room, a few at a time, as before, and draped on a scaffolding that had been erected around the room, the duration of the sound being recorded each time. Finally, when all the cushions from a theatre seating nearly fifteen hundred persons were placed in the room — covering the seats, the aisles, the platform, the rear wall to the ceiling — the duration of audibility of the residual sound was 1.14 seconds.

" This experiment, requiring, of course, several nights' work, having been completed, all the cushions were removed and the room was in readiness for the test of other absorbents. It was evident that a standard of comparison had been established. Curtains of chenille were draped in the room. The duration of audibility was then 4.51 seconds. Turning to the data that had just been collected, it appeared that this amount of chenille was equivalent to 30 metres of Sander's Theatre cushions. Oriental rugs, Herez, Demirjik, and Hindoostanee, were tested in a similar manner; as were also cretonne cloth, canvas, and hair-felt. Similar experiments, but in a smaller room, determined the absorbing power of a man and of a woman, always by determining the number of running metres of Sanders Theatre cushions that would produce the same effect." [11]

The thrill of conquest had seized the youthful investigator. Here, at the very beginning of his experiments, he found that his theoretical conclusions were verified by re-

[11] American Architect, 1900.

sults actually obtained. But he kept his own counsel. It was a long road he had taken, and, while encouraged by the progress of his self-constructed vehicle, he realized that each part of it must be reinforced by continued study of the contributing elements of his problem.

An amusing incident occurred in connection with the cushions. While this special research work was supposed to relieve him of part of his academic duties, young Sabine continued to exercise his full functions as assistant professor in the Department of Physics. The strain of his double labors, and the loss of sleep attending his night experiments, made him abnormally apprehensive, so, on one occasion, when he undertook to verify the results of an earlier experiment in Sanders Theatre,[12] he was aghast to discover variations so vital as to cast doubt upon the accuracy of all his data. Had he reached a dead wall? Were his colleagues right in warning him that he was engaged in a hopeless experiment?

Laying aside his figures, Sabine mentally reviewed his work up to that point, and arrived at the definite conclusion that, in spite of errors the latest figures seemed to show, he must be right. Then he calmly began a minute examination of the auditorium and its contents. In one corner he discovered a pile of cushions which the janitor had collected, from various places where the experimentor had carefully located them, to be sent out for repairs. With these restored to their original positions the tests exactly corresponded with the earlier data. The apparent failure had absolutely confirmed the success of his experiment!

Relieved of his temporary apprehensions, Sabine plunged ahead with renewed confidence. In the experiments thus far the problem had been divided into considerations of loudness, of distortion, and of confusion of sounds. Aside from

---

[12] Sabine conducted more of his experiments in Sanders Theatre than in the Fogg Art Museum, as Sanders proved an ideal place for this purpose.

extraneous disturbing sounds — street noises and the noise of ventilating fans, — confusion may arise from the prolongation of the otherwise discreet sounds of music or the voice into the succeeding sounds. " The latter phenomenon," Sabine records in his notes, " known as reverberation, results in what may be called, with accuracy and suggestiveness, residual sound." [13]

He had demonstrated that the duration of this residual sound depended on the amount of absorbing material inside the room, and also on the absorbing and transmitting power of the walls; and now a method had to be outlined for determining the absorbing power of the former in terms of the absorbing power of some material chosen as a standard.

" A moment's consideration," Sabine explains, " demonstrates that this method, while effective in the determination of the absorbing power of furniture and corrective material, and, in general, of anything that can be brought into or removed from a room, is insufficient for determining the absorbing power of wall surfaces." [14] This made necessary a new series of experiments.

" Early in the investigation," Sabine writes, " it was found that measurements of the length of time during which a sound was audible after the source had ceased, gave promising results whose larger inconsistencies could be traced directly to the distraction of outside noises. On repeating the work during the most quiet part of the night, between half-past twelve and five,[15] and using refined recording apparatus, the minor irregularities, due to relaxed attention or other personal variations, were surprisingly small. To se-

---

[13] American Architect, 1900.

[14] American Architect, 1900.

[15] In spite of the fact that Sabine's observations had to be conducted between midnight and five o'clock in the morning, during twenty-five years he never missed meeting his college classes except on the rare occasions when illness actually prevented him from leaving his bed.

cure accuracy, however, it was necessary to suspend work on the approach of a street car within two blocks, or on the passing of a train a mile distant. In Cambridge these interruptions were not serious; in Boston and in New York it was necessary to snatch observations in very brief intervals of quiet. In every case a single determination of the duration of the residual sound was based on the average of a large number of observations." [16]

The extreme simplicity of apparatus and methods Sabine used for studying the reverberation of a room should be emphasized. As a part of his preparation, he dissected and made models of the human ear, and came to know the anatomy and mechanism of this physical receiver of sound so perfectly that he depended largely upon its unaided use in securing his data. His description of this " harp of several thousand strings " is interesting: " The human ear consists of three parts — in the nomenclature of anatomy, of the outer, middle, and inner ear. The outer and the inner ears are connected by a series of three small bones traversing the middle ear and transmitting the vibrations of sound. The inner ear is a peculiarly shaped cavity in one of the hard bones of the skull. That part of the cavity with which we are here concerned is a long passage called from its resemblance to the interior of a snail shell the cochlea. The cavity has two windows which are closed by membranes. It is to the uppermost of these membranes that the train of three small bones, reaching from the drum of the outer ear, is attached at its inner end. It is to this upper membrane, therefore, that the vibration is communicated, and through it the vibration reaches the fluid which fills the inner cavity. As the membrane covering the upper window vibrates, the membrane covering the lower window yielding, also vibrates, and the motion of the fluid is in the nature of a slight displacement from one to the other window, to and fro.

[16] American Architect, 1900.

From between these windows a diaphragm, dividing the passageway, extends almost the whole length of the cochlea. This diaphragm is composed in part of a great number of very fine fibres, stretched side by side, transverse to the cochlea, and called after their discoverer, fibres of Corti. On this diaphragm terminate the auditory nerves. When the liquid vibrates, the fibres vibrate in unison, the nerve terminals are stimulated, and thus the sensation of sound is produced. These fibres of Corti are of different lengths and presumably are stretched with different tensions. They therefore have different natural rates of vibration and a sympathetic resonance for different notes." [17]

For his absorption tests he utilized the simplest and commonest materials. The absorbing power of the walls, floor, windows, etc., of a certain bare room, using the Sanders Theatre cushions as a unit, was found to be equal to that of 146 running metres of these cushions. But presently Sabine discovered that the exposed vertical edge of a cushion counted as much per unit area as the exposed horizontal top. This striking fact was brought out after experiments made with cushions having one edge pushed against the backs of settees had given anomalous results.

" It was then recalled," Sabine records, " that about two years before, at the beginning of an evening's work, the first lot of cushions brought into the room were placed on the floor, side by side, with edges touching, but that, after a few observations had been taken, the cushions were scattered about the room, and the work was repeated. This was done not at all to uncover the edges, but in the primitive uncertainty as to whether near cushions would draw from each other's supply of sound, as it were, and thus diminish each other's efficiency. No further thought was then given to these discarded observations until recalled by the above-mentioned discrepancy. They were sought out from the

[17] Collected Papers on Acoustics.

notes of that period, and it was found that, as suspected, the absorbing power of the cushions when touching edges was less than when separated. Eight cushions had been used and, therefore, fourteen edges had been touching. A record was found of the length and the breadth of the cushions used, and, assuming that the absorbing power was proportional to the area exposed, it was possible to calculate their thickness by comparing the audible duration of the residual sound in the two sets of observations; it was thus calculated to be 7.4 centimetres. On stacking up the same cushions and measuring their total thickness, the average thickness was found to be 7.2 centimetres, in very close agreement with the thickness estimated from their absorption of sound. Therefore, the measurements of the cushions should be, not in running metres of cushion, but in square metres of exposed surface." [18]

Thus the square metre of cushion replaced the running metre as a convenient unit of reference, even though a square metre of open window was taken as the final standard. Sabine explains the general relation of these two units:

" For the purposes of the present investigation, it is wholly unnecessary to distinguish between the transformation of the energy of the sound into heat and its transmission into outside space. Both shall be called ' absorption.' The former is the special accomplishment of cushions, the latter of open windows. It is obvious, however, that if both cushions and windows are to be classed as absorbents, the open window, because the more universally accessible and the more permanent, is the better unit. The cushions, on the other hand, are by far the more convenient in practice, for it is possible only on very rare occasions to work accurately with the windows open, not at all in summer on account of night noises, — the noise of crickets and other insects, — and in

---

[18] American Architect, 1900.

the winter only when there is but the slightest wind; and further, but few rooms have sufficient window surface to produce the desired absorption. It is necessary, therefore, to work with cushions, but to express the results in open-window units." [19]

Experiments now became necessary to determine the absorbing power of various materials used in construction. Sabine had secured data regarding brick set in cement from the Constant Temperature Room in the Jefferson Physical Laboratory. Now he wanted to learn the absorbing power of hard pine sheathing and of glass. Just at this time the new Botanical Laboratory and greenhouses, given to Harvard University for the Harvard Botanic Garden, were completed. Sabine begged the privilege of conducting experiments there before the plants were moved in. Many of the opportunities to measure the influence of various building materials were accidental, and not likely to be offered a second time. The promptness with which Sabine accepted these, and the finality of his action adds much to the merit of his achievements. The Director of the Harvard Botanic Garden recalls the experience:

From Professor George Lincoln Goodale
Professor Sabine found that our unfilled greenhouses offered him a good place to study echoes. Night after night he made use of the opportunity, and obtained some gratifying results. Here, as everywhere, he impressed the visitors who watched him by his extreme accuracy. Of course, these occasional visitors, who had been attracted to the new structure by the novel lights, were unwelcome; but Sabine never betrayed the slightest impatience at their presence. He had often to discontinue his researches until the intruders had gone.

---

[19] American Architect, 1900.

With satisfactory data in hand regarding the absorbing power of various building materials as a back-log to his investigation, Sabine now shifted his scene of operation to the lecture room and the attendants' room of the Boston Public Library, to determine the rate of decay of residual sound. These rooms were selected because they were finished with material of slight absorbing power — tile ceiling, plaster on tile walls, and polished cement floor — which resulted in excessive reverberation.

On the platform Sabine placed four organ pipes, all of the same pitch, each on its own tank or wind supply, and each having its own electro-pneumatic valve. All these valves, however, were connected to one chronograph, key, and battery, so that one, two, three, or all the pipes, might be started and stopped at once, and when less than four were in use any desired combination could be made. One pipe was sounded, and the duration of audibility of the residual sound was determined by repeated observations. The experiment was then made with two organ pipes instead of one; then with three pipes; and, finally, with four. The whole series was then repeated, but beginning with a different pipe and combining different pipes for the two and three pipe sets. In this way the series was repeated four times, the combinations being so made that each pipe was given an equal weight in the determination of the duration of audibility of the residual sound under the four different conditions.

Having added this data on the absorptive qualities of various wall surfaces and the rate of decay of residual sound to his previously acquired data, Sabine attacked as the next problem the absorbing power of an audience. How many public speakers had ever considered that the proportion of men and women among their listeners is a vital factor in having the voice deliver its message? Yet, if the nature of the building materials so clearly affects the quality of sound, it becomes obvious, with the question once raised, that the clothing of men and women introduces an element which demands consideration. In his experiments, Sabine regarded the audience as one side of a room, looking at it as an extended absorbing surface. The story of his efforts to secure new observations reveals the constant difficulties under which he worked, and discloses his ingenuity in creating his opportunities.

In order to enveigle an audience with which he could experiment, he announced a lecture to be given at the Jefferson Laboratory on Wireless Telegraphy — at that time a novel and popular development of Physics. At the end of the lecture he calmly told his listeners why he had lured them there, and begged them to remain to assist him in his experiments. To secure his data in the shortest possible time, Sabine stationed nine observers at different points in the room, three of whom had prepared themselves by previous practice. His own key controlled the organ pipes and started the chronograph, while he and the other observers each had a key which was connected with the chronograph to record the cessation of audibility of the sound. The experimentor derived no little satisfaction when he noted that the point determined six years before, by a different set of observers, exactly coincided with that arrived at by this latest test.

Sabine complimented the audience upon its patience; but what shall we think of the patience of an investigator who, prevented by rain from securing his data at his first attempt, calmly waits years for propitious conditions; or, on another occasion, discards data obtained from over three thousand observations because of failure to record the kind of clothing worn by the observer, or whether his hair had recently been cut!

Another of Sabine's experiments was to determine the absorption of sound by wood sheathing. It had not been an easy matter to find conditions suitable for this experiment. " Quite a little searching in the neighborhood of Boston failed to discover an entirely suitable room," Sabine records. " The best one available adjoined a night-lunch room. The night lunch was bought out for a couple of nights, and the experiment was tried. The work of both nights was much disturbed. The traffic past the building did not stop until nearly two o'clock, and began again about four. The interest of those passing by on foot throughout the night, and the necessity of repeated explanations to the police, greatly interfered with the work." [20]

Scientists and architects were following Sabine's experiments with eager interest, but to the public such painstaking efforts were incomprehensible. Only recently the subject was considered of sufficient " news " value to warrant this editorial in a leading metropolitan journal, under the title of " Clothes Truly Loud ":

From the " New York Sun," March 2, 1932

Many a venerable wheeze has been based on the theme of clamant apparel; a joke that never fails is to speak of clothing of extreme cut and vivid coloring as being loud. The Federal Bureau of Standards has conducted some elaborate experiments to demonstrate that this is not wholly a joke, although quantity and thickness rather than color determine whether garments can accurately be described as loud. These experiments serve to confirm and extend some observations by Professor W. C. Sabine of Harvard in 1895 to the effect that certain phenomena of Acoustics may be traced to the attire of human beings.

It has been discovered, for instance, that an audience of men wearing overcoats absorbs more sound than one of an equal number of men without overcoats; that an audience

---

[20] American Architect, 1900.

of men without overcoats absorbs more sound than one of an equal number of women wearing coats; that an audience of women wearing coats absorbs more than an audience of women without coats. The explanation is that acoustic quality in any room depends almost entirely upon the amount of reverberation that room exhibits. Sound-waves are reflected back and forth with great rapidity from walls, ceiling, furnishings, and floor. At each reflection a tiny portion is absorbed. Because of the fibrous character of clothing, its absorption on this account is relatively great.

As every experienced singer or speaker knows, there may be a vast difference between the acoustic properties of two different auditoriums, even when these are of the same size and shape; that there is a difference between those of a large room when it is filled and when it is half empty. Temperamental performers have been known to express unwillingness to perform when the crowd was not up to capacity; perhaps some of these have been maligned and misunderstood by critics who supposed that a void in the box office, rather than in the auditorium, was at the root of the trouble. Such abused artists find vindication in the report of the Bureau of Standards. It is to be hoped, however, they will not stress the point too far. Imagination staggers before the vision of some future when a temperamental orator may prescribe the quality, weight, and material of the garments to be worn by his audience.

Thus, in 1932, the Bureau of Standards in Washington calls attention to phenomena in Architectural Acoustics, without adding a single scientific fact beyond those established by Sabine thirty-seven years earlier!

If the audience itself was such a factor in studying his problem, what would be the effect of paintings on canvas, or of the presence of decorative plants? Infinitely detailed data of all these elements found their way into Sabine's note-book, and played their part in confirming his now definitely forming theories based on definite scientific demonstration.

Up to this point, Sabine had satisfied himself that the total absorption of sound in a room was due to the walls, furniture, and audience. There remained but one other possible absorbent — the resistance of the vibrating air. Now he undertook to demonstrate that this viscosity of the air throughout the body of the room was entirely negligible in comparison with the other sources of absorption.

Sabine felt that the two rooms in the Boston Public Library, having in their bare and unfurnished condition less absorbing power in the walls than any other rooms of their size, would show the resistance of the air if it was really a practical factor. Fortunately, also, the two rooms differed greatly in size, the volume of one being about thirty-five times that of the other, while the ratio of the areas of the wall surfaces was about twelve. That part of the absorption due to the walls was proportional to the areas of the walls, and the part due to the viscosity of the air was proportional to the volumes of the rooms. The experiments proved Sabine's conviction that the whole absorbing power was accurately proportional to the areas of the walls. Rooms more suitable for the demonstration of this point could scarcely have been designed, and Sabine was fortunate in gaining access to them in settling this fundamental question so conclusively. In 1899 he reciprocated by correcting the defects in these rooms.

It was thus that Sabine grasped for opportunities for experiment. His income was limited, and he was so over-scrupulous that he personally assumed many expenses which rightfully should have been charged against his professional work. President Eliot became much exercised over his stubborn persistence as applied to the Fogg investigations, which did not yield until Sabine received a reprimand which could not be ignored:

From President Charles W. Eliot to W. C. S.

[*Cambridge, Mass., November 3, 1897*

Your explanation of November 3d about your expenditures in making the investigation which Mr. Hooper and I asked you to make is very far from being satisfactory. You have made sufficient progress to be able to prescribe for the Fogg Lecture Room, and you are going to make that prescription. What the Corporation wants is to pay all the costs to this date of that investigation, not of those experiments only which certainly contributed to the result, but of all the experiments made with that object in view which Mr. Hooper and I set before you. Unless you enable the Corporation to do this by rendering an account of your expenditures, you leave the Corporation in the position of having engaged you in work in their interest which not only cost you much time and labor, but also cost you money. It seems to me that, on reflection, you will perceive that this is not a suitable relation for the Corporation to be left in with one of its assistant professors. You will of course be at liberty to continue the investigation at your discretion, and at your own charge; but up to this time all charges ought to be paid by the Corporation, including the traveling expenses, admission tickets, and the purchase of instruments. These expenses do not require any justification — they are matters of course in such an inquiry.

The President had followed the young investigator with intense and detailed interest during these vital years of experimental labor which, step by step, built up a new science, and turned the original assignment into an event of world importance. Quotations from two of Eliot's letters to Sabine during this period show how closely he kept in touch:

From President Charles W. Eliot to W. C. S.

[Cambridge, Mass., November 21, 1895

It seems to me that the gallery is the first experiment to try, because that means perhaps a permanent cure and an increase of seating capacity to boot. Would it cost much to construct a rough and light gallery of wood which would sufficiently represent a permanent structure? It seems to me that that experiment would be more serviceable than a canvas experiment. You can call on Mr. Garfield, Superintendent of Buildings, for his assistance if you need it. The light lumber used would subsequently come in play elsewhere. I suggest that you make no canvas experiment until the gallery experiment has been tried. The gallery might certainly have an open balustrade — in fact, would need one. Could not the experimental gallery be made of furring and laths only? No weight need be put on it. The permanent gallery will have to be constructed with steel beams and a wooden floor, and perhaps wire lathing and plastering underneath the floor.

Here the President betrays how his interest in the experiment is becoming overshadowed by his interest in the man:

From President Charles W. Eliot to W. C. S.

[North-East Harbor, Me., July 28, 1896

When I consider that you are carrying on actively a summer school, it seems to me that you ought not to work nights as well. I should be glad if you would put off your experiments on the different college rooms till after the Summer School is over. Whenever you work between midnight and four o'clock in the morning, make sure that you get in all your usual amount of sleep. To interfere with the sleep habit is always risky.

The Fogg Art Museum case was officially closed in September, 1898, when the final installation was completed.

The three years of experimentation seem a tremendous effort when the simplicity of the final remedy, as Sabine sums it up, is considered. No mystery remains complicated when the solution is once discovered: " Between 1895 and 1898 I determined the relation which existed between the volume, the shape of the room, and the location of its absorbing components, and the resulting acoustical quality. I determined the absorbing power of all the materials that entered into the construction of the room and of its furniture. I then investigated the absorbing power, making accurate measurements of many materials which might be brought into the room for its improvement — oil paintings, carpets, rugs, domestic and oriental, cheese-cloth, cretonne cloth, shelia curtains, cork, and linoleum. Above all these, there stood out in this quantitative investigation, as more absorbent than anything else, felt. The particular grade of felt used at this time is that known as hair-felt, made from the hair of cattle.

" In 1898, in consequence of this investigation, hair-felt one inch in thickness was glued to the walls in the rectangular spaces between the windows and on the recessed lunettes in the ceiling. Over this was stretched asbestos cloth, also of moderately high absorbing power, but greater than that of cheese cloth. However, an important consideration in the use of asbestos was its fireproof quality. The asbestos was placed in contact with the felt, and held against it by an office wire-grating. The use of this construction was immediately successful, and it has since remained untouched, the lecture room being used constantly, not merely for classes, but for public lectures and musical concerts." [21]

Sabine's acknowledgment of the honorarium for his services contains an echo of his unwilling acceptance of President Eliot's insistence that his work be placed upon a commercial basis:

[21] Testimony in the Mazer Case.

To President Charles W. Eliot from W. C. S.

By this evening's mail I have received a cheque for five hundred dollars from the Treasurer of Harvard University " for work in improving the acoustics of the lecture room at the Fogg Museum." It is with some hesitation and reluctance that I give up the keen pleasure of having done this as a part of my regular duties, to which was added zest by its being a special assignment. On the other hand, I appreciate the payment as of more than its face value.

In November, 1898, Sabine read a paper on " Acoustics " at the convention of the American Institute of Architects at Washington, D. C., in which he tentatively gave the results of and conclusions upon his work up to that time. A comparison of this paper with that published in the *American Architect* in 1900 is of peculiar interest in noting the tremendous gain in the author's self-confidence during the intervening two years. There are no radical changes — Sabine's work never had to be corrected — and the later experiments so completely confirmed the earlier conclusions that what had been recorded as personal opinions were now stated as incontrovertible facts.

It was this paper that gave Sabine his first real recognition. The congratulations he received from his colleagues and friends in the University were perhaps the most appreciated:

From Professor Albert Bushnell Hart

[Cambridge, October 16, 1900

I am amazed that a subject so recondite should be capable of treatment so lucid, so interesting, and so conclusive. I have learned something from trained archaeologists about the method of proof by elimination, but I never expected to have the sense of historical evidence quickened by a treatise on Acoustics. . . . I congratulate you equally on the charm of your style, for I do not remember to have read an article so necessarily technical in which the use of the mother tongue seemed to me so excellent. I hope, now that you are great, and mentioned by name on great occasions, you will not forget your old friends!

From Professor John Trowbridge   [*August* 13, 1900
I hasten to congratulate you on what President Eliot would call " a good job." You are now the authority in the subject of which you treat, and I cannot say more.

Sabine acknowledged that he had arrived at an " approximate " solution of the problem, and announced that he was undertaking to reduce his data to mathematical formulae. This was conclusive evidence that in his own mind the mystery had been completely solved; for each step he took was so exactly calculated that he was never once obliged to retrace. Yet, still in keeping with his characteristic caution, he preferred to claim the solution as " approximate," while he pushed on with further experiments to produce irrefutable evidence.

With the publication of this paper the public first became aware that a new science had actually been discovered. The fact, however, that the mystery of Architectural Acoustics was thousands of years old, and that, if really solved, vague uncertainty had at last been reduced to a scientific basis, was too astounding to be accepted without the further conclusive proof upon which Sabine was still engaged. " Because familiarity with the phenomenon of Sound has so far outstripped the adequate study of the problems involved," Sabine declared, " many of them have been popularly shrouded in a wholly unnecessary mystery. The conditions surrounding the transmission of speech in an enclosed auditorium are complicated, it is true, but are only such as will yield an exact solution in the light of adequate data. It is, in other words, a rational engineering problem." [22]

---

[22] Journal of the Franklin Institute, January, 1915.

Then came the announcement that McKim, Mead &
White, architects of the new Symphony Hall, in Boston, had
placed the responsibility for the acoustics unreservedly in
Sabine's hands, and were preparing their plans for the first
time in history in conformity to a scientist's ideas. When the
youthful expert supplemented this announcement by guar-
anteeing that the new hall should be acoustically perfect, he
issued a challenge to the skepticism of architects throughout
the world.

EARLY in his experiments at the Fogg Art Museum, Sabine stated that it *should be* possible ultimately to determine in advance of construction the acoustical qualities of any auditorium; at the conclusion of these labors, he declared that he *believed* this could be done; in accepting the responsibility for the acoustics of what was later to be known as Symphony Hall, in Boston, he flatly declared that the application of the scientific principles resulting from his experiments *would guarantee* successful results. Coming from a man of Sabine's conservative disposition, the accumulative strength of these statements could result only from a confidence based on definite accomplishment.

When the question of a new Music Hall in Boston had been first agitated, Mr. McKim, of McKim, Mead & White, had prepared plans and a model of a most attractive auditorium along classical lines. Later, at the instance of Major Henry Lee Higginson, the master mind of the project, Mr. Mead, visited Europe for the purpose of consulting with musical and scientific authorities in France and Germany. The Greek theatre as a music hall was an untried experiment, and, because untried, was regarded as of uncertain merits for the purpose by the musical Conductors consulted. The whole plan was therefore abandoned. Ten years later, when again revived, the conventional rectangular form was adopted, the intention of the Building Committee being to follow the general proportions and arrangement of the Leipzig Gewandhaus, so enlarged as to increase its seating capacity about seventy per cent; thus making it a little more than equal to the old Music Hall, at that time the home of the Boston Symphony Orchestra.

That this new and important structure was in contemplation so shortly after the completion of Sabine's work at the Fogg Art Museum was a dramatic coincidence which really compelled him to continue his work in Architectural Acoustics. In view of his achievements thus far, the refusal of the youthful investigator to consider his diversion as merely an incident is easily comprehended; yet without some definite new objective he might quite naturally have returned to his research problems of Light and Optics had not Fate taken a hand. Even so, and in spite of his unquestioned success, Sabine took the new commission under consideration with even graver doubts than those he had experienced three years earlier in assuming the problem of the Fogg Art Museum.

Again it was President Eliot who forced the issue. His quiet observation of the youthful experimentor's progress from the beginning had absolutely confirmed his belief that Sabine was destined for work in a field larger than that restricted to an academic classroom. When he learned from Major Higginson how universal were the apprehensions concerning the acoustic properties of the new hall — apprehensions which inevitably formed a disturbing element in the minds of those concerned with the erection of all auditoriums — Eliot naturally thought of Sabine as the solution of the problem.

What Higginson wished to secure was a music hall adapted acoustically to the perfect production of symphonic music as rendered by the Boston Symphony Orchestra, and to nothing else. Even such famous architects as McKim, Mead & White admitted themselves powerless to guarantee that satisfactory acoustical properties would be secured. Eliot related to Higginson the story of Sabine and the Fogg

Art Museum, and suggested placing the problem in the young scientist's hands. Then he told Sabine what he had done.

Sabine's misgivings were wholly scientific. While personally confident that each step he had taken was accurate and to be relied on, he had not as yet succeeded in setting down in scientific form the basic formula upon which his theories rested. He recognized the opportunity the new Symphony Hall offered for demonstration; but with appreciation of the opportunity came a realization that success would not be universally acknowledged unless based upon a scientifically accepted constant. He expressed his interest in the new proposition to President Eliot, and then took the matter under profound consideration.

As always, in such instances, his *confidante* was his mother, who, with the exception of Sabine himself, knew more than any one concerning the subject upon which he was now engaged. For a fortnight he devoted himself feverishly to a perusal of his notes, representing the labors of the preceding three years. Then, suddenly, at a moment when his mother was watching him anxiously, he turned to her, his face lighted with gratified satisfaction, and announced quietly, " I have found it at last! "

Madame Sabine herself has recorded the incident in a letter to her daughter. While somewhat technical, this letter serves to demonstrate how closely she was able to follow her son's work:

From Madame Sabine to Mrs. Siebert
What do you think Tinto has found! He took the set of experiments he made two or three years ago, when he covered the seats, floor, and walls with cushions, taking successive observations, and plotted them. By letting the abscissas equal the amount of the cushions, and the ordinates be the duration of sound, he gets a perfect hyperbolic curve,

$xy =$ a constant $= k$. This makes everything definite. His whole face smiles, although he is very tired. . . .

You see,

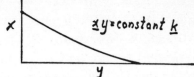

as $x =$ cushion increases, $y =$ duration of residual sound diminishes (see equation $xy =$ k.) When x becomes infinite — that is, when the whole space of the room becomes completely full of cushions — the residual sound — y — would become zero: that is, the curve would cut the axis of x at infinity, practically. This axis of x, from the beginning to the place where the curve cuts it, is called the parameter of the curve. Then, about the displacement of the origin of the hyperbola; you see, there was some deadening of sound by the walls before he began putting in cushions. That would represent the space between the origin and the axis of y.[1]

He rattled it off to me so fast, and when I said " Hold on," he said, " Let me tell it to you; it clears it up in my own mind to explain it to you." (Rather a new departure for him!) So I let him go on, and caught what I could.

In simple words, this formula, the outcome of his intensive study of rooms of different shapes and sizes, enabled Sabine to calculate with scientific precision, and in advance of construction, how long the reverberation would last in a given auditorium, by ascertaining the absorbing power of the different materials and the area of their several surfaces, in relation to the volume of a room in cubic metres. Simple enough when once reduced to words of one syllable, yet so baffling until thus set down as to defy all earlier investigators!

---

[1] See Sabine's letter to President Eliot, which follows.

To President Charles W. Eliot, from W. C. S.

[*October* 30, 1898

When you spoke to me Friday in regard to Music Hall, I met the suggestion with a hesitancy the impression of which I now desire to correct. At the time, I was floundering in a confusion of observations and results which last night resolved themselves in the clearest manner. You may be interested to know that the curve, in which the duration of the residual sound is plotted against the absorbing material, is a rectangular hyperbola with displaced origin, that the displacement of the origin is the absorbing power of the walls of the room; and that the parameter of the hyperbola is very nearly a linear function of the volume of the room.

This opens up a wide field. For example: from results obtained two years ago, during the remodeling of University Hall, it is possible to deduce the absorbing power per square yard of wall surface, plaster on lath. Thus from the work in the Recorder's Office is obtained the result .064, and from the work in the Faculty Room .063. It is only necessary to collect further data in order to predict the character of any room that may be planned, at least as respects reverberation.

No one can read this letter without recognizing the new note of triumph which had entered into Sabine's life. At this point he knew himself to be Master of Architectural Acoustics. It now remained for him to demonstrate this to the world.

From President Charles W. Eliot to W. C. S.

[*Cambridge, October* 31, 1898

I understand from your note of yesterday that, if you can determine the absorbing power with reasonable accuracy of a square yard of plaster on lath, of plaster on wire, and of plaster on brick, you can predict with some accuracy the character as respects reverberation of any room that may be planned. It would seem to follow that the shape of the room did not make much difference, so far as reverberation is concerned. I understand also that you have already got some data for determining the absorbing power of those different materials.

I have written to Major Higginson, telling him the kind of help I think he could get from you towards the construction of a satisfactory Music Hall for Boston.

At the first conference between the two men, Major Higginson was deeply impressed by the young scientist's replies to his searching questions. Sabine's exposition of any subject always possessed unusual clarity, and his quiet conviction imparted to his hearer his own calm confidence. Higginson was a man of equally strong individuality, slow to entrust his affairs to others; but, when once satisfied as to the ability of his agent, he backed him with all the force of his dynamic temperament. Before Symphony Hall was finally completed, this characteristic was to stand young Sabine in good stead!

In prosecuting his work at Symphony Hall, Sabine's problem was concerned with the scientific application of principles already established rather than with the conduct of further experiments to secure new data. His " foundation " was firmly built. Until now, his work had represented a legitimate problem in Physics, and as such he knew that his conclusions were accepted as authoritative. In assuming this new commission, therefore, Sabine took pains to make his position clear. As usual, he minimizes the confidence he really felt:

" The question as to what constitutes good and what constitutes poor acoustics, what effects are desirable in an auditorium designed for speaking, and even more especially in one designed for music, is not a question in Physics. It is therefore not one for which the writer is especially qualified, and would not be undertaken were it not in the first place absolutely necessary in order to give effect to the rest of the work; and, in the second place, were it not the plan rather to gather and give expression to the judgment of others acknowledged as qualified to speak, than to give expression to the taste and judgment of one. It is thus the purpose to seek expert judgment in regard to acoustical effects, and, if possible, to present the results in a form available to architects. This will be slow and difficult work, and it is not at all certain that it will be possible to arrive, even ultimately, at a finished product. It is worth undertaking, however, if the job as a whole is worth undertaking, for without it the physical side of the investigation will lose much of its practical value. Thus it is of little value to be able to calculate in advance of construction, and express in numerical measure the acoustical quality which any planned auditorium will have, unless one knows also in numerical measure the acoustical quality which is desired. On the other hand, if the owner and the architect can agree on the desired result, and if this is within the limits of possibility, considering all the demands on the auditorium of utility, architecture, and engineering, this result can be secured with certainty — at least there need be no uncertainty as to whether it will or will not be attained in the completed building."

It is greatly to the credit of such distinguished architects as McKim, Mead & White that they should have been willing to accede to Major Higginson's insistence to accept the coöperation of a young and little known physicist in preparing their plans for the new building, yet by so doing they became the first of their profession to make use of the new science. Sabine tested the plans from the standpoints of loudness, of interference, of resonance, and of reverberation, and the architects made such alterations as were necessary to conform to the epoch-making ideas on which rested his guarantee of the acoustical perfection of the new auditorium.

From Major Henry L. Higginson

We went over many points, and Sabine gave me his ideas. I remember his saying that angles were necessary; that clear sound did not come well from curves, and, therefore, in making the stage we must remember that fact; also that the room of the stage should not be too high nor the stage too deep. He not only gave the advice, but examined the plans with care and settled the points of doubt. He explained to me why the sound was better when the raised floor was taken out. At the same time, it was necessary for the great concerts of the season that the floor should rise from front to back, and he marked out how that should be done.

The first fundamental criticism made of the original plans was in regard to taking the Leipzig Gewandhaus and the old Boston Music Hall as models. These, he declared, could only be used as " definitions and starting points on the acoustical side of the discussion ":

To Major Henry L. Higginson from W. C. S.

[*February* 14, 1899

The seating capacity of your hall is so different from that of the Leipzig Music Hall [2] that it cannot be a copy, and a comparison would be misleading — as misleading as any attempt at either linear or proportional imitation. The old hall approaches more nearly the new in seating capacity, and, moreover, it is a more familiar standard.

The restriction of the space around the stage, and the removal of the galleries at the sides of the orchestra, will increase the loudness or volume of the sound, and at the same time will better that which on the part of the hall corresponds to " attack " on the part of the musicians. The reflected sound, and the sound coming directly, will more accurately unite. To illustrate, with a stage of the depth originally planned, and the ceiling the full height of the

---

[2] Symphony Hall seats 2579 persons; the Gewandhaus 1517.

room, the difference in time of the two arrivals might amount to a fifth of a beat *allegro* time — the reflected sound, of course, being the fainter of the two. I hesitate to make an estimate of this gain in loudness and distinctness, but, if you wish me to express my impression, I should place it at twenty-five or thirty per cent.

The question, then, stands whether this gain and the advantage arising from the inclination of the floor — for these are your only gains — will be more than offset by the bare walls and the increase in length. Here again I infer that you wish me to take responsibility of a definitely formulated opinion, and, you wishing it, I gladly do so. In respect to loudness, I do not think that the new hall will, on the whole, be at a disadvantage in comparison with the old; in respect to echo, I very much fear that it will. In respect to reverberation or residual sound, the two halls will be very nearly the same, the materials of the walls being the same — but this is an important reservation.

In a theatre, loudness and distinctness are the acoustical properties chiefly to be considered, but in Symphony Hall the problem was much more comprehensive. Here, just enough reverberation had to be preserved to convey musical notes satisfactorily when measured by cultivated musical taste. " This," Sabine declared, " is fundamental; for unless musical taste is precise, the problem, at least as far as it concerns the design of the auditorium for musical purposes, is indeterminate." Wilhelm Gericke, Conductor of the Boston Symphony Orchestra, bore out Sabine's contention when he stated that music is never heard to best advantage in a theatre, because the added reverberation is necessary " to prevent a sensation of oppression."

In the course of the discussions, Major Higginson, Mr. Gericke, and others connected with the Building Committee, expressed opinions in regard to the acoustical properties of a number of auditoriums. These included the Leipzig Gewandhaus; the old Boston Music Hall; and the places visited by the Orchestra during its winter trips — Sanders Theatre in Cambridge, Carnegie Hall in New York, the Academy of Music in Philadelphia, and the Music Hall in Baltimore. At Major Higginson's request, Sabine accompanied the Orchestra on one of its trips, made measurements of all the halls, and calculated their reverberation. The dimensions and the material of the Gewandhaus had already been published, and from these data its reverberation was easily calculated. As for the other auditoriums, Sabine's figures, made in advance of the concerts, indicated with absolute precision in which halls the reverberation would be satisfactory, excessive, or too small. After this successful demonstration, Major Higginson accepted without qualification Sabine's statement that the physical problem was real, and the end to be attained definite.

Sabine gives an elaborated statement of the basic situation with great clearness: " In a theatre for dramatic performances, where the music is of entirely subordinate importance, it is desirable to reduce the reverberation to the lowest possible value in all ways not inimical to loudness; but in a music hall, concert room, or opera house, this is decidedly not the case. To reduce the reverberation in a hall to a minimum, or to make the conditions such that it is very great, may, in certain cases, present practical difficulties to the architect — theoretically it presents none. To adjust, in original design, the reverberation of a hall to a particular and approved value requires a study of conditions, of materials, and of arrangement. . . .

" It is not at all difficult to show *a priori* that in a hall for orchestral music the reverberation should neither be very great, nor, on the other hand, extremely small. However, in this matter it was not necessary to rely on theoretical considerations. . . . An examination of all the available plans of the halls cited as more or less satisfactory models, in the preliminary discussion of the plans for the new hall, showed that they were such as to give greater reverberation than the ordinary theatre style of construction. While several plans were thus cursorily examined, the real discussion was based on only two buildings — the present (old) Boston Music Hall and the Leipzig Gewandhaus; one was familiar to all and immediately accessible, the other familiar to a number of those in consultation. It should, perhaps, be immediately added that neither hall served as a model architecturally, but that both were used rather as definitions and starting points on the acoustical side of the discussion. The old Music Hall was not a desirable model in every respect, even acoustically, and the Leipzig Gewandhaus, having a seating capacity about that of Sanders Theatre, was so small as to be debarred from serving directly, for this if for no other reason. . . .

" The often-repeated statement that a copy of an auditorium does not necessarily possess the same acoustical qualities is not justified, and invests the subject with an unwarranted mysticism. The fact is that exact copies have rarely been made, and can hardly be expected. The constant changes and improvements in the materials used for interior construction in the line of better fire-proofing — wire lath or the application of the plaster directly to tile walls — have led to the taking of liberties in what were perhaps regarded as non-essentials; this has resulted in a changed absorbing power of the walls. Our increasing demands in regard to heat and ventilation, the restriction on the dimensions enforced by location, the changes in size imposed by the demands for seating capacity, have prevented, in different degrees, copies from being copies, and models from successfully serving as models. So different have been the results under what was thought to be safe guidance — but a guidance imperfectly followed — that the belief has become current that the whole subject is beyond control. Had the new Music Hall been enlarged from the Leipzig Gewandhaus to increase the seating capacity seventy per cent, which, proportions being preserved, would have doubled the volume, and then built, as it is being built, according to the most modern methods of fireproof construction, the result, unfortunately, would have been to confirm the belief.

" No mistake is more easy to make than that of copying an auditorium — but in different materials or on a different scale — in the expectation that the result will be the same. Every departure must be compensated by some other — a change in material by a change in the size or distribution of the audience, or perhaps by a partly compensating change in the material used in some other part of the hall — a change in size by a change in the proportions or shape. For moderate departures from the model such compensation can be made, and the model will serve well as a guide to a first approximation. When the departure is great, the approved auditorium, unless discriminatingly used, is liable to be a treacherous guide. In this case the departure was necessarily great." [3]

From the known dimensions and materials of the Leipzig Gewandhaus, Sabine found 2.30 seconds as the duration of reverberation of tone C_4, 512 vibrations, and his calculations foretold that the new Symphony Hall, provided the architects followed his suggestions, would reverberate 2.31 seconds with the same tone. These calculations were completely verified in the final tests.

Sabine's crowning triumph in readjusting the Symphony Hall plans was in relation to the stage. For this he designed what was practically a square wooden sounding box, which throws the music directly forward to the audience. The delicate perforated design above the cornice of the organ, the sloping down of the ceiling, the sloping up of the floor, and

[3] Collected Papers on Acoustics, page 60.

the inward slope of each side, forms the unusual construction. He indicated that the orchestra must sit behind the line of the proscenium arch, and warned that if rows of seats were removed to enlarge the stage for choruses, the acoustics would have to be sacrificed.

An amusing incident occurred in connection with the installation of the organ:

From Major Henry L. Higginson to W. C. S.

[*November* 6, 1899

In order to accommodate the organ in the new Music Hall, Mr. (George S.) Hutchings has asked to have the height of the stage — *i.e.,* the distance from the floor to the roof — increased from 36 feet to 44 feet. This may affect the pitch of this room from front to back, and, if not, it will raise it just so much higher. Will this affect us at all in the matter of the sound? Mr. Hutchings wishes this space for his pipes, but of course I am unwilling to grant it to the injury of the Orchestra. They are waiting for our reply, and I shall be much obliged to you if you can tell me. . . . The height of the room in the present Music Hall is 25 feet at the back and 38 feet 6 inches at the front. At present the new Music Hall is 36 feet at the back and 44 feet at the front. Mr. Hutchings wishes to raise it still eight feet more. Can we let him do it?

Sabine immediately investigated the problem, and reported to Major Higginson that if Mr. Hutchings would change the arrangement of two pipes, his organ would not only fit the space allotted, but, in Sabine's opinion, would be greatly improved in tone. This was heresy! " That young man is very courteous," Hutchings sputtered when Major Higginson gave him instructions to follow Sabine's suggestion; " but I was making organs before he was born! " Higginson stubbornly declined to yield, and the arrangement of the pipes was changed.

To complete the story, it should be added that, during the intermission at the opening concert, attention was attracted by a tall, elderly gentleman, with streaming white locks, pushing his way through the crowd toward Sabine, who was promenading in the *foyer* with his wife. Reaching his arm over the shoulders of those standing between, Hutchings grasped Sabine's hand, exclaiming, " Young man, that is the best organ I ever built. I take back everything I said! " Later, Hutchings had difficulty in securing a satisfactory tone from an organ he had installed in the Houghton Memorial Chapel at Wellesley, Massachusetts. He called Sabine in for consultation, ripped out the work already done, and reconstructed upon plans Sabine suggested, with perfect success. From that time on, the Hutchings organs were built in conformity with the ideas of the " courteous but youthful " critic!

As the new Symphony Hall came to completion, the interest of musicians and musical critics concentrated more upon Sabine's work than upon the architectural design. Less than a fortnight before the formal opening, this letter came to Sabine from the musical editor of the " New York Tribune":

From Henry E. Krehbiel to W. C. S.   [*October* 4, 1900

I have been profoundly interested in your determinations in the matter of Architectural Acoustics and the result of their application in the case of the new Music Hall in Boston, which I inspected pretty thoroughly last Saturday. I expect to print an article in the " Tribune " next Sunday, but have written only a passing allusion to your interesting experiments. At the opening concert I am convinced we shall all find your predictions verified.

For my own edification and that of the readers of the " Tribune " I desire very much to know whether or not you have applied scientific tests to the Hall since its completion, or if you intend doing so at the concert on the 15th. I shall be present on that occasion unless prevented by something unforeseen, and wish to incorporate your observations in my despatch.

Sabine replied that the only real test of his work must come with the actual use of the Hall for the exact purpose of its erection.

From Henry E. Krehbiel to W. C. S.   [*October* 8, 1900

I am much beholden to you for your answer to my letter of inquiry. I had fancied that you had set down a calculation of results with the Hall empty, which you had verified, as well as filled, and that you would be able to make an approximate comparison next Monday at the concert. Of course the test of the Hall will be in its use; but, after the failure of Garnier, who started out to be scientific with the Grand Opéra in Paris, and the builders and designers of the Trocadéro, who were consistently scientific in some respects, I was curious to know, if possible, whether the element of mere chance can be eliminated.

The formal opening of the new Boston Symphony Hall occurred on the evening of October 15, 1900. Mr. Krehbiel's comments follow:

From the " New York Tribune "   [*October* 16, 1900

For the musical students in the audience the question of greatest permanent interest involved in the exercises of the evening was that of the acoustical properties of the new hall. Performances of Beethoven's " Missa Solennis " are not of frequent occurrence anywhere in the world, but, given the determination, the devotion, the money, and the forces, they can be had. At the worst, a poor performance can be atoned for by another and a better one; but a music hall once built, which proves to be unfit for music, is seldom remedied and never made really fit. Hundreds of ears were therefore alert this evening to learn whether the greatest of the problems that the construction of a music hall involves had been solved in this instance.

The responsibility for the concert room's acoustics had been assumed by Wallace C. Sabine, Assistant Professor of Physics at Harvard University. Ever since Mr. Sabine laid his formulas of proportions and materials before the architects of the Hall, he has maintained that there was as little question about the desired outcome as there was in the minds of the architects about the appearance of the structure. In view of certain memorable failures, this attitude seemed very daring. M. Garnier, after studying all that he was able to study about the laws of Sound, and examining in person scores of concert rooms and theatres famous for good acoustical properties, confessed his inability to formulate any law, and built the Paris Grand Opéra on chance so far as acoustics were concerned. He thought the results good, but they were far from satisfactory. The builders of the Trocadéro took not a step without scientific sanction obtained from a long and painstaking series of experiments, and failed much more dismally than M. Garnier. . . .

These French examples of mystery surrounding the laws of Sound made Mr. Sabine's claim, that his determinations concerning Architectural Acoustics left remaining no element of doubt touching the excellence of the music hall yet to be built, seem very venturesome, to say the least. His confidence, it may be said now, has been justified and rewarded. Mr. Sabine's experiments were made in the true spirit of Science. He seems to have the imperturbable patience and perseverance of the German scientific investigator. If he can accomplish as good results in Sayles Hall of Brown University, or the hall of the Women's Musical Club in Grand Rapids, which are the most impossible rooms I have ever tested, he ought to do so at once; and if his formulas are as accurate as the new Symphony Hall seems to indicate, they ought to be adopted immediately by every builder of a public edifice designed for speech or song.

From the New York " Evening Post "   [*October* 16, 1900

It must be remembered that, as the late John Dwight wrote, " The walls of a hall, like those of a violin, must ripen and grow musical by frequent and continuous response to musical vibrations; they must outgrow their crude condition, and become gradually attuned, acclimated to harmony." The Boston Symphony Hall has the advantage of starting out well, and it would not be surprising, therefore, if mellowing time made it a Stradivarius among halls.

The close of the Symphony Hall adventure was the beginning of Sabine's recognition as Master of Architectural Acoustics. The skeptics had been confounded and his critics answered. Major Higginson's note of acknowledgment (October 22, 1900) summed up the attitude of the musical world with characteristic brevity: " Just a word to thank you for your pains and success in the Hall. Of both no doubt exists. I have never heard the music as now.[4] You have proved here that the Science of Acoustics certainly exists in a definite form. You have done a great part of the Hall, and every one thanks you." In another letter (to James F. Curtis) he added: " Sabine never asks anything for his advice or assistance. He made the acoustics in Symphony Hall what they are, and I could never persuade him to take one penny."

Mr. and Mrs. Hylas Sabine were a part of the distinguished audience on the occasion of the opening performance in Symphony Hall — momentous in so many ways to so many people. It was natural that the mother should have been especially excited by her son's triumph. She had followed his work step by step with understanding and with confidence; she had verified all his mathematical data, and

---

[4] The acoustical properties of Symphony Hall for the spoken word were far superior even to Sabine's expectations and promises.

she very properly considered herself personally a part of every detail. Music was an unknown realm to her, for her Quaker family looked upon such indulgence of the senses as worldly and reprehensible. She may have preferred, therefore, to consider this new Symphony Hall as a temple erected to demonstrate the power of Science as expressed in her son's achievement, rather than as a monument to sinful personal gratification!

After this practical demonstration the modest young Assistant Professor became a recognized part of the architectural profession. His opinions were courted and his coöperation sought by architects throughout the country. Such papers as he had published were made part of their office accessories. As sole authority in this new science, Sabine might easily have exchanged his college position, at this moment, for the unlimited field which opened before him; but so firmly was the principle ingrained in him that " the investigator who does not teach serves a diminished constituency," [5] that the undoubted material advantage failed even to interest him. And beyond this was his loyalty to Harvard. " It is due to President Eliot and the Corporation of Harvard University that the work was undertaken and is still carried on," he wrote (November 7, 1900) to John M. Goodell, editor of the " Engineering Record," who called attention to Sabine's " Harvard quality of thoroughness "; " it is the more pleasing that you have placed whatever credit there may be where it belongs — to the spirit and the influence of the place."

President Eliot must have wondered, during this period, whether he had unconsciously encouraged this young scientist to make himself too famous for the academic position for which the President was even then secretly grooming him. Eliot had never abandoned his vision of a great Graduate Engineering School at Harvard. Professor Shaler had

[5] See page 47.

confided to him the possibility of a huge bequest from
Gordon McKay. He believed he had discovered the one man
in all the world to head such a school as he had in mind, but
unless that man instinctively preferred educational opportunity to the glamour of personal acclaim, he would be lacking in the final analysis. Eliot was gratified by the way Sabine met the supreme test, and settled back contentedly to
await the moment to gratify his own ambition.

In the meantime, Sabine, entirely ignorant of what was in
the President's mind, unostentatiously continued to carry
on his academic work side by side with the increasing demands made by his fame in Architectural Acoustics. The
importunities of architects, which would have been considered presumptuous by any one else, were welcomed by him
as further opportunities for laboratory experimentation. As
the sphere of his collegiate work enlarged, he accepted
added burdens of responsibility and service which could not
fail to tax the strongest physique. " He was always so ready
to help," John Goddard Hart records, " that I fear we made
demands on him which we should not have made, and overtaxed his strength. I remember, on one occasion, when very
likely he had been working all night on some problem,
he fainted in a restaurant in Harvard Square. A student
brought him to my office, and I took him to my house and
put him to bed, after summoning a doctor. But we could not
keep him there after he felt strong enough to walk. He insisted on going back to work." Yet Sabine never seemed
pressed, never seemed to lack time for sympathetic coöperation not only with his students but with all with whom he
came in contact. He was living in a world he loved, and that
world gave back to him in kind what he so unselfishly contributed of himself.

SABINE served five years as Instructor in Physics and ten years as Assistant Professor at Harvard University before he reached the position of full Professor, in spite of the fact that he quickly proved himself an admirable teacher and a highly successful investigator." Thus does President Eliot comment on a delayed promotion which has always mystified Sabine's friends; yet naturally the postponement of the higher title rested largely in the President's hands. This may have resulted from the fact that Eliot held him so constantly in mind for the headship of the coming great School of Engineering that he overlooked the importance of the intermediate step; it may have been due to his knowledge of Sabine's indifference to titles, and the fact that a full professorship would not enlarge his field of usefulness nor add to the value of his service. At all events, it is certain that had Sabine made the slightest effort to secure an earlier promotion it would have been given him; but that was not the Sabine way. Then, as if by way of atonement, came a double advancement, which caused him real embarrassment, but to which he unwittingly contributed.

Sabine's actual appointment as Professor of Physics was made on May 1, 1905, to take effect on the first day of the following September. It found him exercising a vital force, not only in the Department to which he was accredited, but in the policies of the college administration. By this time, in spite of his retiring disposition, others on the Faculty besides Eliot had discovered the clearness of his vision and the soundness of his judgment, with the result that he was drafted on important committees and consulted on matters quite apart from his scientific responsibilities.

One of the most far-reaching of these services was in connection with the reorganization of the administration of admissions to the College and the Scientific School. Sabine called attention to the fact that five separate committees existed — four in charge of admissions to regular and to " special " standing in each of the departments administered by the Faculty of Arts and Sciences, and a fifth on admissions from other colleges. If a candidate failed to enter through one of these committees, he frequently succeeded through another. Sabine suggested that a single committee be appointed, charged with the responsibility of determining the fitness of candidates to pursue courses of instruction given by the one Faculty, whatever the departmental classification of the student was to be.

From Jerome D. Greene

To the work of this Committee Sabine gave his time and thought without stint. He was not content with the improvement in administration which the mere establishment of the Committee embodied, or even with the more consistent and painstaking attention to the individual merits of candidates which characterized its work. To him, the most important function of the Committee was that of studying the underlying problem of how to administer admission requirements in such a way as to help both the schools and the College to secure the most promising students, and to make the processes of preparation and examination really educational rather than a merely mechanical sifting of the human material.

One of Sabine's premises was that it was no longer, if it had ever been, the business of the College to impose on the educational systems of the different parts of the country curricula and tests representing one arbitrary standard of mental attainment. Against such a conception he urged that of a system of admission requirements which would take into account wide and wholly justifiable diversities of educational aims and methods, and be expressed in terms that would make the College accessible to youths of demonstrable capacity, however and wherever trained. Out of prolonged discussions of this thesis within the Committee eventually emerged the so-called New Plan of Admissions, not to be adopted by the Faculty, however, until a newly constituted committee, in which adverse views were represented, arrived at a similar conclusion.

Under the New Plan, the *content* of the preparatory-school program is certified by the school itself, while the *quality* of the student is tested by a limited number of examinations. To Sabine, more than to any other man, is due this improvement in the administration of college admissions, leading, as it did subsequently, to a far greater emphasis on the all-round personal quality of the student, as against the more impersonal and mechanical process of scoring points in a formidable array of subjects, preparation in which cannot and ought not to be rigidly standardized.

From John Goddard Hart

Professor Sabine remained officially on the Committee of Admissions from its first meeting, January 20, 1906, until the end of the academic year 1907–1908, but he was always regarded as a member of the Committee as long as I was Chairman of it. We never went before the Faculty with any proposal without obtaining his advice and approval. It was largely because of his advice that we never lost a vote.

Sabine's recommendation of the " New Plan " was but an official expression of principles he had always believed in and personally practiced. Long before the change was put into effect by the University he had formed the habit of visiting different preparatory schools, quietly but effectively doing his part to lessen the abruptness of the transition from school to college. In Sabine's mind the University best served its own interests by first considering the standpoint of the boy:

From George W. Creelman

In June, 1905, Professor Sabine came to Hotchkiss to visit me. We had a boy who was entering Harvard in the fall, in whom the Professor became interested, and with whom he wished to become acquainted before he entered Harvard. This boy was not doing well in school, and we feared he might go all to pieces in college. To prevent this, Mr. Sabine came all the way to Lakeville. He was much interested in the so-called " New Plan " examinations for admission to college. He thought all freshmen should be created equal, so far as possible. He thought that it was a vicious system to load all the conditions on the poor student, who was the last one who could be expected to carry them. " If you must have conditions," he would say, " give them to the good student. He can carry them and no harm done."

From W. L. W. Field

Professor Sabine knew that I had a difficult matter to handle, and he offered to help me. He came out to Milton, arriving about ten o'clock in the morning. He had made engagements in Cambridge, and had experiments waiting for him at the Laboratory, as he expected to be back at noon. On his arrival, he sat down and said, " Now tell me the story." I outlined my problem to him — a pretty intricate problem it was. He thought it over a few minutes, and then said thoughtfully, " You have something on your hands here, haven't you? I may not be of much help, but I'm going to stay right here until we work it out." He remained until four o'clock that afternoon. Then he went back to Cambridge, and I have no doubt that he worked the entire night to make up for the time he had given me.

His connection with Milton Academy [1] was entirely separate from his work at Cambridge. I like to speak of this because it is commonly said that outside of his own field a specialist is not interested. I never found anything that was not of interest to Sabine. He was intelligently and constructively interested in everything. He simply didn't chatter about it.

Soon after attaining his Professorship, Sabine made another move which inadvertently played directly into President Eliot's hands in carrying out his long but secretly cherished scheme for his great School of Engineering, with Sabine ultimately at its head.

By Professor Edwin H. Hall

For many years after Sabine became a member of the Harvard Faculty of Arts and Sciences, he took no prominent part in its meetings. His colleagues were therefore somewhat surprised when, early in 1906, he proposed a radical change in the organization of the Lawrence Scientific School, which was under the control of this Faculty. Discussion of the affairs of this School was active at this time, because proceeds from the great McKay bequest, intended for the promotion of science-teaching at Harvard, were about to come in, and one of the periodical agitations regarding relations between the Lawrence Scientific School and the Massachusetts Institute of Technology had recently occurred.

This McKay bequest was destined to play a vital part in Sabine's life during the next ten years. Gordon McKay had been a successful manufacturer and inventor of machinery, and for more than twenty years before his death had made his home in Cambridge, near the College Yard. During this period he came into friendly relations with many of the college professors and undergraduates, from which contact he gained an appreciation of the advantage of combining train-

---

[1] Sabine was President of the Board of Trustees of Milton Academy for ten years.

ing in the exact sciences with liberal culture in the atmosphere of the University. A particularly close personal friendship became established between him and Professor Nathaniel S. Shaler, who was at that time Dean of the Lawrence Scientific School, and he became greatly interested in its rapid development. In fact, he was accustomed to speak of it as " my school," so it was natural that he should have been influenced by Shaler in his plans for the final disposition of his vast estate.

Mr. McKay died in 1903, and the Corporation of Harvard University formally accepted the Fund " strictly upon the trust conditions and terms, and for the purposes in said instrument, will, and codicils set forth." A year later, rumors became rife that negotiations were under way to effect a merger between Harvard University and the Massachusetts Institute of Technology, with the end in view of establishing a joint School of Engineering, toward which the proceeds from the McKay Fund would be applied. For over thirty years, President Eliot had advocated some sort of working arrangement between these two leading educational establishments of New England which should prevent duplication of equipment and teaching personnel, and offer students from each institution the fullest and highest opportunities for scientific education. As a matter of fact, steps had been taken toward this end as early as 1897, long before the McKay bequest became an influencing factor.

From May 4, 1904, until October 11, 1905, negotiations were conducted by Committees made up of Dr. Henry P. Walcott and Charles Francis Adams, 2d, representing Harvard University, and President H. S. Pritchett and Professor Abbott Lawrence Lowell representing the Institute. A mutually acceptable proposal was drawn up, to be held conditional until an opinion should be obtained from the Supreme Judicial Court, on the legality of using the McKay Trust Funds for any purpose except by Harvard alone.

While the Corporations of both institutions were in favor of the merger, a strong dissenting element sprang up in both Faculties and among the Harvard and Technology alumni. In fact, an Anti-Merger League was established by the Technology alumni, ready to take active steps to prevent what seemed to them to be a threatened loss of the Institute's individuality; while many of the Harvard alumni, especially lawyers, declared that the proposed step was in direct violation of the testator's wishes, and that, if accomplished, would raise a new and serious issue prejudicial to future bequests which might otherwise be made to the University. The whole affair came to a definite standstill on October 11, 1905, when President Pritchett advised the Harvard Committee that the courts had rendered an unfavorable decision concerning the right of the Institute to sell the land and buildings occupied by it on Boylston Street, Boston, which decision made further consideration of the projected plan of merging impracticable at that time.

Thus, at the moment when Sabine made his suggestion to the Harvard Faculty of radical changes in the organization of the Lawrence Scientific School, the spectre of the Harvard-Technology merger seemed to have been effectively laid. His recommendation, or the plan growing out of his proposition, was to establish a Graduate School of Applied Science, the College taking over from the Scientific School the instruction leading to the degree of Bachelor of Science. This proposal was exactly in line with President Eliot's vision, and was approved by the Faculty of Arts and Sciences, being adopted by the Governing Boards of the University in the spring of 1906.

By Professor Edwin H. Hall

It was doubtless Sabine's hope, from the start of his connection with this revolutionary action, to make the Harvard School of Applied Science one of the highest and best in the world; but concerning the wisdom of making it distinctively and only a Graduate School he was not altogether positive, in spite of the fact that the suggestion to make it such is attributed to him. In fact, the decision of the Faculty to approve this policy was arrived at in a curiously casual way. Argument against it was made at a Faculty meeting, and nobody seemed to be confidently in favor of it. Sabine told a colleague the next day that, just before the vote was taken, he tried to get the President's attention, to move a postponement of the question. He did not succeed, the vote was taken and the policy was launched.

The significance of the adoption of Sabine's suggestion is admirably brought out in a paper written by Professor Charles F. Dunbar on " President Eliot's Administration," and published in March, 1909:

From the " Harvard Graduates' Magazine "

In 1906 the Graduate School of Applied Science was established. On two occasions, in the years preceding, negotiations had been carried on by the Harvard Corporation with that of the Massachusetts Institute of Technology, looking to a union of the resources of the two institutions. The second of these negotiations came to an end in 1905. Had the union taken place, this phase of professional training would have had a place by itself, and might have developed on lines not in accord with the general policy of the University.

The prompt creation, in 1906, of the Graduate School of Applied Science, was strictly in accord with that policy. President Eliot had pointed out more than once, in his annual reports, that the work of Harvard College and of the Lawrence Scientific School could be advantageously combined so as to make a course of study covering five or six years, and thus secure a broad as well as technically adequate preparation for the engineering profession. The new Graduate School now looks frankly toward making this also one of the learned professions. Its policy is still tentative. The Lawrence Scientific School, with its four-year professional program of required courses of study, remains in the Catalogue, but as the students now enrolled in those courses complete them, this part of the University's machinery will disappear. Professional degrees in Engineering will then be handed over to the Graduate School of Applied Science.

The further development of this School will be immensely promoted by the great McKay bequest, soon to become available. The possibilities which it offers are realized by few — highly elaborated professional training, based on a preliminary college education, and designed at once to promote research and equip technical experts of the first quality. The preparations have been made, and the organization perfected, for the use of the School's coming resources on a scale and with standards commensurate with its great possibilities. Here, as in so many directions, a far-seeing policy has provided the broad foundations for future growth.

Harvard University has been brought to a unique position among American institutions, and indeed among all institutions wherever situated. It retains the college of the English-speaking peoples, that great instrument for idealism and intellectual uplift. Not independent of the college, not fused or intermingled with it, but as a stage coming after it and dependent upon it, is training for the various professions. Each graduate school receives its students as men of culture and delivers them as trained specialists. Gradually this system has been extended to all parts of the University; inevitably (and therefore first in time) to the School for Research and Pure Science which for many years was the Graduate School; then to the professions of Divinity, Law, and Medicine, which have long been by tradition among the learned professions; and last to Applied Science.

In April, 1906, before the reorganization was fairly under way, Dean Shaler died, and Sabine, to his utter amazement, was selected as his successor. President Eliot had kept his secret well! This appointment was as unwelcome as it was unexpected. The first inkling that Sabine was even being considered came to him in a dramatic way. He and his wife were attending the dedicatory exercises of the new Harvard Medical School buildings, and were standing on the north terrace, chatting with friends, when the President was seen approaching. As the friends moved away, Eliot, instead of speaking to Sabine, but with his attention fixed entirely upon Mrs. Sabine's face, said abruptly, " We want your husband to be Dean of the Scientific School. Think it over." Then, turning to Sabine, the President asked:

" Can you come to my office tomorrow morning at ten o'clock? "

Upon receiving an affirmative reply, Eliot turned and left them. As Mrs. Sabine looked at her husband she saw that his face was deathly pale, but the subject uppermost in their minds was not mentioned until they reached home. Then he said to her: " This is intended as an honor. I dislike to refuse President Eliot anything, but I cannot accept the appointment."

This was the position he took when he discussed the matter with Eliot the following day, but the President was un-yielding. The fortnight that followed was a period full of anxiety and misgivings for Sabine. Eliot was one of his few idols, and, beyond this, he had come to regard him with almost a son's affection. Other assignments suggested by the President, some of them not wholly agreeable, he had accepted blindly, but in this new appointment he saw the frustration of carefully laid personal plans and expectations. He loved teaching, he loved research. Administration and executive responsibility he preferred to leave to other men.

What was surprise to the one was realization to the other.

" The Corporation have a good opinion of your son's attainments, capacity, and character," Eliot had written Madame Sabine in June, 1895; " he is one of the clearest headed and ablest of our younger men," he had told Professor Mendenhall; and, during the period Sabine had served the President as unofficial secretary, Eliot had found ample opportunity to study his personality and test his capacity. His loyalty to Harvard had been proved by his refusal to take advantage of the opportunity for material advancement through his acoustical discoveries. The ideas Sabine had advanced concerning the future development of the Scientific School coincided exactly with Eliot's vision, and the President had not overlooked the added advantage of having as a successor to the popular Shaler a man no less capable, and one who possessed the grip upon the imagination of the students which had been shown so conspicuously in Sabine's courses.

With characteristic adroitness, Eliot accepted Sabine's protests and sympathized with his misgivings. Then, at last, he placed the matter wholly on the basis of a personal request — and against this Sabine had no arguments. Mrs. Sabine recalls the sadness in his attitude when he returned home one day and announced that he had accepted the appointment.

By Professor Edwin H. Hall

Sabine's nature was intense and reserved. Regarding men, and often regarding measures, he had convictions rather than opinions. Dispassionate argument was difficult for him, though he lacked the instinct and temper of the dictator. So the duties of a Dean, the real executive head in this case, of an institution in a period of reconstruction, must have been hard for him at times — harder than they would have been for a man of different temperament.

From Jerome D. Greene

Sabine's diversion to administrative tasks in the Division of Physics and in the Scientific School was in some respects regrettable as an interference with his primary calling; but it brought into play the same spiritual quality along with administrative ability, and left its mark on educational administration in the colleges and universities of the country.

Having once arrived at a decision, Sabine threw himself into the work of this new position with an energy and devotion which showed no reflection of his earlier protests, and from the beginning he demonstrated administrative and executive ability of the highest order. The appointment was at once hailed with enthusiasm not only at Cambridge, but throughout the scientific world. Professor Trowbridge's comments, in a paper published in the " Harvard Graduates' Magazine " (December, 1906), form a most interesting human document. Here is this older man, writing of the boy who first attracted his attention at that scientific meeting in Philadelphia years before, and now promoted to a station superior to his own, with a pride and affection which can scarcely be restrained. It is an expression of idealism one usually associates with religion, but is entirely in keeping with Sabine's own conception of Science:

By Professor John Trowbridge

In considering the appointment of a Dean for the Lawrence Scientific School, which, under a munificent bequest, enters upon a new epoch in its history, one naturally asks what should be the qualifications of an administrative officer to whom will fall the task of building up a Graduate School of Science which shall be to the scientific professions what the Law School is to the legal profession and the Medical School to medicine. The new Dean will have a unique opportunity, for the McKay Fund will in time probably amount to many millions, and the opportunity is offered to train men competent to undertake great enterprises in the applications of Science. To prove that such men are needed, we need only point to the difficulty that was found to secure an engineer competent to direct the work of constructing the Panama Canal. The law student and the medical student now spend at least eight years in preparation for their professions, and yet we trust our lives often to the work of scientific graduates who have not had more than half this period of preparation. The new Scientific School will aim, in great part, to give the most extended training possible; it will have the means, and will not be necessarily dependent upon number of students.

This is certainly a unique opportunity for the man and the University. This man should be a young man, for the School should have the hope of a settled policy for a long period of years. He should be trained in methods of exact research, for these methods lie at the foundations of thoroughness in the practical applications of Science. From a personal knowledge of their importance he can best judge of the fitness and efficiency of the work of professors and students. A physicist naturally believes that Physical Science, with its accurate methods, affords the best training in this endeavor for thoroughness. Moreover, Physical Science lies at the foundation of all practical application of Science, and it would be well that the new Dean should have had the training of a physicist. Last, but not least, he should have the divine gift of enthusiasm and the initiative which arises from it. He should be a man in sympathy with young men and therefore attractive to them, a man free from the entanglements of commercial work and devoted to the University.

The Dean has been appointed. Let us see how he answers to these requirements. . . . He has filled in succession the positions of Instructor, Assistant Professor, and Professor in this University. He is of Huguenot ancestry, and the influ-

ence of the free Western environment on a descendant of the
body of men who resisted tyranny and stood for freedom of
conscience would afford an interesting subject for those
psychologists in literature who now find in such study the
surest analysis of a man's career.

I have seen in Professor Sabine, during the many years
that it has been my privilege to be associated with him, a
devotion to high ideals, a reverence for truth, and an instinctive revolt against all that is unworthy in public life
or in University life. . . . He has built up to a great efficiency the various electives conducted by him, and he is the
authority on an important practical application of Science
— that of Architectural Acoustics.

Not only have students profited by his advice and instruction while still in the University. Among the young men,
who, after their graduation, were endeavoring to get a foot-
hold in their profession, I remember two especially who
waited many weary years for patronage. Professor Sabine's
constant advice to them was: " Do not do cheap work: do
the best you can. You can afford to wait, and, when success
comes, it will be permanent." And it did come. These
young men have now come into their own. This is the spirit
that will make a Graduate School of Applied Science truly
efficient, and it is a striking proof of the perspicacity of
President Eliot and the Corporation, that, under the guise
of a quiet and unassuming man, one who rarely speaks in the
Faculty, they have discerned his high qualities.

From friends came various letters. Professor H. E. Clifford, then of the Massachusetts Institute of Technology, and
later to be called by Sabine to take the chair of Electrical
Engineering at Harvard, wrote (October 15, 1906) : " It is
a keen pleasure and a deep satisfaction to know that you are
to determine the development of the work in Applied Science at Harvard University. Not only is there the delight

which always accompanies a friend's honors, but also the gratification of seeing a man of broad scientific attainment, rather than the professional engineer, entrusted with the responsibility for the highest engineering development."

Professor George H. Palmer, diametrically opposed to many of Sabine's academic ideas, sent him these enthusiastic lines (October 11, 1906) : " My paper has just brought the announcement of this splendid appointment, and I am rejoicing, as all friends of the Scientific School must. What an array of qualifications you bring! — the highest scientific standing, administrative ability, interest in human beings, and acquaintance with schools. And what a delight to exercise such powers in constructing a vast, beneficent engine in a vacant field! To few men does such an opportunity ever come, and none of our colleagues could awaken such a confident assurance of success. I congratulate you, the School, and the public. Don't answer this, but excuse it as a burst of delight."

Dean LeBaron R. Briggs, while more restrained, was no less enthusiastic in a letter (October 12, 1906) to Mrs. Sabine: " The President and Fellows have never — within my recollection — made a better appointment than that of the new Dean. I want you to know that some of the rest of us share the pleasure which must be yours."

Perhaps no letter touched Sabine more deeply than one received from Newton M. Anderson, his old teacher in the preparatory department of Ohio State University (December 25, 1906) : " I congratulate you with all my heart on the reward which has come to you, and I congratulate Harvard even more sincerely. This seems to me the highest result to which any human life could possibly aspire. And yet it is not the position, and its accessories, which has been most in my mind. I have thought mainly on this line: the Officers and Faculty of Harvard represent the very highest type of men — I should say that probably there is no body of men as

well prepared to judge according to the highest standard
known to man. That such a jury should render a verdict saying that here is a man, who, from the life he has led, has
shown himself the best prepared of all men to take this position, which requires of its occupant the purest of living,
the highest integrity, the kindliest nature, the most noble
thoughts, and the greatest attainments, is to me second only
to the ' Well done ' of the Heavenly Father himself. That
you had the ' ten talents ' to start with, and the best of parents to guide you, is, of course, nothing to your credit, but
even this knowledge does not detract in the least from the
honor which is yours."

The history of Sabine's deanship is not of deep significance to his biography, because, as affairs turned, the whole
plan [2] had to be changed, owing to circumstances unforeseen at the time and beyond his control. It belongs " rather
to the prehistoric period of the Harvard Engineering
School." But his administration of his position, and his attitude on the vital problems which arose during his incum-
bency, reveal much that is important.

The Graduate School of Applied Science, at the time Sab-
ine's plan for reorganization was put into operation, was
based on two old foundations — the Lawrence Scientific
School and the Bussey Institution. The Lawrence Scientific
School was the oldest technical school but one in America.
The Corporation and Overseers of the University had first
announced their intention of giving graduate instruction in
Applied Science in 1847. The following year, in recognition
of a generous gift from the Honorable Abbott Lawrence, the
School thus established was called the " Lawrence Scientific
School." At first, the students were holders of bachelor's de-
grees or men of maturity, but, in the course of time, the
School became an undergraduate technical department,
with a body of eminent alumni and with rapidly growing

[2] For Sabine's detailed plans see Appendix A.

numbers and efficiency. Until the reorganization, the Lawrence School comprised the technical work in the University
in Engineering, in Mining and Metallurgy, in Architecture,
in Landscape Architecture, in Forestry, and the technical
sides of such other subjects as Chemistry and Geology,
whose strong presentation in the University were as Pure
Sciences. Now it became a basic part of a Graduate School,
being given the same standing as the Harvard Law and
Medical Schools, thus maintaining the professional purpose
of the training, and greatly increasing the resources and
activity of the University in these particular fields.

The Bussey Institution up to this time had been an undergraduate school of agriculture, established in the University in 1870 on an endowment left to the University in
1845 by Benjamin Bussey. The will, drawn in 1835, by its
far-sighted provisions anticipated by twenty-five years the
Morrill Act in Congress establishing the State Agricultural
Colleges, and conveyed to the University what stood for
many years as its largest single endowment.[3]

This was the foundation upon which Sabine began his
building. What he accomplished is a confusing chapter in
Harvard's history, because so much of his work was structural, and dependent for its fruition upon cumulative, un-
interrupted progress. The destructive effect of the temporary operation of the Harvard-Technology agreement makes
it impossible for the full value of Sabine's actual achievement to be properly assessed.

By Professor Edwin H. Hall

It seems probable that Sabine's methods would in time
have built up a strong School of Applied Science at Harvard, in spite of the great prestige of the Massachusetts Institute of Technology, which had now come under the very
able management of President Maclaurin. But President

---

[3] Condensed from Harvard Records.

Lowell, of Harvard, who, by family tradition, was a trustee of the Institute, and whose main ambition for Harvard did not lie in the direction of Applied Science, either proposed or assented to the terms of the famous merger which undertook to combine the financial resources, the aims, and the teaching staffs of the two scientific schools. His influence, together with the evident economic advantages of maintaining one school instead of two in one community, prevailed, and so the fusion was, for a time, effected. . . .

Any one reading Sabine's brief annual reports for the seven years of his service as Dean must be impressed by the vigor of his administration and by his constant endeavors to improve the effectiveness of the departments in his charge, both by changes of plan and by a careful selection of the personnel. . . . William Morton Wheeler was called from the Natural Museum of History in New York to occupy the newly created chair of Economic Entomology, and other eminent specialists were enlisted in the warfare against the insect pests with which the trees of Massachusetts had been signally afflicted. George F. Swain and Harry E. Clifford were called from the Massachusetts Institute of Technology to chairs of Civil Engineering and Electrical Engineering, respectively, in 1909. In 1911 George C. Whipple came from the practice of his profession in New York City to the professorship of Sanitary Engineering, and Eugene Duquesne, from the École des Beaux Arts in Paris, to the chair of Architectural Design — both of the positions thus filled being new ones at Harvard.

Other colleagues besides Professor Hall have commented on the accuracy of Sabine's estimate of men:

From Professor William F. Osgood
The work he did in helping to secure the great appointments on which the success of the Graduate School of Applied Science would have been founded was extraordinary.

His success, too, in discovering promising youths at an early age, often in the remote high school, should be noted. I have in mind Bridgman, Loomis, Kemble, Lyman, and doubtless there are others of whom I never knew.

Sabine's methods divided themselves into two parts: who was the best possible man for the given position, and how to get him when discovered. He would go from one centre of engineering or architecture to another, chatting informally with various colleagues until he found the one expert all agreed upon as outstanding in his department. Then he would approach this man, offering the lure not of more money but of greater opportunity to carry on his research. And he usually got his man. I have heard Sabine say that his ideal for the School of Engineering at Harvard was to have funds enough, through the McKay bequest, to scrap the whole apparatus of any branch of engineering whenever new knowledge produced new and superior equipment.

Two of the experts thus secured by Sabine to head departments in the Graduate School have recorded their experiences with him:

From Professor George C. Whipple
It was largely his influence which induced me to give up professional work and accept a professorship at Harvard. He believed in the future of the sanitary engineering profession, and did much to make it possible for me to carry out certain plans. Some of these plans were about to come to maturity when the agreement with Technology led to their abandonment, among which was a new building to be devoted to Sanitary Science and Public Health.

Aside from my affection for him, I always admired his cool, thoughtful, scientific method of approaching whatever question he was discussing. His conversations with me were always illuminating, and we were fond of meeting and discussing " the progress of the world." His force lay in his ability to state a subject clearly and follow it along logically step by step. I was always amazed at how much he knew about my own subject.

From Professor William Morton Wheeler

The plans developed by Sabine, with the support of President Eliot, were that the Bussey Institution should not continue the practical applications of agriculture, but should develop research on which those applications rested.[4] That is, lines of research were taken up which seemed promising, that would seem to develop theories and facts that could lead to application later on. The one I was interested in was the gypsy moth and the browntail work in Massachusetts. The Government had established a laboratory at North Melrose for field work, like spraying and things of that sort, and we took up work on the diseases of the gypsy moth, browntail, etc. The work in Genetics — that is, in animal- and plant-breeding — were later introduced, and, after that, the Forestry School was attached to the Institution. Then a Department of Economic Botany was created.

In all these departments we followed rigidly, until the Institution closed in June, 1931, the ideals which Sabine established. I want to emphasize that side of the subject, because it is so remote from the field in which he worked mostly. Sabine was an ideal scientist, both as an investigator and as a man interested in the application of Science — two quite different fields, and a very unusual combination. Following his ideals and plans, the Institution, while it existed, was most successful. It turned out a large number of able young men who went into Government service and agricul-

---

[4] "We can't raise pigs on our side hill equal to those raised by the Amherst Agricultural College," Sabine protested to President Eliot. "Why not restrict our work to scientific lines, supplementing the Agricultural College and collaborating with it?"

Later, in relating this incident to Mrs. Sabine, President Eliot inquired whimsically, "Do you suppose your husband acquired his knowledge of pigs from studying Physics or from his research work in Architectural Acoustics?"

tural-station work, and these young men are now scattered all over the world, some of them occupying excellent positions.

Sabine changed the Bussey Institution from a very rudimentary and unsuccessful undergraduate agricultural school into a research institution of the first order. Extra funds became available largely because of the confidence felt in his work. His interest in the Institution was continuous from 1908 until his death, and anything that was a part of it absorbed his interest.

Sabine was believed to be averse to the popularization of Science, but that was only as applied to his own research. When we opened up the new Bussey he suggested that we engage a competent lecturer to give a course of public lectures on Sunday afternoons. Sabine himself attended these because he thought they might create an interest in agriculture, pest control, etc., and might help in the case of the Arboretum.

Thus was the investigator and the teacher forced out of the customary routine into a highly administrative field which demanded unusual versatility. Sabine met and solved each new problem with his characteristic precision of mind and consummate good sense:

From Barrett Wendell

I slowly came to know Sabine through his duties as Dean, which brought up questions involving personal interviews. When it came to academic business — a matter usually handled in desultory manner — he could dispose of it in half a minute, yet so quietly and so pleasantly that you felt as if you had had a friendly interview. There can seldom have been a more excellent economist of time. And all the while, of course, one was growing to understand that his technical professional work was gaining recognition not only locally but far and wide. He seemed, though, so absorbed in his duties that off-hand one would have supposed them to occupy and to satisfy his whole life.

From President Charles W. Eliot

It was a period of change and development in the scientific departments of the University, which afforded Dean Sabine ample opportunities for the exercise of comprehensive sympathy, considerateness, patience, and good judgment in regard to both measures and men.

As a convincing summary of Sabine's development of the Graduate School, a quotation may be taken from a remarkable analysis by the editor of " Science," in the issue of that journal for November 4, 1910, of the work and position of scientific men in our American colleges and universities, basing his deductions on data furnished by the new edition of the scientific " Who's Who? — American Men of Science." The most comprehensive of Doctor Cattell's tabulations shows the ten strongest departments in each science, together with their gain or loss in a period of about four years:

By Professor J. McK. Cattell

Reviewing the same figures from the point of view of the institutions, the primacy of Harvard among our universities is unchallenged. It stands first in Physics, Botany, Zoölogy, Physiology, and Pathology; second in Mathematics, Geology, Anatomy, Anthropolgy, and Psychology; and third in Chemistry and Astronomy. In every science of the twelve, it is so nearly first that a small change would place it there. This is a remarkable record, and all honor should be given to the men responsible for it.

IX. MASTER OF ARCHITECTURAL ACOUSTICS

THE THREE volumes in which Sabine planned to present the principles of his great discovery in definitive form were never completed. Volumes one and two were to cover the physical and physiological aspects of Sound, and the third was to be devoted to Architectural Acoustics. In 1922, Doctor Theodore Lyman, his former pupil and always his devoted friend, gathered together the important papers Sabine had delivered before learned bodies or published in various architectural journals in a volume entitled " Collected Papers on Acoustics," [1] and it is significant that this publication, fragmentary as its contents must necessarily be, today forms a part of the standard office equipment of leading architects and construction engineers throughout the world. " As these papers were addressed to a changing audience, little acquainted with Physical Science," Doctor Lyman says in his Preface, " a certain amount of repetition was not only unavoidable but desirable." The vital point is that in no instance did the author find it necessary to correct. Fourteen years of opportunity for his followers and imitators to improve upon his work, with the advantage of having his basic principles on which to build, have produced no advancement beyond methods of applying his ideas to new building materials which have come into existence since his death. The " Sabine constant " still stands unchallenged.

As this biography is concerned with the exposition of Wallace Sabine rather than of Architectural Acoustics, the reader

[1] Harvard University Press, 1922.

who is interested in the technical presentation of his work must be referred to this published volume, yet the evolution of his subject, his methods of approaching and solving problems, his ingenuity in acting as " physician-in-chief " to " sick buildings," throw so much light on certain personal characteristics that a brief continuing outline, with no attempt at coördination, is essential to proper understanding.

Sabine divided his problem in Architectural Acoustics into two distinct lines of investigation, each absolutely essential to its complete solution. The first, as developed in the Fogg Art Museum case, was to determine quantitatively the physical conditions on which loudness, reverberation, resonance, and the allied phenomena depend. Thus far the investigation was purely physical, and its conclusions were based wholly upon scientific grounds.

Symphony Hall was the introduction to the second line of investigation in that it offered Sabine an opportunity to apply his scientific conclusions in a practical way to a specific auditorium in advance of construction; and the successful results led him directly into the second phase of his work. This was to determine the intensity which each contributing element should have, what conditions were best for the distinct audition of speech, and what effects were best for music in its various forms. " This," he said, " is a matter of judgment and taste, and its conclusions are weighty in proportion to the weight and unanimity of the authority in which they find their source."

Sabine tells us that his investigation of the absorption coefficient of different materials for the single note of violin C " required every other night from twelve until five for a period of three years " — yet this intensive study, valuable as it was, proved inadequate for the investigator's new problem. Thus, at this point, and during the following five years, Sabine concentrated his experiments upon testing a great variety of structural material and different wall surfaces, and extended his study over the whole range in pitch of the speaking voice and of the musical scale.

The evolution of the musical scale played an important part in Sabine's enlarged and elaborated scheme, and the data he collected for his own guidance suggest many novel ideas to the general reader:

" Turning to Europe, we find the musical scale most rapidly developing among the stone-dwelling people along the shores of the Mediterranean. The development of the scale and its increased use kept pace with the increased size of the dwellings and temples. It showed, above all, in their religious worship, as their temples and churches reached cathedral size. The reverberation which accompanied the lofty and magnificent architecture increased until even the spoken service became intoned in the Gregorian chant. It is not going beyond the bounds of reason to say that in those churches in Europe which are housed in magnificent cathedrals — the Catholic, the Lutheran, and the Protestant Episcopal — the form of worship is in part determined by their acoustical conditions." [2]

In his study of the musical scale, Sabine found Helmholtz' " Sensations of Tone " [3] particularly stimulating:

" Having given a physical and physiological explanation of the harmony and discord of simultaneous sounds, and, therefore, an explanation of the musical scale as used in mod-

---

[2] Vice presidential address, Section B, American Association for the Advancement of Science, Chicago, 1907.

[3] " In our spare intervals Sabine and I often walked together, and I shall not soon forget a Sunday morning in Middlesex Fells in which we neither of us saw much of the spring beauty of the woods, but spent almost all the time in discussing the Helmholtz theory of hearing. I returned with a mind much clarified and enlightened, and with the conviction that in its essentials there was much to be said for the theory. I told Sabine once that Helmholtz made the first measurement of the rate of nerve conduction, and that the measurement had been carried out on a small length of frog's nerve. He remarked that, however it had been done, it was without doubt very close to complete accuracy, for that was the only kind of work that Helmholtz ever tolerated. " Professor George H. Parker.

ern composition, Helmholtz was met by an apparent anachronism. The musical scale, identical with the modern musical scale in all essentials, antedated by its use in single-part melody the invention of chordal composition, or, as Helmholtz expressed it, preceded all experience of musical harmony. In seeking an explanation of this early invention of the musical scale, Helmholtz abandoned his most notable contribution, and relegated his explanation of harmony and discord to the minor service of explaining a fortunate, though of course an important use of an already invented system of musical notes. The explanation of the original invention of the musical scale and its use in single-part music through the classical and the early Christian eras, he sought for in purely esthetic considerations — in exactly those devices from which he had just succeeded in rescuing the explanation of harmony and discord." [4]

In explaining this apparent anachronism, Sabine made an important contribution to the theory of the origin of the musical scale:

" In many rooms of ordinary construction the prolongation of audibility amounts to two or three seconds, and it is not exceedingly rare that a sound of moderate initial intensity should continue audible for eight, nine, or even ten seconds after the source has ceased. As a result of this, single-part music produced as successive separate sounds is, nevertheless, heard as overlapping, and at times as greatly overlapping tones. Each note may well be audible with appreciable intensity, not merely through the next, but through several succeeding notes. Under such conditions we have every opportunity, even with single-part music, for the production of all the phenomena of harmony and discord which has now been discussed by Helmholtz in explanation of the chordal use of the musical scale. In any ordinarily bare and uncar-

---

[4] Vice presidential address, Section B, American Association for the Advancement of Science, Chicago, 1907.

peted room, one may sing in succession a series of notes, and then hear for some time afterward their full chordal effect." [5]

Then Sabine goes farther, and suggests a physical explanation of the differences of musical scale developed by different races:

" Housed or unhoused, dwelling in reed huts or in tents, in houses of wood or of stone, in houses and temples high vaulted or low roofed, of heavy furnishing or light, in these conditions we may look for the factors which determine the development of a musical scale in any race, which determine the rapidity of the growth of the scale, its richness, and its considerable use in single-part melody.

" We have explained for us by the absorptive powers of various materials why the musical scale has but slowly developed in the greater part of Asia and of Africa. Almost no traveler has reported a musical scale, even of the most primitive sort, among any of the previously unvisited tribes of Africa. This fact could not be ascribed to racial inaptitude. If melody was, as Helmholtz suggested, but rhythm in time and in pitch, the musical scale should have been developed in Africa if anywhere. These races were given to the most rhythmical dancing, and the rhythmical beating of drums and tomtoms. Rhythm in time they certainly had. Moreover, failure to develop a musical scale could not be ascribed to racial inaptitude to feeling for pitch. Transported to America, and brought in contact with the musical scale, the negro became almost immediately the most musical part of our population. The absence of a highly developed scale in Africa must then be ascribed to environment." [5]

Concerning other phases of Sabine's advanced work, detached statements have been selected to give the reader an

---

[5] Vice presidential address, Section B, American Association for the Advancement of Science, Chicago, 1907.

idea of his method of approach to his enlarged field, and to emphasize the confidence which accompanied his full realization of the difficulties as the investigator attacked one after another of his involved problems, and arrived at definite conclusions. Speakers and singers will discover here simple explanations of difficulties against which they have personally contended:

Reverberation as applied to entire musical scale
" It can be shown readily that the various materials of which the walls of a room are constructed, and the materials with which it is filled, do not have the same absorbing power for all sounds regardless of pitch. . . . Thus a room may have great reverberation for sounds of low pitch and very little for sounds of high pitch, or exactly the reverse; or a room may have comparatively great reverberation for sounds both of high and of low pitch and very little for sounds near the middle of the scale. In other words, it is not putting it too strongly to say that a room may have very different quality in different registers, as different as does a musical instrument; or, if the room is to be used for speaking purposes, it may have different degrees of excellence or defect for a whisper and for the full rounded tones of the voice, different for a woman's voice and for a man's.

" The following case may be cited: The present pastor of a church near Boston, in describing the nature of its acoustical defects, stated that different speakers had different degrees of difficulty in making themselves heard. He had no difficulty, having a rather high-pitched voice; but the candidate before him, with a louder but much lower voice, failed of the appointment because unable to make himself heard." [6]

Accuracy of musical taste
" The surprising accuracy of musical taste is perhaps the explanation of the rarity with which it is entirely satisfied,

---

[6] Proceedings of the American Academy of Arts and Sciences, June, 1906.

particularly when the architectural designs are left to chance in this respect. . . .

" The immediate effect of reverberation is that each note, if it be music, each syllable or part of a syllable, if it be speech, continues its sound for some time, and by its prolongation overlaps the succeeding notes or syllables, harmoniously or inharmoniously in music, and in speech always towards confusion. In the case of speech it is inconceivable that this prolongation of the sound, this reverberation, should have any other effect than that of confusion and injury to the clearness of the enunciation. In music, on the other hand, reverberation, unless in excess, has a distinct and positive advantage.

" Given a room comparatively empty, with hard wall surfaces (for example, plaster or tile), and having in it comparatively little furniture, the amount of reverberation for the sounds of about the middle register of the violin will be very nearly though not exactly equal. If, however, we bring into the room a quantity of elastic felt cushions, sufficient, let us say, to accommodate a normal audience, the effect of these cushions, the audience being supposed absent, will be to diminish very much the reverberation both for the double-bass viol and for the violin, but will diminish them in very unequal amounts. The reverberation will now be twice as great for the double-bass as for the violin. If an audience comes into the room, filling up the seats, the reverberation will be reduced still farther, and in a still greater disproportion, so that with an audience entirely filling the room the reverberation for the violin will be less than one-third that for the double-bass. When one considers that a difference of five per cent in reverberation is a matter for approval or disapproval on the part of musicians of critical taste, the importance of considering these facts is obvious.

" The coefficients of absorption, when once known, enable one not merely to calculate the prolongation of the sound, but also to calculate the average loudness of sustained tones. Thus it was shown that the average loudness of a sound in a room is proportional inversely to the absorbing power of the material in the room. Therefore, the data, covering the whole range of the musical scale, enable one to calculate the loudness of different notes over that range, and make it possible to show what effect the room has on the piano or the orchestra in different parts of the register.

" To illustrate: if the double-bass and the violin produce the same loudness in the open air, in the bare room with hard walls both would be re-enforced about equally. The elastic felt brought into the room would decidedly diminish this re-enforcement for both instruments. It would, however, exert a much more pronounced effect in the way of diminishing the re-enforcement for the violin than for the double-bass. In fact, the balance will be so affected that it will require two violins to produce the same volume of sound as does one double-bass. The audience coming into the room will make it necessary to use three violins to a double-bass to secure the same balance as before.

" Every musical tone is composed of a great number of partial tones, the predominating one being taken as the fundamental, and its pitch as the pitch of the sound. The other partial tones are regarded as giving quality or color to the fundamental. The musical quality of a tone depends on the relative intensities of the overtones. It has been customary, at least on the part of physicists, to regard the relative intensities of the overtones, which define the quality of the sound, as depending simply on the source from which the sound originates. Of course, primarily, this is true. Nevertheless, while the source defines the relative intensities of the issuing sounds, their actual intensities in the room depend not merely on that, but also, and to a surprising degree, on the room itself.

" The effect of the material used in the construction of a

room, and the contained furniture, in altering the relative intensities of the fundamental and the overtones, is to improve or injure its quality according to circumstances. It may be, of course, that the tone desired is a very pure one, or it may be that what is wanted is a tone with pronounced upper partials. Take, for example, the ' night horn ' stop in a pipe organ. This is intended to have a very pure tone. The room in contributing to its purity would improve its quality. On the other hand, the mixture stop in a pipe organ is intended to have very pronounced overtones. In fact, to this end not one but several pipes are sounded at once. The effect of the above room is to emphasize the fundamental and to wipe out the overtones would be in opposition to the original design of the stop. To determine what balance is desirable must lie, of course, with the musicians. . . . The above bare outline is intended only to indicate the importance of extending the work to the whole range of the musical scale." [7]

Insulation

Sabine's analysis of the sound-insulation problem was perhaps the most difficult he encountered in his investigations. " The insulation of sound," he writes, " as an unsolved problem in Architectural Acoustics, was first brought to the writer's attention by the New England Conservatory of Music, immediately after its completion in 1904, and almost simultaneously in connection with a private house which had just been completed in New York. A few years later it was renewed by the Institute of Musical Art in New York. In the construction of all three buildings it had been regarded as particularly important that communication of sound from room to room should be avoided, and methods to that end had been employed which were in every way reasonable. The results showed that in this phase of Archi-

[7] Proceedings of the American Academy of Arts and Sciences, June, 1906.

tectural Acoustics also there had not been a sufficiently searching and practical investigation, and that there were no experimental data on which an architect could rely." [8]

Sabine's investigations were interrupted by his premature death, and the problem has never been completely solved. Yet the tests recorded in his " Collected Papers " [9] on transmission of sound through sheet-iron and hair-felt, both singly and in combination, still remain the authoritative source of much of the sound-insulation work which is being done today.

Concerning the Pulitzer house, mentioned above, Sabine gives the following particulars: " It was practically a double house, one of the most imperative conditions of the building being the exclusion of sounds in the main part of the house from the part to the left of a great partition wall. In the basement of the main building was the servants' dining room. Rapping with the knuckles on the wall of this room produced in the bedroom, two stories up and on the other side of the great partition wall, a sound, which, although hardly, as the architect expressed it, magnified, (was) yet of astonishing loudness and clearness." [10]

Materials

Sabine had secured reliable data for glass surfaces, for glazed tile surfaces, for plastered and unplastered porous tile, for plaster on wood lath, and plaster on wire lath, for rugs and carpets; but even this information was by no means complete. What he required was not merely the measurement of existing material — how ash differs from oak, and oak from walnut or pine or whitewood; what was the effect of the spacing of the furring on which the wood sheathing was fastened. If the wall was to be plaster on lath, there arose the question as to the difference between wood lath and wire lath, between the mortar that was formerly used and the

---

[8] The Brickbuilder, February, 1915.   [9] Pages 247–254.
[10] The Brickbuilder, February, 1915.

wall, which is made of hard and impervious plaster. What was the effect of variations in thickness of the plaster? What was the effect of painting the plaster in oil or in water colors? What was the effect of the depth of the air space behind the plaster? The increasing efforts at fireproof construction had resulted in the use of harder and harder wall surfaces, with great reverberation in the room, and in many cases poorer acoustics. Was it possible to devise a material which should satisfy the conditions as to fireproof qualities, and yet retain the excellence of some of the older but not fireproof rooms? [11] Or, in considering the interior furnishings, what type of chair was best, what form of cushions, or what form of upholstery?

From that point on, Sabine's investigation was continued with reference to interference and resonance, the effect of peculiarities of form, and the causes of variation in audition in different parts of an auditorium. The fact that as yet little has been said about the form of auditoriums or the position of absorbing or reflecting surfaces, should not lead the reader to think these matters unimportant. " A not unusual fallacy," Sabine once said, " is the failure to realize that in a theatre we are essentially dealing with two large and connecting rooms — that in which the audience is seated, and that beyond the proscenium arch." When he came to consider an auditorium so irregular in shape as a modern theatre, with boxes and deep galleries, and had to meet the requirement that words spoken on the stage should be easily heard in all parts of the house, the problem became more than a consideration of reverberation. In such cases it was necessary to consider whether the details of shape and surface, actual or proposed, were such as to kill off the sound, or to confuse it by an echo. Sabine once shocked a clergy-

---

[11] This self-inquiry eventually led to Sabine's co-invention of the absorptive tile (*see* p. 208), which, while fireproof, overcame excessive reverberation, and was more enduring than the moth-attracting felt.

man, who complained of the acoustic properties of his church, by saying, " You are paying the penalty for adopting an Episcopalian form of building for a Universalist form of service."

The progress of Sabine's experimental investigations was guided along practical lines and greatly enriched by the knowledge gained through frequent consultations from such architects as Messrs. McKim, Mead & White, Carrère and Hastings, Cram, Goodhue, and Ferguson, and Allen and Collens, who sought assistance from him either to correct completed buildings or in the preparation of plans in advance of construction. In March, 1912, Sabine published an article in the " Architectural Quarterly of Harvard University," in which he recorded his experiences and explained the problems involved, supplementing his text by selected examples which are especially typical. To this the reader is referred for technical information. Such detached quotations as follow are taken from copy revised by the author, somewhat differing from the magazine text and from the text as reprinted later in his " Collected Papers." The ingenuity of Sabine's approach to the widely differing problems reveals the versatility of his diagnoses and the sureness of his remedial attack.

" It is proposed to discuss here," Sabine states in his final manuscript, " only such corrective methods as can be employed without extensive alterations in form. It is not proposed to discuss changes in dimension, changes in the position of the wall surfaces, or changes in structural ceiling height. It is the purpose to discuss medicinal rather than surgical methods. Such treatment, properly planned and executed, while not always available, will in the great majority of cases result in a remedy of the difficulty.

" Two old but now nearly abandoned devices for remedying acoustical difficulties are stretched wires and sounding boards. The first is without value; the second is of some value, generally slight, though occasionally a perceptible factor in the final result. The stretching of wires is a method which has long been employed, and its disfiguring relics in many churches and court rooms proclaim a difficulty which they are powerless to relieve. Like many other traditions, it has been abandoned but slowly. The fact that it was wholly without either foundation of reason or defense of argument made it difficult to answer or to meet. The device, devoid on the one hand of scientific foundation, and on the other of successful experience, has taken varied forms in its application. Apparently it is a matter of no moment where the wires are stretched or in what amount. There are theatres and churches in Boston and New York in which four or five wires are stretched across the middle of the room; in other auditoriums miles on miles of wire have been stretched; in both equally without effect. . . .

" Aside from such cumulative evidence of ineffectiveness, it is not difficult to show that there is no physical basis for the device. The sound, whose echo these wires are presumed to absorb, scarcely affects the wires, giving to them a vibration which at most is of microscopical magnitude. How slight the reaction between the air and the wires can be well illustrated by a reciprocal case. If the string of a violin were free from the body of the violin, it would not emit a sound which could be heard four feet away. The string itself cuts through the air with but the slightest communication of motion. Conversely, when the sound is in the room and the string at rest, the vibrating air flows past it, to and fro, without disturbing it, and consequently without itself being affected by reaction either for better or worse.

" The ' sounding board ' so-called, the canopy, plain or curved, over the speaker's head, as a device for correcting acoustical difficulties, has at times a value; but unless the sounding board is to be a large one, the benefit to be expected from its installation may be greatly over-rated.

" Among a number of interesting problems in advance of construction the firm of McKim, Mead & White has brought some interesting problems in correction, of which three will serve admirably as examples because of their unusual directness. The first is that of the Congregational Church in Naugatuck, Connecticut. When first built, its ceiling was cylindrical, as now, but smooth. Its curvature was such as to focus a voice from the platform upon the audience — not at a point, but along a focal line; for a cylindrical mirror is astigmatic. The difficulty was evident with the speaking, but may be described more effectually with reference to the singing. The position of the choir was behind the preacher and across the main axis of the church. On one line in the audience, crossing the church obliquely from right to left, the soprano voice could be heard coming even more sharply from the ceiling than directly from the singer. The alto, starting nearer the axis of the church, had for its focus a line crossing the church less obliquely. The phenomena were similar for the tenor and the bass voices, but with focal lines crossing the church obliquely in opposite directions. The difficulty was in a very large measure remedied by coffering the ceiling, both the old and the new ceiling being of plaster. Ideally a larger and deeper coffering was desirable, but the solution as shown was practical and the result satisfactory.

" The Hall of the House of Representatives in the Rhode Island State Capitol illustrated another type of difficulty. In considering this hall it is necessary to bear in mind that the problem is an essentially different one from that of a church or lecture room. In these the speaking is from a raised platform and a fixed position. In a legislative assembly the speaking is in the main from the floor, and may be from any part of the floor; the speaker stands on a level with his fellow-members; he stands with his back to a part of the audience and often with his back to the greater part of his audience; in different parts of the house the speaker directs his voice in different directions, and against different wall surfaces. In this hall the walls were of stone to approximately half the height of the room; above that they were of stone and plaster. The ceiling was coffered. The difficulty in this room was with that part of the voice which, crossing the room transversely, fell on the side walls. With the speaker standing on the floor, the greater volume of his voice was directed upward. The sound striking the side wall was reflected across the room to the opposite wall and back again, to and fro, mounting gradually until it reached the ceiling. It was there reflected directly down upon the audience. The ceiling sloped, and had some curvature, but the curvature was not such as to produce a distinct focusing of the sound. During these reflections the sound met only feebly absorbent surfaces and therefore returned to the audience with but little loss of intensity. Its return was at such an interval of time as to result in great confusion of speech. Only the fact that the voice, rising at different angles, traveled different paths and therefore returned at varying intervals, prevented the formation of a distinct echo.

" The difficulty was remedied in this case by a change in material without change of form, by diminishing the reflecting power of the two side walls. This was done by placing a suitable felt on the plaster walls between the engaged columns, and covering it with a decorated tapestry. Fortunately, the design of the room admitted of a charming execution of this treatment. It is interesting to note that this treatment applied to the lower half of the walls would not have been acoustically effective.

" The Lecture Room of the Metropolitan Museum of Art illustrates the next step in complexity. This hall is a semi-circular auditorium, with the semi-circle slightly continued by short, straight walls. The platform is nearly, though not wholly, within a broad but shallow recess. The body of the auditorium is surmounted by a spherical ceiling with short cylindrical extension following the straight side walls. In the centre of the ceiling is a flat skylight of glass. In this room the reverberation was not merely excessive, but it resolved itself by focusing into a multiple echo, the components of which followed each other with great rapidity but were distinctly separable. The number distinguishable varied in different parts of the hall. Seven were distinguishable at certain parts.

" To improve the acoustics the ceiling was coffered, the limiting depth and dimensions of this coffering being determined in large measure by the dimensions of the skylight. The semi-circular wall at the rear of the auditorium was transformed into panels which were filled with felt over which was stretched burlap. The result was the result assured — the reduction of the disturbance to a single and highly localized echo. This echo is audible only in the central seats — two or three seats at a time — and moves about as the speaker moves, but in symmetrically opposite direction. Despite this residual effect, and it should be noted that this residual effect was predicted, the result is highly satisfactory to Dr. Edward Robinson,[12] the Director of the Museum, and the room is now used with comfort, whereas it had been for a year abandoned."

" It should be borne in mind," Sabine continues, " that ' perfect acoustics ' does not mean the total elimination of reverberation, even were that possible. Loudness and reverberation are almost, though not quite, proportional qualities. The result to be sought is a balance between the two qualities, dependent on the size of the auditorium and the use to which it is to be applied. Geometrically, the foregoing cases are comparatively simple. In each, the room is a simple space bounded by plane, cylindrical, or spherical surfaces, and these surfaces simply arranged with reference to each

---

[12] See page 226.

other. The simplicity of these cases is obvious. The complexity of other cases is not always patent, or, when patent, it is not obvious to a merely casual inspection how best the problem should be attacked. A large number of cases, however, may be handled in a practical manner by regarding them as connecting spaces, each with its own reverberation and pouring sound into and receiving sound from the others. An obvious case is the theatre, where the aggregate acoustical property is dependent on the space behind the proscenium arch in which the speaker stands, as well as on the space in front of it. In another sense and to a less degree, the cathedral with its chancel, transept, and nave may be regarded as a case of connected spaces. The problem certainly takes on a simpler aspect when so attacked.

" An extreme and purely hypothetical case would be a deep and wide auditorium with a very low ceiling, and with a stage recess deep, high, and reverberant, in fact such a case as might occur when for special purposes two very different rooms are thrown together. In such a case the reverberation calculated on the basis of a single room of the combined volume and the combined absorbing power would yield an erroneous value. The speaker's voice, especially if he stood back some distance from the opening between the two rooms, would be lost in the production of reverberation in its own space. The total resulting sound, in a confused mass, would be propagated out over the auditorium. Of course, this is an extreme case and of unusual occurrence, but by its very exaggeration serves to illustrate the point. In a less degree it is not of infrequent occurrence. It was for this reason, or rather through the experience of this effect, although only as a nice refinement, that the Boston Symphony Orchestra has its special scenery stage in Carnegie Hall, and for this that Mr. Damrosch in addition moved his orchestra some little distance forward into the main auditorium for his concerts in The New Theatre.

" A cathedral is a good example of such geometrical com-plication, still further complicated by the variety of service which it is to render. It must be adapted to speaking from the pulpit and to reading from the lectern. It must be adapted to organ and vocal music, and occasionally to other forms of service, though generally of so minor importance as to be beyond the range of appropriate consideration. Most cathedrals and modern large churches have a reverberation which is excessive not only for the spoken but also for a large portion of the musical service. The difficulty is not peculiar to any one type of architecture. To take European examples, it occurs in the Classic St. Paul in London, the Romanesque Durham, the Basilican Romanesque Pisa, the Italian Gothic Florence, and the English Gothic York.

" It may be remarked in passing that the lectern is almost invariably a more difficult problem than the pulpit. This is in part because reading, with the head thrown slightly forward, is more difficult than speaking; because, if the lec-tern is sufficiently high to permit of an erect position, it screens the voice; because a speaker, without book or manu-script, seeing his audience, realizes his distance and his difficulties; and finally, because the pulpit is generally higher and against a column, whereas the lectern stands out free and unsupported.

" The auditorium which has received the greatest amount of discussion recently is The New (Century) Theatre in New York. Had it been a commercial undertaking it would have received but passing notice. As an institution of large purpose on the part of the Founders, it received a corre-spondingly large attention. As an institution of generous purpose, without hope or desire for financial return, it was appropriated by the public, and received the persistent criticism which seems the usual reward for such undertak-ings. The writer was consulted only after the completion of the building, but its acoustical difficulties can be discussed adequately only in the light of its initial programme.

" It was part of the original programme submitted to Messrs. Carrère and Hastings that the building should be used, or at least should be adapted to use for Opera as well as for Drama. In this respect it was to bear to the Metropolitan the position which the Opéra Comique in Paris bears to The Opéra. This idea, with its corollary features, influenced the early design and shows in the completed structure.

" It was also a part of the initial plan that there should be two rows of boxes, something very unusual in theatre construction. This was a prodigal use of space and magnified the building in all its dimensions. Later, but not until after the building was nearly completed, the upper row of boxes was abandoned, and the gallery thus created was devoted to foyer chairs. As the main walls were by this time erected, the gallery was limited in depth to the boxes and their antechambers. It thus resulted that this level, which is ordinarily occupied by a gallery of great value, is of small capacity. Notwithstanding this, The New Theatre seats twenty-three hundred, while the usual theatre seats but little more than two-thirds that number.

" The necessity of providing twenty-three commodious boxes, all in the first tier, of which none should be so near the stage as to be distinctly inferior, determined a large circle for their front and for the front of all the galleries. Thus not merely are the seats far from the stage, but the great horizontal scale thus necessitated leads architecturally to a correspondingly great vertical scale. The row of boxes and the foyer balcony above not merely determined the scale of the auditorium, but also presented at the back of their shallow depth a concave wall which focused the reflected sound in the centre of the auditorium.

" Finally, it should be borne in mind that, while the acoustical demands in a theatre are greater than in almost any other type of auditorium, because of the great modulation of the voice in dramatic action, The New Theatre was undertaking an even more than usually difficult task, that of presenting on the one hand the older dramas, with their less familiar and more difficult phrasing, and on the other the more subtle and delicate of modern plays. The conventional type of theatre-construction is fairly, though only fairly, well adapted to the usual type of dramatic performance. The New Theatre, with a very difficult type of performance to present, was forced by the conditions which surrounded the project, to depart from the conventional type far more radically than was perhaps at that time realized.

" Here, as usual in a completed building, structural changes and large changes of form were impossible, and the acoustical difficulties of the auditorium could be remedied only by indirection. The boxes were changed from the first to the second level, being interchanged with the foyer chairs, while the excessive height of the main body of the auditorium was reduced by means of a canopy surrounding the central chandelier. This ingenious and not displeasing substitute for the recommended lowering of the ceiling was proposed by Mr. Hastings, although of course only as a means to an end. The canopy is oval in plan, following the outline of the oval panel in the ceiling, its longer axis being transverse. Its major and minor horizontal dimensions are 70 feet, and 40 feet. Its effective lowering of the height of the ceiling is 20 feet. A moment's consideration will show that its effective area in preventing the ceiling-echo is greater than its actual dimensions, particularly in the direction of its minor axis. The improvement brought about by this was pronounced and satisfactory to the Founders. The distances, however, were still too great, even visually, for the type of dramatic performance for which the theatre was primarily intended, and such use was therefore discontinued. The New Theatre is much better adapted to Opera than to dramatic performances, and it will be a matter of great regret if, with its charming solution of many difficult architectural problems, it is not restored to such dignified purpose."

In concluding this chapter, a single instance is recorded, by way of contrast, where Sabine's knowledge of his subject, now in its maturity, was applied to a building in advance of construction, " with unusual precision." Mr. Winthrop Ames had been deeply impressed with the way Sabine had attacked the problem of The New Theatre, and when he came to build his own Little Theatre, in New York, he instructed his architects to make their plans in accordance with Sabine's ideas. But let Sabine tell the story in his own words:

" The purpose was the production of plays which could be adequately rendered only by the most delicate shades of expression, which would be lost in considerable measure if the conditions were such as to necessitate exaggeration of feature or of voice. The definition of its use was that it should seat just less than three hundred, and that all the seats were to be as nearly as possible of equal excellence, with the important assurance that every seat would be occupied at every performance.

" The first calculations, assuming probable materials and plausible details of construction (plaster on tile walls, plaster on wire lath ceiling, solid plaster cornices and moulding), gave a reverberation in excess of that in many theatres whose acoustical qualities are not especially questioned. But the unusual requirements of the plays to be presented in this theatre, and the tendency of the public to criticize whatever is unconventional in design, led both Mr. Ames and the architects to insist on exceptional quality. The floor was therefore lowered at the front, the ceiling was lowered,

and the walls near the stage brought in and reduced in curvature, with, of course, corresponding changes in the architectural treatment. The rear wall, following the line of the
rear seats, remained unchanged in curvature. The side walls
near the stage were curved. . . . In order to reduce still
further the reverberation, as well as to break acoustically
the curvature of the side and rear walls, ' acoustic felt ' was
applied in panels. Throughout, consideration was had for
the actual path of the sound in its successive reflections."

The successful outcome of Sabine's plans for The Little
Theatre demonstrated beyond dispute the existence of a
new science. " Neither Mr. Ames nor I," Mr. Ingalls wrote
him (March 12, 1912) , " would ever build another building, where good acoustics should be a feature, without first
consulting you and asking you to work with us from the
very beginning." At this moment Sabine stood upon the
pinnacle of his success, without a rival, without even a recognized competitor, as Master of Architectural Acoustics.

X. The Dean and the Prophet · 1909–1917

Wᴴᴇɴ Sabine sailed for Europe on the " Finland," on April 29, 1909, the thought farthest from his mind was that any possibility existed which threatened the continuation of his work as Dean of the Graduate School. The plans originally worked out with President Eliot were maturing with gratifying exactness; the various departments were now headed by distinguished leaders in their subjects; the vastly increased opportunities thus offered were attracting the kind of men Harvard wished to educate; the high standard of the School was universally acknowledged.

On the dock in New York, Sabine accidentally met Henry S. Pritchett, head of the Carnegie Foundation for the Advancement of Teaching, whom he had earlier known as President of the Massachusetts Institute of Technology at the time of the projected merger with Harvard in 1905; and during their informal conversation casual reference was made to the failure of that historic event to be consummated. Even as they talked, unknown to Sabine, affairs were shaping themselves in Cambridge to revive the subject, which he had thought settled for all time. Pritchett had come to see Andrew Carnegie off on the boat, and, when he introduced the two fellow-passengers, Carnegie insisted that Sabine join him and his family at table. A curious study in contrasts — this talkative, publicity-loving little Scotchman and the tall, reserved, retiring Harvard professor!

Sabine had two special objects on this trip — to secure Professor Stodoler, of Zurich, to become head of the Electrical Engineering Department of the Graduate School, and to inspect the testing-tanks of Europe. President Eliot had sent in his resignation, to take effect at the end of that academic year, and Sabine hoped, as a last official service to him, to establish a course in Naval Engineering, with a testing-tank, at the University, knowing how great was the President's desire to have Harvard offer such facilities to students through testing models of boats for private yachts and for the Merchant Marine.

Sabine landed at Naples. Thence he went directly to Spezia, the naval construction base in Italy, and was afforded every opportunity for studying the model testing-tank of the Italian navy. From Spezia he proceeded to Genoa, intending to visit Marseilles, but decided instead to go north to Zurich, where he spent several days at the Polytechnique Institute. Then he journeyed to Carlsruhe and later to Stuttgart, especially to inspect the Technische Hochschulen, which at that time had attained a remarkable development of efficiency in Germany. He was shown the German naval base and testing-tank, and again he was impressed by the " efficiency." Then he crossed to England, and devoted a fortnight to studying the technical schools in London, Sheffield, Manchester, Birmingham, Edinburgh, and Glasgow. Mr. Fronde, of the British navy, accompanied him during his inspection of the British Admiralty Tank at Gosport, Stokes Bay, and in a letter home Sabine described this day as " the meat of my trip."

At Zurich he experienced one of his few disappointments in failing to persuade the man he wanted to accept a position in the Harvard Graduate School. This he attributed to his limited ability to speak German. " Never again," he wrote, " will I be caught in the humiliating position of visiting a country of which I am unable to speak the language." [1] Although dazzled by the pecuniary inducement

---

[1] Stodoler's innate courtesy restrained him from mortifying Sabine's somewhat uncertain German by acquainting him with the fact that he spoke English!

of $5500 salary from Harvard, and an additional $5000 offered him as consultant in the General Electric Research Laboratories at Schenectady, Professor Stodoler firmly declined to take up a new life in an unfamiliar country. This was the same Stodoler who developed the turbine which made possible the electrification of the Swiss railroads, and, during the War, invented the marvelous mechanical hand for mutilated soldiers. His name came into the news when he expressed his righteous indignation that Germany prevented him from placing his invention at the disposal of wounded soldiers of every nation.

Sabine was particularly interested in his intensive study of the German method of teaching Science, so emphasized at that time, because in his own teaching he had steadfastly held out against it.

From Dr. Hollis Godfrey

When Sabine began to have his effect upon Science, the teaching of Science and its use were highly technical. The Germans were writing bibliographies, making formulae, and crystallizing Science. They did not understand the relationship of research (determining the fact), teaching (transmitting the fact to the human being), and practice (the use by human beings). They were putting mathematics into all kinds of decimals. They were creating a fog, and didn't know where they were going; they were developing a scientific mysticism that was going to make all kinds of trouble. One of the most important contributions that Sabine made was his principle of " significant figures." He constantly repeated that only what a man could use was significant in applied Science. In that he preached a fundamental philosophy.

Later, the educational world came to agree with Sabine. He insisted that keen as the German mind was to apply a new idea, it seemed incapable of originating one. To prove his contention, he once went through the so-called scientific discoveries credited to the Germans, and found that Helmholtz' theory of Sound and Roentgen's X-ray were the only discoveries not adapted from the inventions of others.

Just before sailing for home, Sabine wrote: " I am learning a great deal about model testing-tanks, about the teaching of Architecture, about Engineering, about the educational systems of Europe generally, and feel that I have a good grip on the general situation of the Applied Sciences and laboratories and *men*."

There is more significance to the italicized word than appears on the surface. Sabine found much in Germany beyond that which he went to seek. Trained by years of intensive practice, his eye, his ear, and his mind were abnormally acute in observation and conclusion. The efficiency in the Technische Hochschulen was a bit too highly developed to be explained by natural conditions; the standardization, the discipline, the equipment he found at the German naval base at Wilhelmshaven exceeded any necessity of a nation at peace with the world; the over-excited toasts to " Der Tag " sounded more exultant and more expectant than when he had heard them before. To gain first-hand knowledge of the attitude of the German people, he devoted the early morning hours to poling on the various branches of the River Spree with the truck gardeners, bringing in their vegetables to the Berlin market, and at other times mingled intimately with the common people. These he found to be contented and peace-loving — as against the Prussian-ruled Kaiser, who jealously feared the growing popularity of his warlike son.

Sabine left Germany with so strong a conviction that the Kaiser was already engaged in definite war preparations that no amount of incredulity could change it. He discussed the matter frankly with the British Admiralty during his later conferences, particularly contrasting the ease with which the Germans could exchange standardized parts in their warships with the clumsy, unstandardized situation in the English navy; but he made little impression. He reported his observations at Washington on his return home, only to have them received with the same polite indulgence. His Harvard associates laughed at the hysteria which had so suddenly attacked their erstwhile peace-loving colleague. Sabine came to refrain from further mention of his convictions, but in his own mind there was no doubt. He knew, from his observations of 1909, that Germany accepted the Agadir settlement in 1913 only because the Kiel Canal was unfinished. The declaration of war in August, 1914, which shocked the supine world, surprised him only in that it had been so long delayed.

Possessing full data concerning the projected testing-tank, Sabine, on his return home in August, 1909, devoted himself to perfecting the plans for consummating the undertaking. He personally prepared the drawings for the dry-dock and the tank; he formulated the detailed plans for the course to be given in Naval Engineering, for which he received President Eliot's unqualified approval; he secured the assurance of W. Starling Burgess that he would accept the professorship in this course; he succeeded in arranging with wealthy friends of the University, interested in the project itself, to underwrite the necessary expense.

Then, before formal announcement had been made of the plans, word came that the Massachusetts Institute of Technology had taken up the same idea, and was prepared not only to build a testing-tank on the Charles River, but to add the course on Naval Engineering to their curriculum! That this news was in the nature of a shock to Sabine goes without saying, but matters were in progress between these two institutions at this particular moment which prevented even a discussion as to which one should retire from the field. Harvard dropped all thought of continuing the project, and turned over to Technology the data Sabine had collected. Starling Burgess directed his energies away from Naval Engineering into Aeronautics. Out of this accident to Sabine's carefully laid plans came a friendship [2] and a personal association with Burgess and Aviation which was largely to affect his war experiences.

It was a curious coincidence that when Sabine returned from Europe he should have found on his desk an official invitation from Washington to be present at Fort Myer to witness the trial test of a single airplane which the Government was considering buying from Wilbur Wright. Unofficial exhibitions were being daily reported in the press, and the invitation stated that the exact date of the Government test would be announced in the newspapers, giving sufficient time for guests to reach Washington. But as Sabine had been away from Cambridge since April, and the inauguration of President Lowell was to take place at the beginning of the new term, he felt that he might not be able to leave at a moment's notice, yet perhaps, by observing one of the daily public performances, he could see enough to enable him to give his opinion.

Late one afternoon he telephoned Mrs. Sabine in Lexington, where the family had taken a bungalow for the summer, asking if it would be possible for her to accompany him to Washington that night, suggesting that he would invite Mr. and Mrs. Starling Burgess to go with them, so that together they could see not only this airplane demonstration, but also inspect the testing-tank at Washington. The little party of four carried out this plan, and the next day saw Wright in the air. During an interview granted Sabine and Burgess by this pioneer aviator, Wright stressed the point that he and his brother had striven only to prove by these engines that flying machines were an accomplished fact,

---

[2] Burgess had been a student of Sabine's at Harvard. After one of the lectures in Physics C, in which the instructor had demonstrated the resolution of forces by introducing the subject of yachts, Burgess came up to Sabine and said, " I suppose my father followed those rules you laid down, but I'm sure he didn't know why! "

adding that he saw no future utility for airplanes — that wealthy men might possibly take up flying as a fad, and should there ever be a war, such machines might possibly be used for scouting. Sabine often referred to this incident when, five years later, the world became air-minded, and the power of the opposing forces during the World War came almost to be measured by their comparative strength in the air.

The attitude of passive acquiescence which Harvard had assumed in the matter of the testing-tank became entirely comprehensible to Sabine when he was made cognizant of what had been taking place while he had been in Europe. In 1909 the first instalment was received by the Harvard Corporation from the McKay trustees, and this revived the project of the merger with the Massachusetts Institute of Technology. Obviously, with this suggested union a definite possibility, it would be more natural for the Institute to establish the course in Naval Engineering. Sabine therefore picked up the threads of his routine work and awaited developments. There was a new President to be inaugurated at Harvard; Professor Trowbridge, his guide and mentor since his earliest days at Harvard, was about to retire; the demand upon his time as acoustical expert had become so great that he had to make plans for transferring some of the burden onto other shoulders; and an insidious attempt to rob him of the fruits of his thirteen years of investigation had to be legally resisted.[3]

The Harvard-Technology affair dragged slowly along until it culminated in an " agreement " which was entered into by the two institutions in December, 1913. This was subsequently modified, and assumed its final shape in March, 1915. President Eliot had been succeeded by President Abbott Lawrence Lowell at Harvard, and President Pritchett by President Richard C. Maclaurin at Technology. The

---

[3] See page 236.

new land on the banks of the Charles in Cambridge had been acquired by Technology, and the plant was in process of erection. Harvard had the money and Technology would soon have the buildings. This time it seemed certain that the merger, which twice before had failed to be consummated, would surely be put through, and Sabine, as Dean of the Graduate School, was faced by the necessity of readjusting the courses at Harvard to prevent disruption during the merging period.

Trowbridge's resignation, inevitable as Sabine knew it to be, came to him as a shock. From that first day when, as a boy in Philadelphia, he had approached him for advice, and was influenced by his personality to come from Ohio to Harvard, Sabine had felt for him an affection comparable only to his devotion to his parents. Trowbridge had warmly reciprocated this sentiment, and had been generous in taking his youthful assistant into close collaboration with him in his experimental work and in the preparation of his published papers.

Sabine felt deeply but was not given to outward demonstration of his feelings. These letters which passed between the older and the younger man — the teacher now far outdistanced by his brilliant pupil — show a phase of collegiate life not often duplicated:

To Professor John Trowbridge from W. C. S.
[*September* 27, 1910

As the beginning of the academic year approaches, I feel more and more keenly the loss of that kindly and sympathetic administration of the Laboratory which I have so much enjoyed during the past twenty-four years. This, although I am not in the Laboratory as much as in those earlier and happier days when it was my great privilege to work with you, or rather for you, with personal loyalty and keen satisfaction.

I wish you could realize how the Department feels in regard to you and your directorship of the Laboratory. Time and again, everybody connected with the Laboratory has spoken about your generous and kindly administration. They have spoken thus not merely during the past summer, while looking forward with some uncertainty as to the future, but during all the time that I have been in the Laboratory. It is not easy to pass the barriers of your reserve, and to express the regard in which we all hold you. But I feel such gratitude for your great kindness, for the stimulation and encouragement which you have continually given me, for my original appointment, and for my subsequent promotion and advancement, that I hope you will pardon me if, after being so long a recipient of such attention, I give expression to my appreciation. I am grateful to you for my whole academic career.

From Professor John Trowbridge to W. C. S.

[*October* 7, 1910

I found your affectionate and appreciative letter on my arrival in Cambridge. My home-coming to an empty house — for my housekeeper and servants are still in Prince Edward's Island — was a unique experience: I seemed to be officiating at my own funeral! Your letter was, therefore, extremely warming.

It has been a most happy experience — one which I believe has fallen to the lot of few men — to have been associated for twenty-five years with such appreciative and forbearing men as yourself, B. O. Peirce, and Hall. After all, what are scientific distinctions compared with that made in human hearts? You assure me that I have really achieved the greatest thing in life; and I have given your expression to my daughter, Mrs. Parker, as an *apologia pro vita mea.*

I must, however, dissent from your belief that your success has been due in such great measure to me. It has been due to your own ability and personality; and I have been only a feeble instrument.

In Sabine's letter here quoted he speaks of " earlier and happier days," and he spoke with reason. To no other colleague would he have admitted it, but Trowbridge knew what he was going through. Loyally as he accepted the new situation created by the suggested merger, no man could see the results of his labors absorbed by an outside institution without having the fact itself pull upon his vitality. And the more loyal the man, the keener the pain:

By Professor Edwin H. Hall

As to Sabine's general conception of what the Harvard Schools of Applied Science should be, I think that the educational world, hereabouts, after some experimenting with other plans, is pretty much coming back to it. Of course this combination involved the extinction of the office he held as Dean, and he might well have felt that it imperiled some of the aims he had been striving for. Any man, however slight may be his natural ambition for executive power, is likely to become somewhat enamored of it after years of possession. Moreover, Sabine was strong in the respect and confidence of influential men. I have heard, though I do not profess to speak with authority on this point, that the Harvard Corporation would have rejected the proposed merger if he had opposed it. But he did not oppose — he advocated it. Did he do so with full conviction? I do not profess to know; but my conjecture is that, when once the change had been suggested, and he saw that it would involve in some degree a sacrifice of himself, he was no longer able to view the matter with a free mind. Where another might have shown resentment and made opposition, he took inevitably the path of self-effacement. For he had in large measure that quality of gentle heroism which finds allurement in self-sacrifice.

Then came an additional shock from the research side of his work. An individual named Jacob Mazer took advantage of Sabine's refusal to commercialize his discoveries. He even had the effrontery actually to announce himself as the inventor, and to submit evidence on which he tried to secure patents for himself on everything Sabine had perfected during his thirteen years of experimentation. The story of the celebrated " Mazer Case," [4] which excited the attention of Senators, the Secretary of State, and even the President of the United States, belongs to another chapter, but the baleful effects of the irksome trial, on top of all other strains, made the years 1911–1912 the most unhappy of any in Sabine's life.

The summer of 1911 was one of the hottest in history — when even the asphalt melted in the streets, and horses dropped dead in their harness. Sabine was kept in town throughout those oppressive months, deprived even of home relaxation by the absence of his family in Berlin. " I am keeping too many balls in the air," he wrote his mother — " in my experiments at night; the merger with the Institute of Technology by day; testimony against Mazer all day tomorrow, after I get back from giving prizes at Milton Academy; plans for the new high-tension laboratory; last Saturday in New York over the acoustics of The Little Theatre — the smallest in the world, seating 297; and Friday in Philadelphia over an auditorium, the largest under cover in the world, to seat 20,000. Next Sunday I have to go to New York to look over the Cathedral of St. John the Divine,[5] the architect, Cram, having asked me to help him out. *Ich bin sehr müde.*"

Yet neither heat, nor overwork, nor physical fatigue could keep him from giving personal assistance to any movement

---

[4] See page 236.

[5] " The music of the choir rises wonderfully to the ear. . . . There are no echoes, and the voices of the choristers come up gloriously clear." *New York Times*, January 29, 1933.

which had for its objective the advantage of Harvard University, or to apply to it the full quota of his scientific knowledge:

From Dr. J. Collins Warren

In 1911 the Harvard Cancer Commission was in process of reorganization, in order to adapt its energies to the increasingly pressing demands for a solution of some of the many questions which were then being brought forward in connection with the campaign against this disease. A hospital had been built by the Commission, and an opportunity was then given to test some of the remedies which were supposed to exert a favorable influence as curative agents. Prominent among these was Sero-therapy, which, after trial, went the way of its legion of predecessors, and was promptly followed by others which failed to realize the hopes of their advocates.

The treatment of disease by light rays was, however, accomplishing much in many forms of ailments, and was producing results which gave encouragement for future trial and research. The Roentgen-ray had been found to exert a favorable influence on certain types of cancer, but had failed with the apparatus then available to accomplish all that had been hoped for it.

At this time the new substance known as radium was beginning to excite a world-wide interest, and I chanced to hear of the recent return from Europe of a former pupil and co-worker of Professor Sabine's who had followed up his training in the Jefferson Physical Laboratory by a long course of study under Madame Curie. The Commission was thus brought in contact with the proposition to establish a department of Radio-therapy, and was referred by Dr. William Duane to Professor Sabine for an opinion upon the advisability of this new departure.

It was an undertaking of considerable magnitude, involving, as it did, not only the establishment and endowment of what was practically a new professorship, but the purchase of an extremely rare and valuable mineral, and much elaborate equipment.

It was under these circumstances that I appealed to Professor Sabine for advice, and I shall never forget the whole-hearted way in which he entered into a discussion of the new problem, and the wealth of information which he was not only able but glad to contribute. His method of approaching and dealing with his subject was admirable. A patient listener, his answers were carefully considered and delivered with a brevity and decision which was satisfying and convincing. During the discussion there unfolded itself, to my vision at least, a new line of medical investigation — the application of the physical science to the problems of the cure of disease.

Here was a scientist, in charge of a great department of the University, prepared to offer its resources to a new field of research, not indeed in a spirit of rash enthusiasm, but as the result of a capacity to weigh judicially the arguments *pro* and *con,* and to form a clean-cut opinion — all was done apparently without effort, and as the expression of a quiet mastery of the situation.

A feeling was borne in strongly of an object lesson of the great benefit to be derived by reciprocity and intelligent coöperation between different departments of an institution of learning, each possessed of stores of knowledge, but too often hidden under the bushel of academic isolation.

The application of Bio-physics to medical research, and still more recently to Therapeutics, is now becoming universally recognized by the medical profession. It is pleasant to recall this indebtedness of Medicine to Physical Science.

From Dr. William Duane

Shortly after I returned from working in the radium laboratories of Paris, I met Professor Sabine at a meeting of the

Physical Society in Cleveland. He asked what I was planning to do, and I told him I was trying to develop radiation methods of treating malignant disease in this country, and was about to accept a position in a cancer commission in New York for that purpose. He immediately asked me to wait until he could talk to the Harvard Cancer Commission about it. I did so, and, as a result, the work was begun at Harvard instead of in New York.

Among other " balls in the air " which Sabine mentioned in his letter to his mother, just quoted, should have been included his experiments to discover a substitute for the hairfelt which had served extensively in his correction of acoustical faults in buildings already constructed, and was the material most used in his plans for new construction. The objection against the use of felt was that the material was subject to deterioration and was neither fireproof nor vermin proof. Early in July, 1911, therefore, Sabine instituted a series of experiments with the idea of producing a substitute which should be less subject to excessive reverberation and echo and the injurious focusing of sound than brick, tile, wood sheathing, plaster on wall or wire laths, or plaster applied directly to a solid support, which represented the materials in general use by architects for structural walls and ceilings.

These first experiments were purely preliminary. They were carried out by placing sand on the floor of the testing laboratory room in a retaining frame, the experiment being made with sand of different sized grains, and laid to different depths on the cement floor. By this method he determined the best sized grains and the best thickness, these being the two important factors. At that time no binding material was used.

These investigations were interrupted by other and more imperative demands upon Sabine's time, and, as the laboratory was fully utilized in other experiments, he welcomed the suggestion of collaboration which came to him from a skilled ceramic worker of Brooklyn, New York, who had been making experiments along the same line:

From Rafael Guastavino

Up to the year 1911 the construction of vaults in our churches had a finish of ceramic tile which had practically no property of sound absorption — in fact, very little more than stone. Many of these churches were poor acoustically. I had read in one or two of the architectural magazines articles on Architectural Acoustics by Professor Sabine, which interested me very much, and in view of the fact that at about that time Cram, Goodhue and Ferguson, architects, were designing prominent Gothic churches, in which it was desired that the acoustics should be good, and, as the interiors had to be of a masonry material (for felts were not desired for acoustical correction), I decided to write Professor Sabine for an appointment. He kindly granted me an interview in March, 1911.

We went over the whole situation, and arrangements were made to carry on experiments, first on a ceramic tile. Experiments were made up to 1913, and by that time we were able to produce a rather efficient product,[6] for which a patent was granted to us December 1, 1914. So far as we know, this was the first patent on an acoustical ceramic tile. For a while, further experiments were conducted, and it became apparent that the process was a rather difficult one, requiring great care in manufacture, and finally it became evident, as quantities of these tile were made for two or three important buildings, such as St. Thomas Church, New York, for Cram, Goodhue & Ferguson, architects; The First Congregational Church of Montclair, N. J., B. G. Goodhue, architect; and the B'Nai Jeshurun Synagogue,

---

[6] The ceramic product was called " Rumford Tile," and the non-ceramic " Akoustolith." Sabine never permitted his name to be attached to any product of any description.

Newark, N. J., Albert S. Gottlieb, architect, which were among the first installations, that we would have to conquer manufacturing difficulties.

We then decided to look forward to making a non-ceramic acoustical material of masonry character, or stone-like, that would not present the difficulties of a ceramic product. The first successful samples of this new material were produced about September, 1915. These were improved upon from time to time, and a patent was issued to us September 12, 1916, and reissue filed July 24, 1918, as co-inventors. This material, owing to its high efficiency and economy in manufacture, has practically superseded the ceramic product.

This non-ceramic product has been used in a great many of the prominent buildings in the United States, among them St. John's Cathedral, New York, N. Y.; Nebraska State Capitol, Lincoln, Neb. (both the ceramic and non-ceramic materials were used in this building) ; the Princeton University Chapel, Cram & Ferguson, architects; Duke University Chapel, Durham, N. C.; New York Central Railroad Station, Buffalo, N. Y., Fellheimer & Wagner, architects (this latter building has probably the largest installation) . And there are several hundred other installations.

The relation in the collaboration between Professor Sabine and myself was that of the scientist and the practical ceramic worker.

By Professor Edwin H. Hall

Sabine had found the absorptive power of a painted brick wall to be only about half that of the same kind of wall unpainted. This is because of the porosity of natural brick, which enables the sound waves to penetrate the material slightly and so lose a little of their energy. Gradually, through Sabine's suggestions and " the skill and great knowledge of ceramic processes " possessed by Mr. Rafael Guastavino, a kind of tile was developed which " has over six-

fold the absorbing power of any existing masonry construction and one-third the absorbing power of the best-known
felt."

The words just quoted are found in a paper printed in
1914. We may say that, so far as the properties of auditoriums are concerned, Sabine had, in less than twenty years,
brought Architectural Acoustics from the empirical state, in
which success with any new structure was a happy accident
and failure was a misfortune often made ridiculous by such
attempted remedies as the stringing of wires, to the status of
a reasoned science and a precise art.

He had done this by force of his own qualities, with but
little favor of circumstances and with so little financial assistance or reward that he was probably a poorer man by
thousands of dollars than he would have been had he never
attempted it. Moreover, he had published his formulas and
his devices freely to the world, for any one to use who could,
patenting only, and this with Mr. Guastavino, the kind of
tile described above.

Three times during that summer of 1911 Sabine fainted,
the terrific strain culminating in a physical and nervous
breakdown which brought Mrs. Sabine hurrying back from
Germany. He had pledged every one to keep the facts from
her, but they leaked through. On reaching home she found
that he had suffered a slight cerebral hemorrhage, his right
hand and right leg being slightly paralyzed; but it so an-
noyed him for her even to show anxiety that she was forced
to conceal her great concern. He gradually grew better, but
for a while he was so abnormally sensitive that his wife had
to caution the maids and the children to avoid noticing his
infirmity. He would leave the table with meal unfinished if
he became aware that he was being watched. It is from this
summer of 1911 that the great change came in his health,
and from that time on he was never a well man.

Instead of reducing his activities, Sabine drove himself

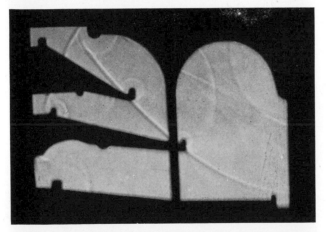

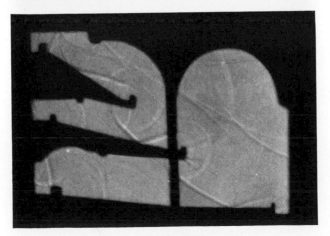

PHOTOGRAPHS OF SOUND WAVES AND ECHOES
the first ever taken passing through a small model
of a theatre. *See* page 211

even harder, with Stoic indifference to the greater demands upon his decreased vitality. In 1913 his acoustical experiments took a new turn which fortunately fascinated him, and these hours of added labor were lightened by the sheer joy of accomplishment. He had always been interested in the subject of photography, and one of the earliest gifts he made to Jane Kelly, after they became engaged, was a camera, made by his own clever hands, for her use in microscopic work. During the following years he manufactured some extraordinary instruments, and out of this came his idea of photographing sound waves and echoes:

To his Mother from W. C. S.

[*Cambridge, Mass., March 27,* 1913

I am enclosing three photographs which will interest you, of sound waves and echoes passing through a small model of a theatre. I have been working night and day to get this for the past two months. Don't you think it will be interesting? Can you follow the main wave and its echo from the ceiling, and the echoes from the balcony fronts? And then echoes of the echoes? It is going to be great fun now that I have got it. I just succeeded yesterday. Now I am having models made of The New Theatre in New York, The Little Theatre, and one or two others of special interest, and I think I shall have the architects excited.

From Professor Walter Le Conte Stevens

The graphic representation of waves of sound, whether simple or compound, after all components have become known, is familiar to all physicists; but in the present case the inverse problem was presented with such complications that theoretic curves were quite useless, even if possible. Professor Sabine resorted to the method of instantaneous photography [7] as developed of late years by Toepler in Germany and improved by Foley in America.

---

[7] Sabine's experiments, of great beauty and of inestimable value, are fully described in the American Architect, December 13, 1913.

Assuming an auditorium of known form and dimensions, a sectional model of it may be made on a small scale. In this the snap of an electric spark is produced on the stage, and the progressing waves of short period are photographed in mid air, sometimes before reflection, sometimes after. From the photographed wave-lengths and wave-fronts may be computed the corresponding wave-dimensions in the actual auditorium. Information is thus secured quite independent of that obtained by the well-trained ear of the musician.

Beyond applying his scientific knowledge in photography to Acoustics, Sabine appealed to the Director of the New York Zoölogical Society for assistance in securing data to satisfy his curiosity concerning animal vision. Basing its construction upon the information received, he actually produced a camera which gave, shall we say, " a cat's-eye view! "

To Henry F. Osborn from W. C. S.   [*June* 2, 1914

There is a subject which lies between the field of Natural History and that of Physics which I believe is unknown to zoölogists, and which, so far as I know, has not been commented upon anywhere. It is a curious fact that, whenever the pupils of the eyes of carnivorous animals depart from circular, it is with the major axis of the ellipse vertical, while in herbivorous animals the major axis is horizontal. This difference can be traced also in an interesting manner through the group of reptiles. The shape of the ellipse and the direction of its axis vitally affects the character of vision. For example, in looking at a mosquito netting a cat can see the horizontal wires better than the vertical, while a deer can see the vertical more easily. I will not go into the full discussion of this at the present time except to say that it is a matter wholly aside from astigmatism.

Possibly you have photographs showing the shape of the pupils, and if not you might, time permitting, be able to make some for me. Of course if you have photographs on hand I should be glad to have any that may show what I have above explained. If not, I should very much like to secure photographs of the eye of the boa-constrictor, for a vertical slit, of the king cobra, for the round pupil, and of any reptile whose iris is of such color as to show the shape of the pupil and a horizontal slit. Mr. Ditmars pointed out to me a most interesting phenomenon which I should very much like to show by means of photographs — that when a snake's head is inclined up or down, the eye so rolls in the socket that the slit remains substantially vertical. If it were possible to secure it, I should very much like a photograph of the eye of the boa-constrictor when the head is pointed straight forward, when inclined at a considerable angle up, and when inclined down, maintaining otherwise the same point of view.

In addition to adjusting the Harvard courses to meet the new requirements of the Harvard-Technology merger, Sabine was one of the most active participants in the diplomatic negotiations between the two institutions. It was Sabine, in fact, who made the official report to the President and Treasurer of Harvard College, giving in detail the agreement as drawn up. This " agreement " of 1913–1915 provided, in substance, that all the University instruction in Mechanical, Electrical, Civil, and Sanitary Engineering, Mining, and Metallurgy, and in the promotion of research in these branches of Applied Science, should be transferred to the Institute; that all this instruction was to be conducted in the Institute buildings; that the full control of the curriculum and professors should be vested in the Faculty of the Institute, which, after the agreement was put in operation, consisted of fourteen Harvard men to one hundred and six Technology men; that, besides other property and income belonging to the University, three-fifths of the income of the

McKay Endowment was to be devoted to the maintenance of this instruction at the Institute; and that the executive head for all the work carried on under the agreement was to be the President of the Institute, who was made an agent of both Corporations for the purpose.

While opposition still existed among some of the alumni, it was not so violent or so well organized as in 1905, yet it was sufficiently active to impress the college authorities with the importance of securing a ruling from the Supreme Judicial Court as to the legality of their action. During the two years between the filing of the suit to obtain this opinion and the final rendering of an adverse decision, the agreement between the two institutions was actually put into active and practical operation. Sabine's own courses, however, which he had continued to give even after his appointment as Dean, were not included in the merger.

The legal argument for the Corporation was, in brief, that, in the absence of express statutory limitation, a corporation may adopt any reasonable means of accomplishing its purposes; that there was no express statutory limitation upon the means to be adopted by the President and Fellows of Harvard College in accomplishing the purposes of their incorporation which prevented them from carrying out the agreement in question; and that the means, coöperation with the Massachusetts Institute of Technology in accordance with the terms of the agreement, were reasonable. It was further submitted that the School of Applied Science on the Charles River Embankment, contemplated by the agreement, was in effect a Harvard School and a department of Harvard University; that the agreement did not divest the President and Fellows of Harvard College of their control over the affairs of the Corporation; and that the specific directions of the McKay trust were not inconsistent with the general proposition that he was giving money to the President and Fellows of Harvard College to be used by them in any way that their general funds could be used in the field of Applied Science.

The main argument which, in the minds of the Harvard authorities, conscientiously justified their construction of Gordon McKay's terms of trust was that coöperation was a part of the modern system of education, and was more in keeping with the spirit of educational effort than was competition; that Harvard University was a charitable corporation; that its funds were charged with a trust for the public; that to use them in duplicating the plant of the Institute with the result of creating two competitive Schools of Applied Science rather than one school of higher efficiency would be to waste a public charitable fund; that limitations imposed by testators upon the use of their funds had frequently, within comparatively short periods, rendered charitable trusts of little public value; and that a decision against the agreement would be a severe blow to coöperative effort in education, and would greatly retard educational progress.

The Supreme Judicial Court handed down an adverse opinion on November 17, 1917: " It may be assumed that a coöperative plan like that proposed would be advantageous to both of these great institutions by creating one School of Applied Science of the highest efficiency, with economy in expenditure and effort, to take the place of two competitive schools. But so far as the agreement attempts to dispose of the income of the McKay gift, the controlling question is whether it is authorized by the terms and conditions of the trust upon which the gift was made and accepted. . . . In our opinion this intention of Gordon McKay is not in fact carried out in the agreement in controversy, as we have construed its provisions in their practical operation."

Was this decision a disappointment to Sabine, or did he see in it a return, accomplished by an outside agency beyond his control and in spite of his efforts to prevent, of the opportunity he had loyally relinquished to build up at

Harvard a Graduate School of Applied Science such as he had visualized in his original plans? No one of his friends or colleagues could authoritatively answer that question. Throughout those six years during which the negotiations were carried on, every one was amazed by his disinterested attitude, and admired the whole-hearted enthusiasm and diplomacy with which he conducted the delicate situations naturally arising as the new relations gradually became established between the two great institutions.

" I was struck by his tact and complete self-abnegation," Professor F. W. Taussig observed: " during the negotiations which took place from time to time for bringing into closer relations the University and the Massachusetts Institute of Technology. It is given to few men to subordinate so completely personal questions to the achievement of that which was best for the institution."

Eliot Wadsworth, at that time Chairman of the Overseers' Committee, said: " It was evident from the most careful study of the proposed plans for coöperation that the very important position of Dean, held by Professor Sabine, would either disappear or would lose much of its prestige. In all our talks I never recognized the slightest intimation or thought in his mind that this feature of the plans was in any way a factor. He dealt with the problem as it came before us in a purely impersonal way, considering first, last, and all the time the welfare of scientific education as a whole, and the future position of Harvard University."

Professor James H. Ropes comments: " Sabine told me that the reason he finally withdrew his objection to the Technology combination, and threw himself enthusiastically into the new enterprise, was that he felt that an engineering school of the first quality — equal to the Western university schools with their great public support — could be built up in New England only by combining *all* the resources of the New England constituency. His magnanimity in the whole matter was noteworthy and characteristic, for it must have been perfectly evident to him that there would be no adequate permanent place for him, who had been Dean, in the combined enterprise."

And when the details were completely adjusted, to all intents upon a permanent basis, Henry L. Higginson wrote him this wonderful letter of congratulation (January 14, 1914) : " To strive for a noble end, forgetting oneself completely, and then to succeed, is to reach high-water mark — and to set a fine standard. That you have done, and we all know it and value your countenance, your help, your power, your character, very, very highly.

" Constantly I've heard the question, ' What does Sabine say to that? ' ' How does he regard this or that point? ' And when our learned and critical bulwark of rights and duties of Harvard University, Dr. Walcott, asks such questions, and is content with the answers, it means much — for no man holds these duties and interests dearer or higher than our old friend.

" I am only writing the opinion and feeling of the President and Fellows when I say that your attitude and acts in this negotiation with the Institute have been very fine — nothing could be higher, and without you we should not have succeeded. I have had the pleasure and honor of your fellowship for many years, and owe you much. What can I say more than that I honor and thank you from my heart? "

Again we come back to our question, only to ask ourselves another. Was the public recognition of a deed well done sufficient recompense for the undoubted sacrifice which had now proved to have been of no avail? It was impossible for Sabine to pick up the threads he had dropped, and continue on from that point. America had entered the World War. Harvard was a military unit instead of an educational institution. Great scientists were working for their country, and youth had its eyes centered on a glorified ideal which unhappily was never to be realized. Sabine could not have been keen to resume his old position as Dean, for the Harvard Graduate School of Applied Science in 1917 had become a shadow of what had been and what might have been.

My answer to the question of Sabine's reaction to the adverse decision in the merger case, gleaned from a study of the man's mental attitude at all times, is that no one of all those interested was more keenly disappointed than he. I agree with Professor Hall's statement that " he had in large measure that quality of gentle heroism which finds allurement in self-sacrifice," but I cannot believe that " he was no longer able to view the matter with a free mind " when self-sacrifice was involved. Sabine believed that the merger was a great thing for education, or he would definitely have opposed it. The personal element would have been barred from one door as definitely as from another.

From President Abbott Lawrence Lowell

Sabine felt, as I did, that the real object of all such institutions is to do good, do the greatest service to the public, and to bring about the greatest advancement in knowledge that is possible, and that for this purpose a combination, rather than a competition, of the two institutions working in the same field, within two miles of one another, would be a great benefit. He was too large a man to allow the pride of institution or his own personal interests to sway at all his sense of duty. All that has been said about his unselfishness, his magnanimity, his single-minded desire to do his duty without the slightest regard to personal feelings, is not too much. Indeed, his nobility of nature could hardly be exaggerated.

But if I read Sabine's character correctly, he favored the merger for more than its mere educational advantage. Ever since he visited Germany in 1909, he had been obsessed by the belief that war was actually in sight. His convictions, so lightly received by the authorities in England and America at that time, had become a grim and devastating fact. Had the merger been unopposed in 1915, the full scientific resources of a united and powerful engineering school would have been at the disposal of the Government from the moment America entered the War. This, I believe, was Sabine's compelling reason for enthusiastically coöperating toward an end he considered more vital than education, more gratifying than self-advantage. When the merger became impossible, Sabine's thoughts centered themselves upon other methods by which he could serve his country in the crisis he saw approaching, and the great vision which opened before him, when once that point was reached, lifted him above the ordinary conception of educational work, even though his mind and body continued to perform their usual academic gestures.

XI. The Master and His Clients

Throughout his work, Sabine was needlessly handicapped by a lack of financial resources with which to build necessary apparatus and to carry on his experiments, without drawing too heavily upon his restricted income, or demanding too much of his personal strength to overcome this limitation. " It is difficult," he admitted, " to find rooms whose walls are in a large measure of glass, especially when one bears in mind that the room must be empty, that its other wall surfaces must be of a substance fully investigated, and that it must be in a location admitting of quiet work. Or, to investigate the effect of the different kinds of plaster and of the different methods of plastering, it is necessary to have a room, preferably underground, which can be lined and relined. The ' Constant Temperature Room,' which is now available for the experiments, is not suitable to that particular investigation, and for best results a special room should be constructed. Moreover, the expense of plastering and replastering a room — and this process, to arrive at anything like a general solution of the problem, would have to be done a great many times — would be very great, and is at the present moment prohibitive."

The word " needless " is used deliberately because, except for Sabine's over-conscientiousness, the material value of his contribution to Architecture might easily have supplied him with legitimate income far beyond the resources he required and craved.

From President Charles W. Eliot

Sabine's primary ideal for a university teacher and investigator was that everything such a scholar could learn or discover should be placed immediately at the service first of his students and scientific colleagues, and then of the public. He paid me an official visit early in his Harvard career to inquire if I thought justifiable the copyrights and royalties of a man of letters, or the patent taken by a scientist on some process or instrument which he had come upon in the course of his studies, and imagined might prove profitable. He preferred the mental and moral attitude of the physician or surgeon who, having invented a new treatment or operation, or a new instrument, makes it known to the whole profession for the benefit of the public, as soon as he himself regards it as of demonstrated value.

He could not bring himself to charge proper fees for his own services, and his mind often misgave him as to the propriety of his spending on outside work time which belonged to the University and to Pure Science. I repeatedly pointed out to him that Harvard University gained much whenever its professors contributed to the public welfare, although their services were directly rendered to commercial or industrial bodies or individuals; and, further, that no sharp and fixed line can be drawn between Pure and Applied Science, since what is pure today may easily have valuable applications tomorrow. He politely appeared to accept my views for the moment, but soon relapsed into his own.

When Sabine began his investigations at the Fogg Art Museum he was a young Assistant Professor receiving a salary from the College of $2000 a year, with no outside resources; yet President Eliot found it almost impossible to persuade him to render bills covering the legitimate expenses incidental to his work.[1] Even later, when Sabine

---

[1] See page 125.

rendered valuable services to architects or to committees he was absurdly reluctant to make adequate charges. The constantly increasing demands for advice on acoustical matters, coming from almost every state in the Union, finally compelled him, in self-defense, to stipulate a nominal honorarium of $200 for professional consultation and advice, which was always conscientiously used for apparatus or experiment. This in theory permitted him to decline many trivial and uninteresting requests, was a protection to him and to the University, and left him free personally to undertake the larger problems. But even this practice was distasteful to him, and in rendering a bill he always specifically stipulated that it must be a direct charge against the client rather than assumed by the architect. He would have considered it a breach of professional etiquette to withhold anything in connection with his work, and his personal service to architects was never placed upon a commercial basis:

To R. Clipston Sturgis from W. C. S.   [*November* 17, 1910

I am a little suspicious of the check which I have just received from you — not as to its cash value, but I fear from its form that the bill which I sent you was disallowed by the Trustees of the Perkins Institute, and that you have sent me your personal check instead. Will you be so kind as to let me know whether this is the case? If so, I certainly cannot accept it. . . . Let me repeat, that the only condition on which I am willing to make any charges whatever is that they neither are paid by the architect nor are embarrassing in their transmission.

Throughout Sabine's correspondence are found letters of protest from clients who would have preferred to place their relations upon a professional basis. Some of these would be amusing except for the knowledge that Sabine's quixotic attitude placed an added strain upon his willing shoulders, already too heavily loaded. There was a constant struggle between his professional ethics, exaggerated by the beautiful impracticality in financial matters inherited from his father, and the longing to give his family the material comforts which come with affluence. For himself he asked nothing. " I want to surround you with a beautiful home, with pictures, and rugs," he wrote to his wife; " but I want to do it myself. I want to feel that it is my own effort, and a measure of my own competence."

From Richard W. Hale to W. C. S.   [*January* 28, 1914

You ought to have a scolding for not sending in a bill, and I take the liberty of offering you one. Talking to me at the Union Club you told me the story of the financial results of this work. Later I asked President Eliot about it, and he told me a little more. Now, one of the reasons why the financial results have been bad is that, although you are a good expert on Sound, you are not a good expert on how to charge for services, and when to do it. That is not unusual. Mr. Ralph Waldo Emerson never got anything for his work until his daughter married Mr. William Forbes. You will probably continue to suffer unless you hire an expert bill-collector and charger. But that is no reason why the Old South Meeting House should not pay a proper *per diem* for the high grade of professional time which you have given to it.

To Richard W. Hale from W. C. S.

I hope the fact that I make no charge for my services will not give the impression that I fail to appreciate the responsibility which I am assuming in making the recommendations in such a subject as Sound Exclusion. My experience is such that I probably appreciate this responsibility more than any one else.

Mr. Hale responded by sending him a check accompanied by the following note: " Please remember that this is a professional retainer. Your bill is going to be paid whether you like it or not, and whether you send a bill or not."

Handicapped by inadequate laboratory facilities, as already explained, Sabine seized upon the unusual problems offered him by architects as opportunities for experimentation. " I was very much impressed with the complete absence of any commercial instinct in Professor Sabine's make-up," Winthrop Ames writes. " While he went to great trouble and pains to help us solve our problems, he always gave us the impression that our problems were so interesting that it was we who were conferring a favor upon him by giving him an opportunity of helping us solve them rather than he who was conferring a favor on us by giving us the benefit of his great wisdom and experience."

From Henry Creighton Ingalls to W. C. S.

[*March* 12, 1912

Mr. Ames asked me yesterday to obtain from you a statement of your expenses and fee in connection with The Little Theatre proposition. I dislike to ask you for this, as once before, when I mentioned the subject, you did not take kindly to it. He is quite insistent, nevertheless, and I am sure that he will be upset if you do not allow him to reimburse you for your time and trouble. Please do send me the statement, then, in order that he may feel happy about the matter.

To Henry Creighton Ingalls from W. C. S.

[*March* 18, 1912

I appreciate the kindness of Mr. Ames' request that I send a statement of my expenses and professional fee. So far from his being under any obligation to me, it is quite the other way. It has been a privilege to me to have had even this small connection with The Little Theatre, and to have been of some service. Indeed, I should have regarded it as grievous had I not been consulted after the difficulties in The New Theatre.

The lack of practicality, curiously enough, applied only to the financial side of his relations with his clients. Sabine showed himself to be thoroughly practical as a scientist, as a teacher, as an investigator, and in the application of Science — a most unusual combination. His ingenuity in surmounting obstacles which appalled practical engineers amazed laymen and scientists alike, and caused one of his friends to remark, " Sabine changes his personality when he takes off his laboratory coat and puts on his business suit." It is from his clients, therefore, that we must learn of this other — almost contradictory — expression of the teacher-investigator's characteristic:

From Winthrop Ames

My relations with Professor Sabine began when I called him in to remedy the acoustics of The New (Century) Theatre, in New York. It was before he had publicly established the scientific value of his work, and I had a bitter struggle with the architects and some of the Trustees to allow the changes he suggested to be made.

I have rarely met a man who seemed to me more effectively to combine the qualities of the scholar, the practical engineer, and a charming gentleman. The problems with which Professor Sabine had to deal in connection with The Century Theatre were not only technically complex and difficult, but called for great tact and practical skill. He met all these requirements. He solved our problems with a rare combination of tact and technical skill, and won the admiration and respect of everybody. The result was that when the same group of gentlemen considered the erection of another theatre, the first thought of all of them was not to take a step without the approval of Professor Sabine.

It is rare that in any department of human activity a man earns a position of such universally acknowledged preëminence as that held by Professor Sabine in the field of Acoustics. Many times I have sat in conferences in which the question arose as to whose advice should be sought on that subject. The unanimous response always was that Professor Sabine stood alone, and that no one else should be considered if he proved available.

In connection with the statement made by Mr. Ames at the beginning of this letter, a former associate of Messrs. Carrère and Hastings records that " there was a tradition in the office regarding a celebrated conference on the acoustics of The New Theatre between its designer, Mr. Thomas Hastings, the promoter of the theatre, Mr. Winthrop Ames, and Professor Sabine. This was an all-night discussion, and from the point of view of the architect's office it was an historical affair! "

From Dr. Edward Robinson

In his professional capacity, my experience with Professor Sabine was characteristic of the man and his ability, and illustrative of his methods of work. It was in connection with the Lecture Hall of the Metropolitan Museum of Art. In beginning the story, I may say, parenthetically, that the plans for the part of the building in which the hall was embodied had already been completed, and I believe the contract had been signed, before I became associated with the Museum, else I should have hoped to see them worked out under Sabine's guidance. However this might have been, the hall as designed and constructed was semi-circular in shape, with a seating capacity of about five hundred, the platform occupying the flat side, and the seats arranged much as they are in the lower part of the Sanders Theatre at Harvard. Esthetically, it was a disappointment, first of all because the walls were disproportionately high, though it is fair to say that this was due to the architect's desire to leave space for a balcony, should one be needed later. But in addition to the poor proportions there was a general barrenness of effect, owing to the fact that the lofty, curving wall of the auditorium was left perfectly smooth throughout, without either niches or projections of any kind to relieve it, and it was surmounted by an equally smooth semi-dome, the cornice which separated the two being the only interruption to the monotony of the surface. To be sure, the wall behind the platform was broken up by the large, massive frame for the lantern screen which was built upon it, but this gave variety to only one side.

As the builders removed the staging, and the hall stood nakedly disclosed to view, our doubts as to its acoustic qualities began to grow, and they were not allayed by one or two attempts to address its emptiness, which proved only too responsive. Then we thought, or rather hoped, that the introduction of the seats might quiet the painful reverberation which seemed to come not from any one place but from all parts of the hall. The seats did not remedy matters, however, and our last hope lay in the presence of an audience, as it is well known that a hall which is bad when empty may prove at least possible if well filled. Here again we were doomed to disappointment. An experimental lecture was given to a good-sized audience, and it demonstrated beyond any further possibility of doubt that acoustically the hall was a lamentable failure. The speaker heard his own voice three or four times in a confused jumble of sounds, and his hearers had the greatest difficulty in following him even when there was perfect quiet, while a slight scuffle on the floor neutralized all other sounds, and added proportionately to the confusion.

In despair I went to the architect of the building, explained our predicament, and suggested the advisability of consulting a specialist in Acoustics to see if anything could be done to remedy the situation. Possibly he did not take the matter as seriously as I, but at all events he said that he did not think it necessary to go outside for assistance, as he had an excellent expert in such things in the office whom he would send up to investigate and report. The " expert " came, and, after hearing what I had to say about our experiences, and making what he called an examination, told me that if we would put a heavy carpet on the platform and lay strips of carpet along the aisles, he believed we would have no further trouble. After all that we had been through, and with the knowledge that experiments of this kind had not been successful in other places, this recommendation did not sound at all convincing or satisfactory. What we wanted, of course, was to ascertain definitely the faults in the building, and then adopt some certain and thorough means of eliminating them if it could be done. Further experimentation did not appeal to us.

Fortunately for us this happened at a time when Professor Sabine was making frequent visits to New York in connection with his endeavors to correct the acoustic defects in The New Theatre, or Century Theatre as it now is. I therefore laid our case before the Trustees of the Museum, and obtained their consent to engage his services upon our problem. He accepted our invitation at once, and began an investigation, the thoroughness of which astonished all who followed his work. He went carefully through the architect's working drawings, made tests of the sounds in the hall, examined the walls inside and out, as well as the various materials used in their construction, and did much else besides which I could not follow. But I well remember how impressed I was at the importance he attached to details which to others, and especially to a layman, would have seemed negligible, showing how little he left to chance in the solution of his problems.

As a result of his tests and examination, he brought me a

plan [2] which to my untutored eye I confess looked more like a map of a western cyclone than the interior of our hall. From this he explained that he had found three distinct sources of echo in the hall, the sounds from which, by crossing and mingling with one another, had produced the confusion that rendered it hopeless as a place for speaking. Two of these sources, he said, could be done away with, but the third could not, and if we were to carry out all his recommendations there would still be a small group of seats on each side of the hall in which there would be some difficulty in hearing, though by no means as great as it was at the time; and there were two spots on the platform, about midway between the middle and the ends, where the voice would produce a slight echo. His recommendations were radical, as was to be expected. The height of the hall was to be reduced a considerable number of feet — I forget just how much, but he was precise on the point. The smooth dome was to be replaced by a coffered one, the number, size, and depth of the coffers to be exactly as indicated by him. Pilasters were to be set at certain definite intervals around the walls, their projection specified to a small fraction of an inch, and the spaces between them were to be filled with a sheeting of felt, the thickness and even the make of this prescribed with the care of a physician. " For," he said, " unless you carry out my recommendations to the minutest detail, I cannot guarantee the result."

His report, with its instructions, was turned over to our architect, the interior of the hall was altered accordingly, and his predictions were absolutely fulfilled. The hall is not perfect today, — there are still those two groups of seats of which he spoke, where one is conscious of a slight confusion, though far less than before, — but as a whole it is vastly improved. To one who knows how to use his voice, speaking in it is easy, and does not produce that sense of strain or

---

[2] See page 187.

fatigue on the part of either the speaker or his audience which is not uncommon even in small halls. And, finally, it is perhaps significant that the changes which were made under Professor Sabine's instructions, though undertaken for a purely practical purpose, have resulted in a much more beautiful interior than we had before.

From Richard W. Hale

My attention was directed to Sabine's genius early in 1892 by a man named Fewkes, of the Smithsonian Institution, whom I met going to South America. On my return to Boston, I had the good fortune to meet Sabine, and enjoyed the pleasure of his friendship. My one professional relation with him was in connection with the acoustics of the Old South Meeting House. I saw his genius more clearly on that occasion because of the training which Christopher Columbus Langdell and his disciples gave me at the Harvard Law School in the case-method of teaching and investigation, which now dominates the teaching in the Harvard Law School, the Harvard Medical School, and the Harvard School of Business Administration.

Speaking in terms of that system, I would say, " Genius is not merely an infinite capacity for taking pains, but a combination of the divine spark with that capacity." Sabine worked in the Old South case with the foundation of a body of observation upon Acoustics which had been taken with infinite pains and accuracy. He added to that a similar body of observations about the Old South Meeting House itself. From his assembled facts he produced his premises, and from these premises he worked to accurate logical conclusions, testing his premises all the while by the nature of the working and the validity of the conclusions. Part of what I saw had been in his previous lucid exposition of his work; part was in his examination and exposition of the particular problem. And you could always feel that spark! At the end we had a quarrel as to whether he should be paid, and he was victorious in presenting us with his valuable services!

During all this period, Sabine's colleagues saw in him a scientist of constantly expanding horizon; his students looked upon him more and more as an extraordinarily helpful co-worker; despite the constantly increasing tax upon his time, his friends found him ever ready to respond to their approach, even though seldom disposed to take the initiative; to his family he was the tender, affectionate husband and father, finding his greatest joy and relaxation in the development of his unusually responsive daughters; to the world at large, who came to know him through his continued achievements, he was a veritable necromancer, able to solve hitherto unsolvable mysteries, and make Nature subservient to his will.

This same world was becoming more and more sound-conscious. Whatever may be said of modern, labor-saving inventions, no one will dispute the fact that they have made a less idyllic abiding-place for those whose sense of hearing remains unimpaired. One might think that Sabine would have found his specific problem sufficiently demanding to limit himself to Architectural Acoustics, but, as an investigator, his mind was ever reaching out for the unusual, from which to secure additional data. What Sabine's friends, aghast at the burden he voluntarily assumed, considered as presumptuous intrusions on his time, he continued to look upon as opportunities for unexpected research which placed him under obligation.

But Sabine's friends could not comprehend that for an investigator of his thoroughness to be indifferent to anything which related to his subject, however trivial it might seem, without testing its importance, would be at direct variance with the cumulative record of his work. It was this characteristic that made his results so basic. His success came from the inexhaustible store of isolated facts he was continually collecting, and his skill and ingenuity in drawing upon it when the occasion demanded. He once compared Architectural Acoustics to Medicine, where book knowledge is wholly inadequate unless broadened by versatility of application gained through experience in cases which fail to classify under general laws. Two instances may be cited to illustrate:

In 1900, the Superintendent of the Baptist Hospital, situated on the crest of Parker Hill, in Boston, came to Sabine with the story that for several weeks, between the hours of midnight and four A.M. every night except Sunday, peculiar sounds were heard as if a large and heavy body had fallen directly overhead. Those sleeping on the top floor said that the noise came from the roof, and those on the lower floors declared that it was on the floor directly above their heads. The mystery bade fair to create a haunted hospital, as not only the attendants but several of the patients became alarmed and begged to be removed.

Sabine casually inquired if there were any blasting going on in the vicinity, but the Superintendent declared that there was no building whatever anywhere in that neighborhood. He reassured her by promising to look into the matter. On the following day he telephoned to the Public Works Department, where he learned that blasting was taking place under Parker Hill in connection with the installation of the Metropolitan Water Works. To the uninitiated this ghost-hunting would seem a trivial and diverting incident; to Sabine it furnished a demonstration that, under the given circumstances, sound created below is transmitted as if just above the varying levels of the hearers.

What could seem more incongruous than for the famous Rockefeller Institute to consult the great authority on Architectural Acoustics regarding the deadening of noise in the dog-kennels on the roof of its Central Building! Yet Sabine saw in this request an opportunity for assisting Dr. Alexis Carrel in his services for mankind by insulating his suite, and for himself new and valuable experimentation in sound transmission. No wonder that he accepted the commission with the same serious consideration he gave to a great cathedral!

From the records of his work with architects in lesser undertakings may be gleaned an idea of the clearness of his diagnoses and the directness of his remedial attack even more strikingly than from his more important services on public buildings. In 1903, for instance, Stanford White consulted him in regard to difficulties existing in a hall which McKim, Mead & White had built for Colonel Astor, in his Courts Building at Rhinebeck-on-the-Hudson. The letters which passed illustrate the reliance architects had come to place upon Sabine's judgment, and the authority with which he rendered his opinion. In all correspondence of this nature, the promptness with which Sabine arrived at his conclusions is shown by the comparative dates:

From Stanford White to W. C. S.   [*November* 4, 1903
. . . Under the dome in the centre there is a very pronounced echo which practically makes the room unlivable, and I write to ask you if you can suggest any way of getting over this by stretching wires, or any other way. . . .

To Stanford White from W. C. S.   [*November* 12, 1903
. . . The dome is no more concerned in the echo than is the floor. . . . One reflection from the dome would not be formed at any point within the room, but would fall normally, and almost uniformly normally, over the floor. It would then be reflected normally, again strike the dome, and this time be focused at the centre of the room again — a pronounced echo. In other words, the single reflection from the dome will not result in a serious echo, but the triple reflection from dome, floor, and dome will. In this

case you have an unusually ready remedy — break up the reflection at the floor. To this end you may either put down a heavy rug or irregular objects of furniture (chairs as distinguished from large, flat-topped tables), or both rugs and furniture. From the symmetrically distant walls you will also get reflections, but the same furniture that stops the ceiling-and-floor echoes will also stop the wall-echoes.

This is an interesting and unusual case, in which the furnishing should be at the centre of the room instead of at the wall. If this treatment can be made dominant in furnishing the room, I feel entirely confident that you will be free from difficulty.

I may venture the prediction that if, instead of standing erect, you stoop to within a foot or so of the floor, you will find this an excellent whispering gallery, and in its way almost unique. I have traveled long distances to see less interesting ones. All this will disappear if the room is furnished as above. . . .

From Stanford White to W. C. S.   [*November* 13, 1903

Thank you very much for your letter. . . . Here, however, is a very much harder problem. The Astors have built an inside lawn-tennis court. The original design was to be built of brick with an iron truss and a wooden roof, but, for constructive reasons, it was necessary to get a circular roof, and this I built of iron and masonry. Although it has an earth floor, the echo and reverberation are very unpleasant. The only reason I am anxious about this is that high-born gentlemen " holler," and very beautiful ladies " scream," and get their remarks back in their faces from the vaulted wall! What shall we do about this?

That Sabine should have become interested in the general subject of subduing noise was inevitable. " The whole development of building construction and building materials during the past twenty-five years," he declared in a public statement, " has been in the direction of poor acoustics and more and more noisy offices. Recent efforts at fireproof construction have resulted in the use of harder and harder wall surfaces, with consequent increase in reverberation. The plaster, too, is usually applied directly to the tile or brick walls, and is much heavier and denser than the old hair-lime-mortar plaster. As a result we have exceedingly noisy rooms."

Sabine's work attracted so much attention that it became news in the public press:

From the " Literary Digest " [*March* 28, 1914

Several large industries and banks have already profited by the results of Dean Sabine's repeated experiments. In one typical instance, the general offices of a Chicago packer employing four hundred were turned from bedlam into workrooms so quiet — considering their size and the activity of their inmates — that the absence of noise is remarkable.

The various propositions submitted to Sabine were so varied and so far-reaching as to emphasize the growing interest in deadening sound. He could not avoid giving them consideration, and he contributed his advice freely even though the subject in general did not interest him so much as the specific application of his scientific knowledge to architectural problems.

A very early experience (1898) may have confirmed his oft-expressed statement that commercial association destroyed the deep-seated satisfaction he gained from his gratuitous relations with architects. In the case referred to, the Boston Elevated officials had tried to interest him in an effort to reduce the noise in the Boston subway, but, realizing that this work would necessitate his giving up all his work at Harvard for at least a year, he declined to consider the proposition. They were so insistent, however, that they even appealed to President Eliot, who urged Sabine to take a year's leave of absence, on the ground that he would be serving the College in serving the community as a public servant.

President Eliot's influence overcame Sabine's personal objections, and he agreed to meet the officials in a final conference, having previously laid out his plan of attack. They expressed great interest in his outline, but when it came to the question of compensation, and he stated that President Eliot had stipulated that he charge $5000 for a retaining fee, the Elevated officials protested that $1000 was as much as they felt themselves warranted in appropriating for the purpose. Sabine was relieved to have the matter thus settle itself, but he could not resist the satisfaction of remarking to them that he had paid $1200 out of his own pocket during a single year to a mechanic who manufactured for him the special instruments he designed for the investigation of Sound!

As illustrative of the variety of the appeals which came to Sabine may be mentioned a request from the Director of Public Works in Philadelphia to relieve that city of the curse of street noises; from the manufacturers of a nationally known sewing machine to assist in the design and construction of an instrument for measuring the noise produced by the working mechanism; from a granite company to solve the problem of the excessive noise caused by their blasting; from a friend and pupil to express a definite opinion on the practical value of lightning rods; from a well-known piano company to assist it " along the line of scientific investigation on the theory of piano scale and tone production." His responses to these inquiries were so full of practical application of scientific principles that they would form a text-book in themselves!

In February, 1911, Sabine received a telegram from Mr. Mead, of McKim, Mead & White, which brought him suddenly and uncomfortably to a realization that the highly altruistic position he had assumed in refusing to patent his discoveries in Architectural Acoustics was in danger of permitting the accomplishment of exactly what he had endeavored to prevent. This letter contained the startling information that the Johns-Manville Company, of New York, a highly reputable firm, had served papers of restraint upon the architects to prevent the continuation of their work for the improvement of acoustics in the auditorium of the Metropolitan Museum of Art, on the ground that one Jacob Mazer, of Pittsburgh, had taken out a patent for the use and application of the material employed, and had entered into a contract with their firm for its exploitation.

It had never occurred to Sabine that idealism on his part could lay himself and his work liable to misappropriation on the part of any one unscrupulous enough to take advantage of this lack of commercial instinct. In fact, even after receiving this letter from Mr. Mead, he believed that, as his methods and processes had been given so much publicity for so long a period of time, there was no possibility of any one, whatever his intentions, securing a patent to prevent a general use of what he himself had freely given to the public. He immediately wrote to the Commissioner of Patents, asking for information, and discovered that Mazer had not only made application for a patent, as stated, but that the citation had already been printed in the official Gazette of the United States Patent Office.

Sabine's own story of the events which led up to this attempt to take from him even the satisfaction of placing his work at the disposal of the public, is as follows:

To Allen and Collens from W. C. S.
                    [*Cambridge, February* 12, 1915
In 1909 a young man, named Mr. Jacob Mazer, wrote to me from Pittsburgh that he was starting as an architect in that city, and would like to correct the acoustics of Mr.

Hornbostle's synagogue, of which congregation he was a member. I sent him copies of all the papers I had written, and in addition wrote letters giving him all the advice that I could. I gave my services without charge, while he charged a fee of $1000 and $400 for what he called investigations. While the congregation as a whole squirmed a little at having to pay this fee, some of the members of the congregation organized a company with a backing of $25,000 to make a business of it. Mr. Mazer came on to see me, and spent two days asking all sorts of questions. I was glad to be of service, and wished him success in his undertaking. Two years passed, and I received a telegram from Mr. Mead, of Mc-Kim, Mead and White, saying that they had been threatened by an injunction from carrying out my recommendations for the lecture room of the Metropolitan Museum of Art in New York City, that a young man by the name of Jacob Mazer had applied for a patent, and that the patent was within one week of issue. I took the train immediately for New York, Mr. Mead in the meantime getting a copy of the patent. It appeared that Mazer had applied for a patent at the very time he was consulting with me, taking sentences, paragraphs, and even tables out of the papers which I had given him, and claiming them as his own.

The situation was indeed serious, and demanded immediate action, as the Mazer patent had reached a point where within a few days it would automatically become final. Sabine's friends quickly rallied to his support:

From Henry L. Higginson to James F. Curtis [3]

[February 25, 1911

DEAR JIM: You know Professor Sabine, his knowledge, his character, and his deserts. . . . This Mazer came to Sabine, got his information, used it, found it successful, and now has enjoined Sabine from using his (Sabine's) own

---

[3] In the United States Treasury Department.

ideas, and has gone to Washington and got almost to the top notch with his patent for this method which he proposes to appropriate.

The matter has already been laid before Senators Crane and Lodge, and I only ask you and Andrew, both of you, to take the matter up and see that the necessary thing is done, that the patent be not granted to this man, and to explain that Sabine is not asking for any patent, nor asking for any reward of any name or nature, but that this robber should not be allowed to steal other men's ideas in that way for his own good. As you know, Sabine never asks anything for his advice or assistance. I do not know a man who is more unselfish or more ready to help his fellow-creatures than he, and you know his very high position and merits.

May I rely on your energy and your influence? I cannot think that anything but a clear statement of the case is necessary to stop Secretary Ballinger from granting this patent, and I know perfectly well what I am talking about.

President Lowell and Doctor Walcott both have written to the Senators, and we want to stop this outrage, for the sake of the public and for the sake of decency.

From Henry L. Higginson to Senator Henry Cabot Lodge
[February 25, 1911
MY DEAR CABOT: . . . I wish you would do me this great kindness, if you never speak to me again. Go with this letter to the President, and show him the matter, and have the thing stopped now.

From Henry Cabot Lodge to Major Higginson
[Telegram, February 27, 1911
Have seen Patent Commissioner. Sabine must file protest at once on ground that principles and ideas in Mazer patent were in public use at least two years before application for patent. It would be well to have Mr. Fish draw this protest, and it should be mailed at once. In the meantime telegraph

Mr. Moore, Commissioner of Patents, that such a protest is on its way, and ask him to withhold patent. I will show your letter to the President.

[*Telegram, February* 27, 1911

DEAR HENRY: I have just received the following message from the White House: The President has asked the Secretary of the Interior to order the Commissioner of Patents to withhold the issuance of a patent to Mazer until he can see him at the Cabinet meeting. He has also asked him to bring the Commissioner of Patents to the White House with him. I think from this that the matter is sure to have full consideration before any action is taken, but the papers should be sent on at once.

From Bertram Grosvenor Goodhue to Senator Elihu Root
[*February* 24, 1911

It has just come to my knowledge that a very great injustice is likely to be done by the Patent Office in issuing a patent to one Jacob Mazer of Pittsburgh. This patent covers the use of a certain felt for the correction of acoustical defects. . . . As a matter of fact, Mr. Sabine used precisely this same process at least twelve years ago in the case of one of the rooms of the Boston Public Library, and even earlier in the case of the Fogg Museum at Harvard, and many other times since then. The *argumentum ad hominem,* so far as architects are concerned, is, of course, the stipulation made by Mr. Mazer's concern that, in cases where they are called in, their authority is supreme, and the architect ceases to exist as a force of any kind. This is, on the face of it, absurd, and seems to show how the principles upon which Mr. Mazer's company as formed run absolutely counter to Mr. Sabine's own views; for Mr. Sabine, ever since he first began to be interested in the subject of Acoustics, has freely and most kindly placed his knowledge and experience at the disposal of us all. . . .

From Elihu Root to Mr. Goodhue   [*February 27,* 1911

I have your letter of February 24th in regard to the patent which Jacob Mazer has secured on an invention, the credit of which properly belongs to Professor Sabine. My understanding is that the issuance of this patent is to be withheld pending a further investigation into the merits of the case.

From Charles W. Eliot to President Taft

[*February 25,* 1911

DEAR MR. PRESIDENT: I venture to bring before you an atrocious case of injury to the public, wrought through a fraudulent use of our patent laws, in the hope that you may find some way to prevent the consummation of the fraud. It is a subject in which the public has a large and widespread interest, because it concerns the acoustics of all buildings in which people assemble to listen to public speaking, religious instructions, drama, and music. . . . I venture to hope that you may be disposed to call the attention of the Commissioner of Patents to the importance of preventing the consummation of this fraud.

The Patent Office found itself placed in a very uncomfortable position, as it was obvious that the officials had proceeded without due investigation, and that a palpable fraud had almost been accomplished with their unintentional assistance. If Mazer had restrained his impatience before having the Johns-Manville Company write their letter of restraint to McKim, Mead & White, it is a question whether the patent could possibly have been revoked. As it was, the insistence brought to bear upon the Patent Office by the President, based upon protests from such eminent men, resulted in having the issue of the " Patent Gazette " held up, and, when published, the notice referring to the Mazer patent was altered by means of a rubber stamp, which printed the word " Withdrawn " over the entry of " Issued."

The case was duly tried before an examiner, Sabine being

represented by Fish, Richardson, Herrick, and Neave, while Kay and Totten appeared for Mazer. Sabine's witnesses included those who had taken part or been completely conversant with the work which he had done in connection with various buildings where the acoustical properties were corrected, including such well known architects as McKim, Mead & White, Carrère and Hastings, and Cram, Goodhue and Ferguson. His published papers were submitted in evidence, the plagiarism was clearly proven, and by the time the case before the examiner was closed, Mazer's claims were shown to be so audaciously fraudulent that the verdict in favor of Sabine had become a foregone conclusion.

This experience taught Sabine a lesson which previous arguments and urgings of his friends had failed to impress — namely, that even in Pure Science, if a discoverer desires altruistically to place the results of his work at the disposition of the world, patents are necessary to prevent the miscarriage of his intentions. Mazer, even after the adverse decision, continued to solicit acoustical work, brazenly announcing himself as a student of Sabine's.

Johns-Manville Company were chagrined at the part they had been led inadvertently to play through Mazer's misrepresentations, and they now offered their entire commercial facilities to promote the application of the Sabine principles along such lines as he himself would approve, in order to offset the counterfeit work which Mazer was continuing to do. Sabine still declined to make any commercial affiliation, as this would interrupt his direct relationship with architects, which he valued highly, but he saw in the suggestion a protection to his own ideals. The Johns-Manville Company were the manufacturers of the felt he had used in his experiments, and thus agreeable business relations had already been established. He therefore agreed to an arrangement with this firm on the condition that they place their Department of Architectural Acoustics in the hands of Clifford M. Swan, whom he recognized as his only pupil,[4] and in whose ability he had every confidence. " I am holding myself," Sabine wrote (June 19, 1911) " in a position to act in a consulting capacity for them in all cases that may need my services. A part of this arrangement, and that in which I am the most interested, is that it gives me an opportunity to carry on the investigations in the development of new and practical materials of construction."

From Clifford M. Swan

The work of the Johns-Manville Company was directed particularly towards the development of suitable materials for sound-absorption and the technique of their application in buildings in such a way as to produce effective acoustical results without injury to the architectural appearance. During the period up to Professor Sabine's death, that company had made over eight hundred installations of acoustical treatment, including many prominent buildings both during and after erection, these corrections being accomplished by the use of a highly sound-absorbing felt specially designed for the purpose, and known as " Akoustikos Felt."

The invention of the sound-absorbing tile [5] largely did away with the use of felt in Sabine's acoustical work. Taking a lesson from the Mazer case, he consented to a patent on the tile, the proceeds from which he used for furthering his experiments Even this, however, did not prevent an attempt from being made to obtain possession of this invention. Owing to a second exhibition of carelessness in the United States Patent Office, John Comerma, a Spanish laborer in the Guastavino Company, actually secured a patent in June, 1917, which was a direct infringement upon that which Sab-

---

[4] Of Mr. Swan, Sabine writes, " He is the only student I have had, and, as matters now stand, my sole hope of making the subject of Architectural Acoustics an engineering science."

[5] See page 208.

ine and Guastavino held. As in the Mazer case, however, when the facts were presented to the Patent Examiner, Sabine's claims were fully allowed. A reissue was made by the Patent Office, adding the Comerma claims to the original patent.

XII. THE PROPHET JUSTIFIED · 1914

B

Y THE close of the academic year in June, 1914, the pressure of Sabine's Harvard responsibilities had somewhat lessened, despite the fact that he had been appointed to the Hollis Professorship of Mathematics and Natural Philosophy — the earliest and most important endowment for Science possessed by Harvard University. With the plans apparently matured for the merger with the Massachusetts Institute of Technology, his work in the Graduate School consisted of carrying on rather than in reaching out for fuller development, and he saw the opportunity to devote the vacation months to an extension of his acoustical practice abroad instead of searching out new heads for departments or studying new educational methods. Mrs. Sabine and the children, following their usual summer custom, were already installed at Berlin, and this year Sabine looked forward to spending more time with them than had hitherto been possible.

During this same month of June, 1914, was completed what will always stand as Sabine's masterpiece in the practical expression of his discovery of the Science of Architectural Acoustics. This is the concert room in the Paine Memorial Music Hall at Harvard University, of which Howells and Stokes were architects, and which proved to be the last building in the planning of which Sabine coöperated, and whose construction he supervised. Curiously enough, this final monument to his work is across the driveway from the Jefferson Laboratory, in which was located the Constant

Temperature Room, in which he began his acoustical experiments!

In the concert hall are to be found Sabine's famous " bouncing walls," which represent the successful accomplishment of uniting the qualities of brilliancy with the total absence of echoes — a combination of scientific and professional taste which, as a result of long evolutionary experiments, came out exactly as planned, in a degree beyond any expectation except that of the inventor.

These " bouncing walls," instead of offering the usual rigid resistance to sound, are built with felting placed over the solid outside retaining walls, and with a five-inch air space between that and specially prepared, flexible canvas. This billowy canvas surface receives and returns the sound in such a way as to secure absolutely perfect reverberation. Sabine expected to be back in Cambridge for the formal opening of the building the following October, but affairs so shaped themselves in Europe that he was denied the satisfaction of personally hearing the expressions of surprise and delight over the unusual acoustic properties made by such artists as the Flonzaley String Quartet, the American String Quartet; by Miss Maude Powell, Albert Spalding, and Georges Enesco, violinists; by Arthur Whiting, Heinrich Gebhart, and Hans Ebell, pianists; by Miss Povla Frisjch, soprano; and Maurice Barrère, flutist.

Rumors of his success in Architectural Acoustics had filtered through to England as early as 1905, but little credence was placed upon the reports by the English architects, who had been content to accept the theory that " good acoustics are due to accident." Had not the great Sir Christopher Wren declared that " the limits of a moderate voice are fifty feet in front of the speaker, thirty feet on either side, and twenty feet behind him, provided he does not drop the last word? " Had not Albert Hall, in London, with poor

acoustical properties when first built, actually corrected itself until now it was passable? What if the voice of the speaker
in St. Paul's Cathedral was inaudible in certain locations so
long as it could be picked up again by any one advancing
down the building toward the west door? The Reverend
C. H. Spurgeon expressed the general attitude, during the
erection of his Tabernacle, when he said, " I don't believe
any of us knows anything about Acoustics, but if we let the
architect have his own way, we shall have the small consola-
tion of blaming him in case of a failure."

But the failures proved so frequent and the blame so consistent that the English architects became more eager to
secure relief, even at the expense of sacrificing their pride
through admitting that any one in the New World could
teach them anything in their profession, which had been
basically established before America was discovered. One of
the earliest inquiries Sabine received was from the Deputy
City Architect of Edinburgh:

From J. S. Williamson to W. C. S.
[Edinburgh, February, 1905

There is in contemplation the erection in this city of a
large concert hall for about 3,000 of an audience, with orchestra provision, in addition, of 80 of a band and 320 of a
choir. Naturally, there is a desire to ascertain what has been
done on this scale elsewhere, especially in America, and I
learn from the professional prints that you have in recent
times given considerable thought to the question of acoustics, especially in connection with the Symphony halls in
New York, of which Messrs. McKim, Mead & White were
architects. I venture to enquire whether the results of your
investigations have been published, and, if so, whether you
would be good enough to direct me where such can be obtained. It would also be obliging if you could say whether
any plans or other particulars of the Symphony halls are
procurable, and, if so, where.

During the next few years inquiries continued to come from English architects — still interested and still skeptical; but gradually Sabine's reputation reached a point where they could do no less than recognize him as the unique authority in his subject. This recognition came slowly because the limited publicity his early work received was in scientific circles and in American architectural magazines which were not generally read by the profession in England. As a matter of fact, the brief outline Sabine wrote on Architectural Acoustics in Sturgis' " Dictionary of Architecture and Building " attracted more attention abroad than all the magazine articles that had appeared.

Significant requests for information came from high sources. The magnificent new Criminal Courts, which had replaced the famous Old Bailey, had proved distressingly unsatisfactory in their acoustical qualities, and Sabine was consulted as to the possibility of correcting the Central Court. At his suggestion, Mountford and Chapham, the original architects, sent details and drawings to America for his examination. This correspondence aroused the interest of Frank Baines, Principal Architect in Charge of Royal Palaces, and he added inquiries as to possible improvements to be made in the theatre in the Civil Service Commission, in Albert Hall. The Director of Examinations in the Civil Service Commission had also sought his assistance in correcting acoustical defects in the Hall of the building at 6, Burlington Gardens:

From David Mair to W. C. S.

[*London, September* 13, 1913

In this Department we have been for some time attempting to improve the acoustical properties of our examination rooms, and have in that connection studied with interest and profit your lectures on Architectural Acoustics which appeared in the " American Architect and Building News " of the year 1900. In those lectures some prospect is held out of further lectures, and I should esteem it a favour if you would be so kind as to inform me whether any further lectures are available.

It was natural that the deepest interest should be shown by the younger school. The following correspondence formed the beginning of a definite understanding and application of the Sabine principles on the part of English architects:

From H. Bagenal,[1] A.R.I.B.A., to W. C. S.

[London, March 25, 1914

I venture to write to you because I am an architect interested in Acoustics, and I have read what I can find of your researches in print here in London. With your article in the " Brickbuilder " for January before me, I note your most interesting diagrams on absorptive coefficients. Could you oblige me by telling me whether your later researches cancel those published by you in Sturgis' " Dictionary of Architecture " in 1901. In this latter you give a formula which is equivalent to the statement that the duration of residual

---

[1] " Sabine was ' called in ' about the problem of the lecture room of the Fogg Art Museum — as Reid and Tyndall had been called in about the House of Parliament. But whereas the British scientists were content with a statement of ' reverberation ' as the root of the practical problem, Sabine saw in it much more than that. There is no doubt that he was the first physicist to define reverberation as ' residual sound,' and to attempt to measure it. The necessity of accurate measurement led him to undertake the difficult and long-drawn-out experiments that yielded his absorption results. These experiments required a remarkable combination of practical ability and theoretical acuteness. At every step he weighed and sifted his evidence: and he perceived the separate factors in the problem. Thus he was fully aware of the reaction of the room upon the source of sound, and carefully defined the energy conditions upon which his formula rests. He laid down the principles of research in sound-transmission as well as absorption. The importance of historical evidence was fully recognized by him, and is embodied in his remarkable essays on ' Melody and the Origin of the Musical Scale ' and on ' Theatre Acoustics.' Thus it is true to say that the whole structure of the modern study of Acoustics in relation to buildings is based upon his work." From " Planning for Good Acoustics," by Hope Bagenal and Alexander Wood. Methuen, London. 1931.

sound is inversely proportional to the absorbing power of
the room, the constant being proportional to the volume of
the room. This statement I imagine holds good, though you
do not mention it in the " Brickbuilder " article for January.

Also, in connection with the formula, you give in the
" Dictionary " a table of the relative absorbing power of a
few materials, not apparently for any definite note, but stated
in such units that the constant k can be calculated for a corresponding value by multiplying the volume of the room
in feet by a figure 0.0082. Would you also tell me whether
your coefficient of last January's publication can be taken
in any similar way for calculating the residual sound in a
room or for any practical application?

I trust you will not consider these questions a liberty.
I need not say how obliged and interested I should be to receive an answer from you. The younger members of the
profession over here are particularly interested in American
architecture, and Science applied to Architecture.

To H. Bagenal from W. C. S. [*Cambridge, April* 13, 1914
. . . All subsequent experiments have verified the value
of k determined in the earlier work. However, the value of
k, .164, reduced from the metric to foot system, is not .0082
but .050, for one must bear in mind that the coefficients of
absorption enter into the formula as absolute values and not
relative values. It is necessary to reduce not merely the volume of the room, but the area of the surfaces as well.

I am not certain that I understand your next inquiry,
but if I do, the answer is that the value of k, .164 for the
metric system and .050 for the English system of units, is
the constant to be used for calculating the reverberation
of a room for any note of the musical scale. The coefficients
given in the table are absolute coefficients, and are therefore
available for any problems which may arise bearing in mind

one condition only — that, under certain peculiar forms of auditoriums, it is a matter of no inconsiderable importance as to where in the room the absorbing material is placed. These conditions which make the placing of the absorbing material important in the computation of the reverberation of a room are also the conditions which make echo and interference even more serious factors.

I am looking forward to being in London a part of this summer in my quest for interesting data, my summer search having heretofore been mainly on the Continent.

From H. Bagenal to W. C. S.
[Hampstead, N. W., April 24, 1914

I must thank you most sincerely for the information. My ignorance is largely due to the difficulty of seeing American journals. Your article in Sturgis' " Dictionary " was something of a revelation. I shall hasten to send for the subsequent articles you have so kindly mentioned, if I can obtain them.

I hope if I can be of any service to you in London you will let me know. Knowing architectural London well, I might help you. As far as interesting data is concerned, I wonder if you know the beautiful plain song and polyphony of the new Catholic Cathedral at Westminster? The Cathedral is large, but the acoustical effect excellent. The interior walls are of London stock-brick, still nine-tenths undecorated, roofed with four concrete domes (no mosaics) .

I could give you the name and address of the organist. It is difficult to determine how far the musical excellence is due to the building and how far to the Gregorian modes and the acoustical mastery of choirs trained in them. The only other places I can suggest at the moment are the Tube stations, 300 feet long, where *absolute silence* can be obtained (on Sunday mornings) . They have, of course, a wonderful capacity of transmission.

Thus, at the beginning of that fateful summer of 1914, Sabine looked forward with great anticipation to the opportunities already at hand to study examples of good and bad acoustics in England, to meet the leading English architects, and to apply his scientific principles under new conditions.

It so happened that at this time the Royal College of Surgeons, in London, had invited the American College of Surgeons to be their guests, and Mrs. Sabine was eager to attend the Congress in her professional capacity. This set a fixed date, and Sabine made a point of joining his family in Berlin on July 21, in order to assume charge of the children during her absence.

To his Family from W. C. S.   [*July* 11, 1914

MY DEAR SWEETHEARTS: We are just leaving New York, and there are tears in the eyes of the other passengers, for they are leaving their friends, but there is a smile on my lips and my shoulders are back as I walk alone to the prow of the ship, for my sweethearts await me, and I am going to all that I hold dear in the world.

I am so happy, so content, in my three little girls. So happy that I am going to you. Will my little girls be talking German when I get to them, and will they try to teach me? Oh! what a summer we are going to have together!

I shall mail this at Cherbourg. It will reach you two or three days before I do, for I shall come straight on to Hamburg and thence to Berlin.

The first comment Sabine made after rejoining his family was that, as he entered Southampton, and all the way along the coast, he had observed English men-of-war, returned from a naval review, still at full steam when they would naturally have been banking their fires. " When is your war coming? " Mrs. Sabine asked jocosely, sensing the significance of his remark. " Within twelve months," was his grave reply. As a matter of fact, he might have stated the number in days rather than months!

On Saturday, July 25, after an early family luncheon, Sabine and the children escorted Mrs. Sabine to the station to see her off for London, full of enthusiastic anticipation of attending the meetings which had attracted some fifteen hundred American surgeons and their families. After the train moved out, Sabine took the children back to the apartment, and during their rest-period he suddenly realized that he had handed to his wife all the ready money he had with him. Taking an old-fashioned, high-set taxi at the door, a model he had supposed long since relegated to the dump heap, he started for the American Express Company to cash a draft, and, knowing that the office closed early on Saturday afternoons, he urged the driver to proceed as rapidly as he could. Whichever way they turned they found the streets hopelessly blocked by massed troops. This date of July 25 is significant, as Germany has always insisted that no military organization existed until defensive action was forced upon her by the belligerent attitude of the Powers! Here was the explanation of the old-fashioned taxi! Not even a policeman was in evidence on any street, such interest was being taken in the military activity. Sabine knew what this meant, and he also knew that the conclusions he had formed in 1909 were now being confirmed.

As the taxi driver was doing his best to make up for the lost time caused by a long detour, a little child dashed from the sidewalk, and the taxicab passed over its body. In his horror, Sabine forgot his own necessities, picked up the child, and took it to the Charité Hospital, where, after a careful examination, the authorities pronounced it absolutely unhurt, save a few surface scratches. Even this accident had failed to attract the attention of any policeman, and Sabine found much difficulty in locating the home of his near-victim and depositing the little body safely in the arms of his mother, who took the matter quite calmly, not having even noticed the child's absence!

That evening, Sabine joined with the crowds which had gathered on Unter den Linden before the Kaiser's Palace. The story from this point on is better told first-hand by Sabine's elder daughter. These are recollections of a ten-year-old child in passing through one of the most dramatic incidents in the history of the world:

From Janet (Sabine) Ley

The turbulent days in Germany immediately before the War made very little impression on my childish mind at that time. I vaguely knew that great events were taking place, and that at last Germany was attempting to gratify her long suppressed ambition of *Deutschland über alles*. That Germany was the aggressor I never knew until father suddenly realized that my limited knowledge was German in sentiment, picked up from conversations overheard between my German governess and the German housemaid.

That night, after we saw mother off to England, when my little sister and I were safely tucked in bed, he was drawn by the ever-increasing tumult into the street, and mingled with the crowds surging in one direction up Unter den Linden to the Kaiser's Palace with cries of " We don't want war! " It was not until the order was given for the Uhlans to charge the mob that the cries changed to those of pain and fear, as the people tried to flee through side streets. The censorship never allowed news of this demonstration to find its way into the foreign press.[2]

---

[2] Lest this statement be questioned, I quote from Emil Ludwig's volume, " July '14 ": " But only in closed meetings was the protest allowed — only indoors, that God's ear might not catch it too easily. Under the open sky nothing but cheering was permitted, nothing but loud anticipation of the ' victor's laurel ' for the Kaiser, nothing but hatred for the brothers across the political frontier.

" For all that, a few hundred men dared to march from the Friedrichstrasse up the Linden, resolutely singing the ' Workers' Song.' From the other side, through the Brandenburger Tor, a procession of youths marched in to the strains of ' Deutschland

The routine of the children's days had already been established by their mother, and Sabine settled down to enjoy
the novel experience of leisure in which to enter into their
lives. He was disturbed by the warlike atmosphere, but as
yet had no premonition of personal inconvenience. In fact,
at that moment he was planning to install the apparatus he
had presented to the new Charlottenberg Technischeschule
in the Berlin suburbs, to the dedication of which he had
been invited.[3]

To Mrs. Sabine from W. C. S.   [*Berlin, August 2,* 1914

MY VERY DEAR JENNIE: It is hard to say what the situation
is here, for it changes so rapidly from day to day and moment
to moment. Each new announcement on the official posts
changes our possibilities and our plans. Just at the earliest
moment we shall join you, but it looks as if we should not be
able to do this before the tenth of August.[4]

Little Janet and Ruth are wonderful companions — never
flurried, never anxious, always ready, resourceful, and level-
headed. During the past week they have had skating lessons
every day, and horseback riding almost every day. They
wanted to have a surprise for mama when she came back,
so they have made wonderful headway. Ruth is no longer a
windmill in skating, stands straight, swings well, and skates
backward with real grace. Janet has a beautiful carriage;
not merely skates backward, but cuts half circles backward,
and has had some lessons in dancing on ice. It would please

über alles.' Mounted police — affray — tumult — the pavements cleared — the crowd
driven off by the horses' hoofs — fresh demonstrations at the corner of the Wilhelm-
strasse — fresh collisions at the Schadowstrasse. The middle of the roadway of the
Linden shakes under the hoofs of the mounted police as every fresh reinforcement
rides up. Any one who resists is arrested. The hoofs of the horses, the batons of the
foot-police drive the workers back, despite their growing excitement — lest any of the
surrounding Embassies should see it from their balconies, and telegraph home that
some at least in Germany are against a war."

[3] The sudden turn of war events naturally prevented this dedication from taking
place. Some of the apparatus was unique and was never duplicated.

[4] Sabine and his daughters left Berlin on August 3 — the day following the writing
of this letter.

you to see them riding through the Tiergarten, as it does every one they pass, for all stop to look and comment. The teacher riding between them is as proud as you can imagine. The children's horses are larger than his. Janet is a perfect Valkyrie, Ruth a perfect Jeanne d'Arc.

The Admiral's Ice Palace is closed on account of the War, but the riding school is still open and crowded with officers, who all stand and admire Ruth and Janet. Two or three days more and the officers will be all gone.

From Janet (Sabine) Ley

Enlightened by father as to what an invasion of Belgium would mean in the way of broken promises, and warned that we might be obliged to leave abruptly, I had the trunks brought up for an emergency. A few mornings later I noticed a worried look on father's face as he hurriedly left us, so I began putting a few things in the trunks. Then, dressing in our riding clothes, we waited for him to take us to our lesson. Instead, he came rushing home, thrust money into my hands, told me to do the best I could to close the apartment, pay off the governess and maid, and pack. The last train out of Germany left in three hours!

How I managed this I shall never know. I only remember that I packed carefully our best clothes in the trunks, because of the sad consequences! I had been thriftily taught that old clothes, even if nearly outgrown, were good enough to travel in. The youthful tragedy of it was that for a year the trunks were lost, and by the time they were recovered, our best clothes were outgrown!

At last father returned, exhausted but triumphant — he had secured a cab. He had been running for two hours after every taxi he saw. By good luck, a taxicab approached, and a German officer stepped out. Father immediately engaged it, making an agreement with the chauffeur that he would take him and our baggage to the train, and return to the apartment for us. This he did, but, while father was checking the baggage through to London, a mob seized the taxi, and the police had to interfere to make it possible for the driver to keep his agreement, to which he was honest enough to adhere although large sums were offered by German officers who wanted the cab. Father saw our baggage on the train to the Hook of Holland, and then came back and got us.

My responsibility was now over. I have a confused recollection of father's commanding, pleading, and bribing his way into a train filled to overflowing, through a station jammed with cheering troops and tearful women and children. At last we found ourselves wedged into a compartment bound for the Hook of Holland. When we finally sorted ourselves out, and the luggage was stacked away, we could count the occupants — fourteen Americans, and actually, though it is hard to believe, one parrot, in a compartment for eight! Besides ourselves and two ladies the rest were men — one a friend and well known Unitarian minister from Boston, the late Paul Revere Frothingham. How father rallied these escaping delegates of the Geneva Peace Conference!

The corridors were just as crowded. At best we could sit down only in relays. Father and I took turns, mine much longer than his, for he insisted that he preferred to stand. Some kind person would always take my sister Ruth on his lap. When it came time for meals we made a sad discovery. English gold would not be accepted. Pooling all the resources of the fellow passengers netted a very meager total in paper money; but by all going to the dining car at once, and occupying the same seats in shifts, changing between courses, each managed to get a third of a meal.

Returning from a sketchy dinner, we found the train in an uproar. It was being searched, and Americans were protesting loudly, if not grammatically or even intelligibly, at the confiscation of cameras and undeveloped films. Father became anxious. In his pocket he carried a large official letter, with seals of the British Crown, from the Royal Architect. It was not that these papers would ultimately cause any trouble, but he feared that we might be held in Germany by the red tape of official investigation, and this was the last train out. These papers he could not very well get rid of, serving as they did as letters of introduction; but our camera, our pride and joy, he quietly lowered on a string out of the window of the moving train. When the inspectors came to us, only our luggage was opened, and as father had a passport, rarely carried by any traveler in those days of peace,[5] his person was not searched. What a comfort that passport was to the two scared ladies with the child and parrot! At sight of it they immediately attached themselves to us and became the " and family," in what relationship the harassed officials never took the time to figure out!

The frontier was finally reached, but what weary hours we had spent in waiting in out-of-the-way places for troop trains to pass — the men cheering and gaily calling out their destination, " Nach Paris! "

The discomforts of that trip to the older people were real enough; to a child of ten they were no doubt magnified by tired legs, hunger, and thirst. In the end we had to give in and drink the water passed around in mugs for the troop trains, to the later horror of poor mother. When she heard of this, it caused her weeks of anxious waiting and watching for symptoms which never developed!

Once out of Germany, some of these discomforts ceased, for there was at least sitting room on the Dutch train. The Channel crossing was another nightmare. The sea was rough, and we were in no condition to withstand its effects. But even that came to an end. England brought another financial

---

[5] This was an " emergency " passport, issued at his request by the American Embassy at Berlin, and dated July 31, 1914! Sabine was among the first to recognize the possibility of serious complications for Americans abroad.

crisis in our pooled resources. But this time father was able to save the situation with some small currency, which, spread very thin, got us all to London and into cabs, each for his own destination. We had joined mother none too soon. The news vendors everywhere were shouting extras. England had just declared war on Germany!

Mrs. Sabine greeted her husband and children with profound relief. The surgeons from Germany and France had abruptly departed from the Surgical Congress for home, leaving their learned papers to be read by substitutes. As at that time she expected to join the family in Germany, she went to the American Embassy, seeking information. A young attaché whom she had known in Boston, took the matter up with the German Embassy, which forbade her to try to go back to Berlin with the threat that, should she make the attempt, she would be held in Holland. Then came a cable from her husband asking her to remain in London, as he and the children were trying to join her.

The " official envelope " which was on Sabine's person during the journey from Berlin to London, to which Janet refers, included the additional conclusions and recommendations he had prepared in answer to the inquiries he had received from the Royal Architect in connection with the acoustical difficulties in the Civil Service Commission Hall in Burlington Gardens, and the New Old Bailey. Sabine had promised to confer in person with the authorities " before the Bank Holidays " in August, and, even though he had arrived at a moment when England had declared war on Germany, he kept his appointment!

Before getting in touch with the architects, however, there were immediate and serious personal matters to receive attention. One of the first questions he asked his wife after his arrival was, " How much cash have you? " She mentioned a sum so much larger than he expected that he was relieved of all immediate anxiety. Just before his arrival, and with no thought of the impending *clôture* to be placed by all banking concerns on ready money, she had drawn on her letter of credit an amount absurdly in excess of any immediate needs. Her husband blessed her for her uncanny if unconscious foresight!

Joyously Sabine sought out the American friends who had advanced him money during the momentous trip from Berlin, repaid his loans, and in several instances made advances to them. Then he presented himself at the temporary headquarters established to advise and assist distraught Americans stranded in London, and offered his services in any capacity. He was promptly placed in charge of the baggage department, which was undertaking to locate and retrieve luggage which the fleeing travelers had lost or unceremoniously abandoned in various countries of Europe as they flocked to London, striving hectically to secure passage homeward on some steamer.

One American woman, who had turned over to Sabine, in his new capacity, registration slips of her luggage, supposed to have been on the same train as that on which she herself escaped from Germany, became highly indignant when, a day or two later, the volunteer " baggage master " was unable to make a full report on her trunks. His attempted explanation that his own luggage, which he had personally seen placed on the train a fortnight earlier, was still missing, was scornfully cast aside, and the irate woman proceeded to administer what she no doubt considered a well deserved rebuke, culminating with the direful threat that, unless he produced the errant baggage within another twenty-four hours, she would report his negligence to William Jennings Bryan! In passing, it may be mentioned that the Sabine luggage, to which Janet refers in her notes, unexpectedly and mysteriously appeared at their home in Boston a year later, through the American Express — nothing lost, though opened several times as stamps indicated. Such was German efficiency!

After the first excitement moderated, Sabine put himself in touch with the English architects, and found them deeply concerned but by no means subject to war hysteria. They were enthusiastic over the professional suggestions he had made, some of which had already been tested with highly beneficial results. To complete the work in the New Old Bailey it was necessary for Sabine to make a personal investigation, and also to secure additional data, which was supplied by the Royal Architect after Sabine's return to America:

From Frank Baines to W. C. S.
[*London, November 23, 1914*

It was agreed between us that I should supply you drawings of our Royal Courts of Justice, giving clearly the sizes to scale, together with notes of all the materials of which the Courts are constructed. I now send under separate cover ten detail drawings of some of the Courts, which you saw when you visited the building with me, and I have attached to each photographs showing clearly the character of each of them.

I also send a site plan, giving the positions of the Courts in the general plan of the building, and on the detailed plans of the Courts I have shown by colour, with the reference on each plan, the material of which the Courts are built.

I trust you do not regret, when you see this mass of material, the kindness of your offer to advise us on this difficult question of acoustics. Pray consider, however, that we are entirely in your hands, and would not wish you to take up this difficult problem unless you find both the time and inclination to deal with it. I should sincerely regret troubling you if I felt that we were imposing on your good nature and kindness in accepting your offer to help. Should you, how-

ever, require any further information, pray command me.
You will see by this that we are still pursuing our usual avo-
cations in spite of this disastrous war, but perhaps that is in
us a sign of our hopefulness as to the ultimate result.

To complete this story, it should be recorded that, in response to this letter, Sabine sent Baines models and directions which resulted in accomplishing all that could be desired. In the New Old Bailey, the difficulty in hearing came
from the fact that the sound rose directly to the dome.
Sabine remedied this by the simple expedient of inserting
a ground-glass roof, thus lowering the height of the ceiling.

Returning to this summer of 1914, the English architects
became so impressed by Sabine's work that a Committee of
Parliament asked him to make suggestions regarding the
Houses of Parliament. In the House of Commons he suggested, among other things, the removal of the grille through
which women were allowed to peek as well as listen to debates on the floor. The suggestion was at first met almost
with horror by those to whom he made this recommendation. Women, they solemnly declared, could not be allowed
to be seen in this august assembly hall, which for centuries
had been sacred to man. Yet, in less than ten years, Lady
Astor and other women were not only seen there but heard,
in their status as full members!

In connection with his work, the Government gave Sabine
official permits to visit the buildings " at any hour of any
day." He used to relate a unique experience he had of being
present as an alien on the floor of the House of Commons
during the early secret war-conferences of England, thus
shattering all English precedent. No charge was ever placed
upon him not to repeat what he heard. Perhaps the most
thrilling session he attended was when he shared the enthusiasm aroused among the members of Parliament by the
reading of Lord Hardinge's famous telegram to the Secre-

tary of State, giving the pledges of the Indian Rajahs, forever silencing Germany's boast that India would prove disloyal: " The Rulers of the Native States of India, who number nearly seven hundred in all, have with one accord rallied to the defense of the Empire and offered their personal services and the resources of their States for the War. . . . The veteran Sir Pertab Singh, the Regent of Jodhpur, in spite of his seventy years, would not be denied his right to serve the King-Emperor, and his nephew, the Maharajah of Jodhpur, who is but sixteen years old, goes with him."

Never again could Sabine be persuaded that the English were a phlegmatic people, but he could not have foreseen that this same youthful Maharajah would one day be sitting in state in the Council Chamber at New Delhi, applauding the perfect acoustical properties of a room constructed, after the plans of Sir Herbert Baker, the Royal Architect, out of Sabine-invented tiles and built in accord with Sabine laws. In reporting this to Mrs. Sabine, Sir Herbert added, " We architects and all interested in public buildings, owe a great debt of gratitude for Professor Sabine's investigations and discoveries."

The weeks in London at this dramatic moment gave Sabine further opportunity to witness the marvelous spirit with which the British people always meet a national emergency, and deeply impressed him. While he continued his professional and patriotic work in London, his family sought a quieter refuge in Oxford. Here Mrs. Sabine found her former professor at Johns Hopkins — Sir William Osler, who, with characteristic initiative, even thus early in the War had started his campaign to secure civilian coöperation. While the children resumed their riding lessons under the direction of an accomplished English master recommended by Sir William, Mrs. Sabine joined him in his patriotic work, devoting her evenings to classes in bandaging, and in other ways contributing to the general cause.

The Sabine family sailed for home on September 10, their party being reinforced by the addition of Madame Sabine and Mrs. Siebert, who had also been in England during that stirring summer.

One of Mrs. Sabine's first acts, on arriving home, was to buy up all the roller bandaging machines in Boston and send them to Doctor Osler!

XIII. WHAT PRICE THE GOOD SAMARITAN? · 1915–1916

THE OFFICE of Dean of the Graduate School of Applied
Science at Harvard University came to an end on June 15,
1915. With the Technology merger supposed to be final, the
position automatically ceased to exist. During his Deanship
Sabine had refused to relinquish the courses he had personally conducted, and, as these were never included in the
merger, the lifting of his administrative responsibilities
simply gave him more time to devote to teaching and research. However unwillingly Sabine may have accepted the
office, his experience during those seven years had greatly
broadened his outlook, and may even have prevented him
from becoming a recluse. The administrative ability, previously latent, was now fully developed, and disclosed itself
in his writings and in his handling of outside interests. His
recognition as the sole authority in the new science of Architectural Acoustics was now international, and the increasing opportunity for demonstration could not fail to gratify
him. Granting that his work as Dean was abruptly terminated, Sabine was left in a position which seemed, at least to
his friends, even more favorable for the consummation of his
greater labors.

But these conclusions fail to take into account the effect
of the Great War upon him and his work. Except for that,
Sabine in all probability would have stood at this moment
at the threshold of a long career of constantly increasing
fame. The War gave him the opportunity to demonstrate
his greatness in Sound beyond its application to Architec-

tural Acoustics, but it also demanded from him the supreme tribute, for Sabine was as directly its victim as if he had fallen in the front-line trenches. He had been an eye-witness of the war activities in Berlin; he had been in London when England declared war against Germany. To a man of his temperament it would have been unnatural not to feel an unconquerable urge to assume a personal and active part in the great conflict.

The opportunity seemed to have come in 1915 when he was invited to deliver the Sorbonne Lectures at the University of Paris.[1] Once on the Continent, Sabine knew that he could contribute of himself to the advantage of the Allies; but the illness of his younger daughter forced a postponement, and this was one of the few summers when the family remained in America. The invitation, however, was repeated, and in March, 1916, the Harvard Corporation appointed him to represent the University at the Sorbonne.

From the Boston Evening Transcript

As scholastic ambassador from Harvard, next fall, Dean Wallace C. Sabine should bring credit to himself and to the institution which he will represent. A physical scientist of profound scholarship, a capable innovator in one or two important and unexplored fields of research, Professor Sabine has steadily resisted the modern tendency to cheapen Science by too much popularizing it. Indeed, his insistence on writing only for technical journals of his experiments in Acoustics has unhappily left the general public in ignorance of facts which it might have used to advantage.

This assignment enabled Sabine and his wife at last to gratify their intense desire to plunge actively into war work. They sailed for Bordeaux with their children immediately

---

[1] Germany had invited Sabine to deliver lectures on Architectural Acoustics as Exchange Professor at the University of Berlin in 1906 and again in 1907. On both occasions, however, these invitations had to be declined for personal reasons.

after the College closed in June, and had scarcely reached
France when they were both invited by the Rockefeller War
Relief Commission to join that organization in promoting
work already in operation, with headquarters established in
Berne, Switzerland. Sabine himself was asked to take charge
of these headquarters, to relieve the Director, thus enabling
Warwick Greene to visit other neutral countries and study
their needs; while Mrs. Sabine was urged to become the
head of a committee at Fribourg, Switzerland, to supervise
the hospitalization [2] of some five hundred Belgian refugee
children — a work which was to be undertaken by the Commission at the personal request of the Queen of Belgium.
As the Sorbonne lectures were not scheduled until November, the opportunity for service thus offered seemed to the
Sabines exactly what they wanted, and they accepted both
propositions, starting their work in mid-July. Compensation was suggested but declined.

Sabine's first war work seemed far removed from the
subjects in which he was accepted as expert, yet the same
completeness of understanding and the same efficiency in
execution were always manifest. In a letter to America he
gives some of the details:

To Clifford M. Swan from W. C. S.   [*October* 10, 1916

My investigations in France have related so far to tuberculosis. This has been extremely interesting, and has resulted in a Report to the Rockefeller Foundation on which
I hope they will be able to take definite action. From now on,
my investigations will probably relate to other forms of war
relief in France. These investigations for the Rockefeller
Foundation are interesting not merely in themselves, but
because of the men with whom they bring me into contact.

---

[2] The word " hospitalizing " is used here in the sense of " housing." The Belgian
children were undernourished, but not sick. Sabine's relation with this work was
simply to pay the bills, as Acting Director of the War Relief Commission, the preparations for installing the children being in Mrs. Sabine's efficient hands.

I was compelled to stay in Berne much longer than I expected — two months in fact — partly on account of the Belgian children which the Rockefeller Foundation is hospitalizing in Switzerland, but more especially because the other member of the War Relief Commission was in Germany and Austria, and it was necessary for me, as the sole representative on the Allied side of the battle front, to be in a position to render immediate service should Mr. Greene be able to get the necessary permission for the sending of condensed milk to the Polish and Serbian babies. The necessary permission was finally secured, and condensed milk is being sent from Switzerland. Of course great care is taken, above all things, that its distribution should be so safeguarded that it shall all go to native Polish children.

Perhaps the war-relief work which makes the greatest appeal to one is that of the blind. It is an affliction almost peculiar to this war, and, curiously enough, I found very few people who have given the correct explanation of the fact that so large a proportion of the disabled are disabled through blindness. The real reason is that the warfare is one of mines, of heavy shells and of trench bombs. All of these throw sand and gravel, which injure the eyes even when the body itself is not hit by an object large enough to produce permanent harm. The impulse to look in the direction of the shell or bomb that is falling seems irresistible.

From Mrs. Sabine

The children and I are in Fribourg. Mr. Sabine telephones me every day while the children are having their supper, and he spends each Saturday night and Sunday with us up to a late train leaving for Berne. He has three problems: first, bread baked in Berne and sent to the French war prisoners in Germany (later the bakeries became so overtaxed by the demands of the interned soldiers and refugees throughout Switzerland that only flour could be sent to these prisoners) ; second, milk (condensed and powdered) is sent to the Polish babies; third, the Rockefeller War Relief heads want to learn how the Commission can best aid France in its tuberculosis problem from a layman's standpoint. To make this report, Mr. Sabine, Baron Henri de Rothschild, Dr. Maurice Letulle, a tuberculosis expert, and I, visited all tubercular sanatoria in and about Paris for a radius of many miles, going out from the city in various directions for several successive days. The French idea is to have trees around the buildings. Dampness and lack of sunshine was the atmosphere we found surrounding the pathetic specimens of humanity.

To Jerome D. Greene from W. C. S.

[*Berne, September 20, 1916*

During the past few days Mr. Warwick Greene and I have had a number of conversations in regard to war-relief work in Europe. He has asked that I write you in regard to the satisfaction which these exchanges of opinion have given both of us. I think we had both become a little apprehensive. Starting with the same views two months ago, separated from each other and almost cut off from communication, on opposite sides of the battle front, under very different influences, we had both changed our ideas greatly, not so much in the component elements as in the emphasis which we would lay on the different considerations which should guide the policy of war relief. Starting from the same point, traveling very different paths, we have come out shoulder to shoulder.

We both feel that very great care should be exercised that relief work of the Foundation should not in any way whatever affect the issue of the war. As an abstract principle this is obvious; as an applied principle it is by no means so simple. Of course there are times when, in the interest of humanity, it should be waived. I do not think that either of us is by nature inclined to make a fetish of a principle, but the point is that the activity of the Foundation in one field depends on what may have been done in another; that in yielding to the impulse of one good call, one may be sacrificing the opportunities and privileges of another. Local committees and ephemeral organizations may well choose their purpose and attain their ends as they will, and in doing so serve a great cause. But the War Relief Commission will remember that the Foundation is an enduring organization, and that goodwill is an important factor in its future service.

Many of the distressing results of the war, such as the mutilated and the blind, appeal directly to patriotic and partisan sympathy, and evoke a spontaneous outpouring of individual, committee, and national relief work which is the one bright side of the War. When such problems are presented to a permanent charitable organization, like the Rockefeller Foundation, it is the opinion of your Commission that the investigation is not complete until it has been extended to both sides, and that the aid given should be in proportion to the needs.

There are still other problems so large and so international in scope that they cannot be touched by any of the agencies at work here, but which, well solved, will yield permanent results. These we believe are preëminently suitable for the Foundation. Tuberculosis is one, and Mr. Greene has another which he hopes to be able to lay before you before long. In the meantime, smaller charities may be recommended which are good in themselves, and which have the additional advantage of bringing with them goodwill for the larger. Even these will be treated internationally if possible.

All this may seem to you trite. I think in America it would have seemed to me trite. Over here, however, it is by no means so, and such considerations have characterized the organizations in Switzerland only. However that may be,

I am quite willing to lay myself open to the criticism of having voiced the obvious, if only for the opportunity which it affords me of expressing my pleasure in finding myself so closely in accord with Mr. Greene in matters both large and small. Of course I should not express any opinion on a matter of policy except to him, were it not at his request. I shall return in a few days to Paris and resume the investigation of the problems to be found there.

On the following day the formal Report,[3] written by Sabine, was forwarded to New York. President Eliot pronounced it " the best medical report I have ever read." With it went the following letter from the Director:

To Jerome D. Greene from Warwick Greene
[*Berne, September* 21, 1916

The Tuberculosis Report of the War Relief Commission was mailed to the Foundation today. The long report was prepared by Mr. Sabine and the letter of transmission by myself.

You may remember that my original recommendation was that the Foundation send Dr. Richard Derby or some other doctor to make a preliminary investigation of the subject. The information that I had gathered led me to believe that there was a real war tuberculosis problem in Europe, but I had neither the time nor the necessary qualifications to make a thorough examination into the subject. Therefore I recommended that an expert be sent.

Before an answer was received from the Foundation, however, we had the great good luck to secure Mr. Sabine as a member of the War Relief Commission. We discussed the matter of tuberculosis at length, and then Mr. Sabine started to make the preliminary investigation, the results of which are embodied in the Report forwarded today.

I recommend that Mr. Sabine be made the Chairman of

---

[3] See Appendix B.

the Rockefeller International Tuberculosis Commission. This recommendation is not contained in the Official Report of the War Relief Commission, as Mr. Sabine naturally did not want to sign a report containing a recommendation concerning himself. Furthermore, his natural modesty made him very reluctant to consider the matter when I proposed it to him. He had no idea of himself in connection with this position at the time he prepared the Report. But I think he is well qualified for the place, and I hope that it will be offered him if the Rockefeller Foundation takes favorable action on our Report, and creates this International Tuberculosis Commission. If the Foundation decides that the American medical expert should be the Chairman of the Commission, I still hope that Mr. Sabine will be appointed to the Commission as the layman member.

Before the Foundation could act upon Warwick Greene's letter, Nature had taken a hand in the game, and Sabine was suffering a collapse from overwork which made his acceptance of the suggested position impossible. The Foundation, therefore, through the International Health Board, appointed Dr. Livingston Farrand, President of the University of Colorado, Director of a Commission which went abroad in July, 1917, to undertake the task of setting up in France, in close coöperation with the French Government and the medical profession, a dispensary, publicity, and training demonstration which should aim at helping to control tuberculosis.

All this work was based upon the recommendations in Sabine's Report, and, during the next six years, the twelve tuberculosis dispensaries he mentioned were increased to a hundred and sixty-eight. Subventions were granted for the building of sanatoria, training-schools were conducted for public health visitors, offering a two-years' course, and a graduate course in tuberculosis was completed by 175 dispensary physicians. This work of the Foundation was transferred to the French Government in 1922.

By the first of October it became necessary for Sabine to relinquish his position with the War Commission to return to Paris in order to prepare for his Sorbonne Lectures, and to place the children in school. There seemed no reason for Mrs. Sabine to give up her work with the Belgian children, so she remained behind at Fribourg. Sabine also persuaded her to spend a fortnight at Doctor Rollier's sanatorium at Leysin, Switzerland, to which he had been much attracted during his official visits, simply for rest before joining him later in Paris. Mrs. Sabine rebelled that he himself could not indulge in similar relaxation, particularly because, just before he relinquished his post at Berne, several of the younger men attached to the Commission expressed their fear that her husband was on the verge of a serious breakdown. Sabine, however, laughed at her fears, and reminded her that scarcely enough time remained to prepare himself for his important lectures.

The little party of four, made up of a French schoolteacher who had been with the children in Fribourg, the two girls, — thirteen and ten years old respectively, — and himself, took temporary quarters in a small and unsatisfactory hotel, while Sabine and Janet set out to discover something more suitable. The father's attitude toward the child was characteristic. For the first time he now explained fully their limited financial condition, and enlisted her assistance in finding the *best* accommodations within his means. Thus the search, which lasted for several days, instead of being a compromise, turned into a game, in which the child took the liveliest interest, and when at last they settled down at the Hôtel du Palais, fronting the Seine, she felt that herself had made the selection, and would not have exchanged their simple quarters for an *apartement* at the Ritz! The ex-

pectation of finding sunshine, which was one of the anticipated attractions of the Hôtel du Palais, was never realized
because of the thickness of the atmosphere caused by the in-
cessant firing of the German artillery at thirty miles' distance.

It was not until early in November that Mrs. Sabine arrived in Paris, having been called from Leysin by Doctor
Joseph Blake to serve as surgeon in his war hospital. She
had heard little from her husband during the previous
weeks, but supposed that this was occasioned by the demands made upon him in preparing for his lectures. When,
however, she arrived in Paris, accompanied by the French
governess she was bringing for the children, and found that
he was not at the station to meet her, she was greatly surprised and not a little hurt, as always before he had been
scrupulously attentive. She telephoned to the Hôtel du
Palais, and inquired if they were expecting her. The clerk's
rather hesitating reply alarmed her, and she asked that her
husband be called to the telephone. " But, Madame," the
clerk replied, " your husband is very ill. The doctor has just
left saying that he cannot possibly live the day out! "

Mrs. Sabine rushed from the telephone booth only to find
complications in connection with her luggage. France had
recently made a rule that no baggage could be transported
from the station to a hotel unless within a certain limit of
size. Not knowing this, Mrs. Sabine had arrived with an unusually large American trunk. Pressing money into the hand
of the governess, and calling a Cook's agent to her assistance,
she explained the circumstances, and rushed to the Hôtel du
Palais, where she found her husband indeed a desperately
sick man — so weak that he could hardly speak or step, and
in such pain that he could scarcely greet her. Quickly getting him back into bed, she learned that he had been ill for
two weeks, and had refused to let the children send her
word. Little Janet had tried in vain to find a doctor or a

nurse, for those not at the Front were home for rest, and un-available. At last Sabine suggested that the child get in touch with James Hazen Hyde, who responded promptly by send-ing his own physician.

As a matter of fact, it is a question whether a letter or a telegram could have gotten through to Mrs. Sabine even if it had been sent. Taking advantage of the right of way given communications to the Rockefeller War Relief Com-mission, she wrote immediately to the office in Berne; the officials there cabled to Jerome D. Greene in New York; Greene sent a cable to Dr. Alexis Carrel, which reached him at the Front; and Doctor Carrel telegraphed Mrs. Sabine that his head surgeon was on the way to Paris, and that he himself would follow immediately. All this took place within twenty-four hours of the time Mrs. Sabine arrived in Paris!

Doctor Carrel's assistant, whom Mrs. Sabine had met when visiting the Carrel hospital at Compiègne, agreed with her that surgical interference was necessary; but on the follow-ing morning, ten minutes before Doctor Carrel and the noted surgeon, Doctor Tuffier, arrived, the abscess broke and drained naturally — one case in a million! The result of the consultation was that a surgical operation should be postponed until the patient had regained sufficient strength to stand it.

After careful consideration, it was decided that Sabine should be removed to Doctor Rollier's establishment at Leysin as soon as he was able to go. Mrs. Sabine had learned from personal experience the efficacious results of the sun cure to other than tuberculous cases, and she felt certain that in these surroundings, with her own careful nursing, the quickest cure would be accomplished. Then the prob-lem arose as to the children. The governess, Mlle. Morel, a finely educated woman, was thoroughly reliable, but, in case of illness, the military censorship made communication almost impossible, which naturally created an anxious situation. But Sabine's condition made separation absolutely imperative.

During Sabine's convalescence at the Hôtel du Palais, carefully husbanding his returning strength, the children did their utmost to supplement their mother's nursing. Little ten-year-old Ruth, the younger child, was particularly ingenuous in keeping her father amused. Some of her devices are disclosed in a letter she wrote to child friends in Boston:

To Marion, Richard, and David   [*Paris, January 22, 1917*
. . . A little while ago I wrote a piece of poetry. I'll recite it when I've told you the when and wherefore of it all. The reason I called it " The Scorpicat " is that in papa's room here in the hotel, on the ceiling, is a place where some water has leaked through, and it forms a horrible beast something like this: it has eyes like cats' and a row of drops forming his back bone; he looks something like a scorpion, and has a leg of tremendous dimensions. We put the words scorpion and cat together and called it the " scorpicat." Papa wanted me to write it, but I didn't know what to say. The end is the little child crying in the night. After a whole lot of trying I found out what I would say, so I wrote this:

THE SCORPICAT

On the ceiling, the room's white sky,
One can see if one looks up high,
The scorpicat, he's a horrible beast
Whom you can see in the ceiling east.
He has claws like a lobster's and eyes like a cat,
And his long, skinny leg goes off like that.
He terrifies me, and he horrifies you,
And his stare is enough to make one blue.
But every night, he takes his flight
On a broomstick. Boo-hoo-hoo!

Quotations from a letter written by Sabine from the Hôtel du Palais during his illness bridge the gap until he found himself strong enough to make the journey to Leysin:

To his Mother from W. C. S.   [*Paris, November* 16, 1916
. . . I have been gaining steadily for the past two weeks and more, and yesterday the doctor — the best doctor in Paris, the best specialist in kidney troubles in the world, Jennie says — declared me practically well, or at least so near it that there is no doubt of the rest of the journey — and that without any operation, which in America would probably have been insisted on. So that I may have no recurrence, he advises a long rest at Leysin and the sun treatment. This has been arranged for, and I shall stay there three months. . . .

A month later he continued the description:

To his Mother from W. C. S.   [*Leysin, December* 11, 1916
. . . At last, after many starts and delays, we are at Leysin. Doctor Rollier looked me over very thoroughly, and promptly put me to bed with orders to lie quietly for — I don't know how long. So here I lie in a narrow but very nice, clean, and comfortable bed, in a simple but attractive and clean hospital room. The window of the room is a door opening out onto a balcony, which runs the length of the building, divided off so as to give a private balcony to each room. Out onto this balcony I shall be wheeled whenever the sun shines, and exposed to the sun — naked. This sanatorium is 5000 feet high. At such an altitude being exposed naked out of doors sounds cold. It is cold, very cold, when the sun is behind a cloud, but on the other hand, very, very hot when the sun shines — so it is said. The sun has not shone since I have been here. . . .

Sabine was in Doctor Rollier's sanatorium from December 11, 1916, until the middle of February, 1917. The en-

forced rest and the sun treatment resulted in steadily regained strength, and gave him an opportunity to study
French six or eight hours a day with a tutor, to perfect his
diction for his Sorbonne Lectures. Perhaps he was inspired
to greater effort by competition offered by his indefatigable
mother:

From Ruth Sabine to her Parents
            [*Hôtel du Palais, Paris, January* 13, 1917
    . . . Papa dear, do you know that you'll have to study
hard at your French? You have more than one rival. In coming home this evening we found a letter from grandmother,
all in French. It was written as though she had known nothing but French all her life, and besides, there were only two
mistakes. Take care, papa! You know your French well,
but grandmother is at your heels! . . .

During this period more letters were exchanged between
Sabine and his family than at any other period in his life.
The following extracts are published in chronological se-
quence as giving a detailed account of his mental activities
as well as his physical progress, and containing statements
upon several significant subjects. Especially do they show
rare and understanding family relations:

From Janet Sabine to her Parents
            [*Paris, France, December* 21, 1916
    We are having a lovely time, but we do miss you so, but
we know that it is in a good cause. We wished the sun would
show his face more and make papa well for us. I was fifth in
my science test. We went yesterday to the Champs-Elysées to
get the toy for Henry Hyde, and we have a nice mama-hen
with three chicks beside her. How I envy those wooden
chicks, for they have their mama!

To his Children from W. C. S.   [*Leysin, January* 4, 1917
    . . . New Year's Eve I left my room for the first time, and

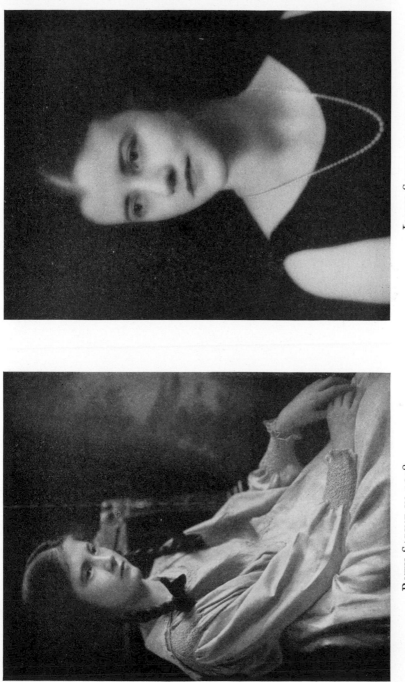

JANET SABINE IN 1932
now Mrs. Frederic T. Ley

RUTH SABINE IN 1918
died October 23, 1922 [æt. 16]

went down to the first floor for both the afternoon and evening entertainments. In the afternoon there was music, piano and song, by Russians. The man who played the piano was "laureat," which means prize man, at the Petrograd Conservatory of Music. The singing was by a Russian young woman. In the evening, the entertainment was less serious — two little plays interspersed with amateur guitar, mandolin, violin, and piano music. The audience was even more interesting than the performance. All the patients except a few, like mama and I, who are very much alive and can navigate ourselves when we are allowed to, came down in their beds, and both wings of the dining room were filled by the white beds with the patients propped up in them. One of the two plays was by the children of Mr. Rollier — not Doctor Rollier, but Mr. Rollier, the Director of Miremont — who are here from Neuchâtel for the Christmas holidays. The other play was given by my French teacher, my *femme de chambre,* who made a very pretty heroine in the play; a young Greek man, who borrowed my cutaway coat for the part; and one of the nurses. The mandolin and guitar music was charmingly informal, all entirely by the patients, except the guitar music, which was by the painter here in the Clinique, who is an Italian with brown mustache and a middle-west American appearance and manner.

Mama's skis have come. I have oiled her shoes, and she is all ready for skiing, but there is no snow. The rains of a week ago washed it all away, and there has been none since. I hope there will be some snow while we are here, for I am anxious that mama should have a chance to try it. . . .

[Leysin, January 7, 1917

Today it is a letter from Janet that comes with its very happy enclosure — her school report for the past three months, so very, very satisfactory, and reminiscent of the reports from Miss Winsor, which mama and I used to enjoy so much. Dear children, you make us very happy with your good work. What we want is good, clear thinking, not merely in your school work, but on all occasions, and in your every action, and this you give us in overflowing measure, both of you, all the time. Dear little girls, we are very happy in our thoughts of you.

Plenty of snow for skiing, but it is pronounced too soft as yet. Apparently it must be neither too soft nor too hard, too deep nor too thin. Like most sports, its conditions are rarely fulfilled. I am afraid the logical conclusion from that generalization in regard to sports — that their conditions are rarely fulfilled — is that one should have a variety of sports. So, when occasion permits, we shall add skiing and snow-shoeing to your other pleasures, and, well, we will go out of our way to make " the occasion permit." You shall have fun as well as work. Then we shall hope that you will carry one with the other — find pleasure in your work, and make accomplishments of your pleasures. . . .

[*Leysin, January* 12, 1917

This is five o'clock Friday afternoon, and mama has just come in bringing three successes! Janet's letter with word that she got $19\frac{1}{4}$ points out of a possible 20 in her French course and nearly a *croix d'or;* Ruth's letter with 18 points out of 20 in her French and a *croix d'or;* and mama's oral report of her first skiing lesson, in which she got a " parfait parfait " and doubtless a *croix d'or* — that is to say, she did not fall down. But I discount mama's report a little, for she only walked on a level with two big English soldiers, one on each side of her. Tomorrow's lesson will be the test, for they are going to take her out on the hill and slide. Then if she gets only a *bien* it will be a success worth recording. I told you about engaging a woman teacher, and that the arrangement was not a success. She wanted to take two pupils at the same time. This time we engaged a man, and it worked just the other way. Two came to take little mama between them. One is an English sergeant and the other a private. They did not have skis today, but walked on either side of mama. Tomorrow they will bring skis, which they will get from the military stores. Then mama's French teacher, who, I think I said, is also teacher in the school at the bottom of the hill right next the skiing grounds, is going to take mama skiing Sunday morning — she and her husband, who is the postmaster here in the village. So you see, mama is working hard over her lessons. . . .

[*Leysin, January* 13, 1917

. . . I see by the papers that the Seine is rising (you probably notice that my pen still has its fingers crossed), and is getting near the danger level. By the time this letter reaches you it will have done one thing or the other — passed the danger mark and begun an inundation, or have begun to fall. All such things cause a good deal more anxiety to the absent ones than to those on the spot. Moreover, I know it would be an inconvenience not a danger to *you,* yourselves, so, however regrettable, I shall not worry. . . .

From Ruth Sabine to her Parents [*Paris, January* 18, 1917

I used to think that it was always you who told us not to worry, but now I see that it is my turn. You oughtn't to bother yourselves about the Seine's rising. It has gone down again, though it isn't yet low enough. It will need just about two metres before it gets really dangerous, and all the water in the clouds before we get drowned.

Dear papa, we found your letter with the drawing in it. Your room looks rather interesting, though I'd much rather have you here than your picture. What was that little three-legged thing (or rather, tripod — I don't think that's the way you spell it) with a little thing the size of a book at the top of the leg? I know I'm expressing myself badly as usual, but I'm sure you don't care.

Dearest mama, don't break a leg on your skis. I'm not scared enough to tell you that I can imagine you tangled up among two enormous sticks, flying over a precipice, and landing on the other side with a broken leg and a crooked ski. I'll not say that, because I don't think it will ever happen; but, to draw a milder picture, I don't want mama to hurt herself. And besides, I'm sure there's no precipice in front of the schoolhouse where she practices.

I won't advise mama to try skiing here. We're quite proud of it because it doesn't snow every day in Paris, but really the snow has turned to slush, and the slush is very slippery. There's only a tiny bit of snow on the grass-plots along the Seine in front of the hotel.

Papa, I began my letter reassuring you, but you're in much danger of finding the end a scolding. You told us in your last letter to relax after we had the *croix d'or*. Do you think we're going to give up? No sir! " Ye're mistook in yer judgments," as the sailor boy said in " Captains Courageous." . . .

On this same day, while little Ruth is declaring the children's determination to continue to win honors in their studies, Sabine, remembering the self-forcing of his own youth, is repeating his admonitions to make excellence rather than superiority their goal.

To his Children from W. C. S.   [*Leysin, January* 18, 1917
. . . I have before me on the bed two precious letters, which mama and I have read over and over again, and in which our two little girls write that they have both won the *croix d'or,* and both were first in their French courses. Each *croix d'or* is the sweeter because of the other. Now that you have won them, relax a little, just a little. Remember that health and a buoyant, joyous spirit, happiness and an interest in people and things, are quite as much to be striven after and treasured as excellence in your studies.

Well educated but at the same time happy and sympathetic children are what we want. This might easily be misinterpreted, but I have no fear that you will do so. . . .

From Janet Sabine to her Parents [*Paris, January* 18, 1917
Oh, how glad it makes Ruth and myself to know that mamma is having a nice time skiing! You take such pleasure in what we do, and I am sure we take as much pleasure in what you do. . . .

To Janet from W. C. S.   [*Leysin, January* 19, 1917
. . . Janet, sweetheart, you don't know how much happiness I have had in the result of your Algebra *concours*. That was our study together. Though the examination came so much longer after I had left than I expected that I cannot claim any share in the result, I still feel a special interest and companionship. I had been intending to hold my celebration of this success until I got back to Paris, and could hold you in my arms, but I really can't refrain any longer from writing about it. . . .

The following letter is of peculiar interest because of the reference made by this ten-year-old child to the echo in the Trocadéro, showing the understanding with which these children, young as they were, entered into their parents' life and work. The Trocadéro was one of the outstanding examples of poor acoustics cited by Krehbiel in an earlier chapter.[4]

From Ruth Sabine to her Parents [*Paris, January* 24, 1917
. . . Isn't it queer that I could forget the most important of all during two weeks? It was a matinee at the Trocadéro. There was a moving picture of the War and a good deal of singing. A soldier in his old uniform sang the very best of all. Before playing the Marseillaise, some great gentleman or

---

[4] See page 146.

other gave a long, long lecture. I didn't understand half of what he said. Besides, all his words, nearly, ended in t-i-o-n. But that was nearly the most interesting part of all. During the whole lecture the *echo* kept up as ardently as he himself, and, as it was up in the roof on our side, we heard the echo much better than the thingamagig personage himself. I wish you'd been here. It would have interested you so, papa dear. . . .

To his Mother from W. C. S.   [*January,* 1917

. . . All Switzerland is much excited now by a very real fear that Germany is contemplating an invasion. On the other hand, Switzerland does not want an early peace. She knows, as the whole world must know, that if peace came now it would be her turn to be swallowed up in a very few years, and an unresisting world, a world incapable of resisting, would look on. If the struggle must come, she wants it now. Do not be misled by the courtesy of her endorsement of Wilson's most ill-advised note. Switzerland, German and French Swiss alike, fears Germany. They fear a Germany defeated, but infinitely more a Germany arrogant in a brutal, vicious, ruthless victory. Holland, Denmark, Norway, Sweden, fear and *know* that the same fate would await them. A world war by the father would be followed by another world war by the son, who is even more militaristic than his father. No worse calamity could befall the world, no more ominous event could occur in history, than peace at the present moment. *Preparation must not mean victory.*

If you were to see out of your window almost every day, as I do, the funeral of French soldiers, with muffled drums, or the touching march of Chopin, and the following files of French, English, Belgian prisoners of war, wind its way down the mountain side to the valley below; if you could see the wounded lying on their cots everywhere, in the houses, on the terraces below, waiting their turn — you would say with *Lincoln,* not Wilson, " They shall not have died in vain." . . .

To his Children from W. C. S.   [Leysin, January 25, 1917

Yesterday your two precious letters came, each characteristic of the sweet girl who wrote it, each as delightful as the other, each as full of affection, each with its sweetly turned thought and expression. Mama and I first read them separately, then we read them out loud to each other, that we might all four be together in the love which we must now send each other by letter. Since then we have taken turns keeping the letters to enjoy as the moments permit, for we are both very busy, each in his own room. I have had the letters of both overnight. It is now four o'clock in the morning, and I have just finished reading them for the fifth time, to extract from them all the precious love which they express and which I may read between the lines. Janet's " You take such pleasure in what we do. I am sure we take as much pleasure in what you do," is the very essence of this family's happiness. Ruth's picture of mama on her flying skis so gently turned into her " milder picture " of sweet concern that she does not hurt herself, is the very essence of our joint affection for little mama. . . .

To his Mother from W. C. S.   [January 26, 1917

. . . We are in the midst of the most intense excitement. I wrote you that the Swiss feared an invasion by Germany. This has grown in intensity. Half the Swiss army is massed on the German frontier, and the other half is holding itself in readiness for a moment's notice. Germany has cut off all communication with Switzerland, and is known to be massing troops near the Swiss border. After this, will any crime be left for Germany to commit! After Wilson has declared America's interest in liberty and the freedom of small nations, can he stand aloof, if Switzerland is invaded — Switzerland, like Belgium, a state of guaranteed neutrality, of guaranteed freedom? What maudlin imbecility could lead a man who had ignored the invasion of Belgium to talk about sharing, and to think about trading in guarantees of immunity! Had America come in and fought like England for Belgium for the guarantees that already existed, it would be a different thing. But what good are guarantees if the guarantors will not enforce them? Why in Heaven's name not at least let the others alone while they are doing their duty! Oh, Lord!

From Janet Sabine to her Parents [*Paris, January* 28, 1917

. . . This letter is rather complicated to write, so I am afraid you will have to be patient. I shall try to go to the point. Algebra is the question. We have finished equations, and have begun problems. Everything has gone on wheels up to now. The 8th grade have all had more Arithmetic than I have; they have had problems on the composition of metals. I think I have translated correctly, and I don't know the first word of them and can't follow when they explain on the blackboard, and other things, and I am afraid I will fall back farther and farther. I tried doing my best yesterday, but you will see by my mark it isn't very good. I had nine points out of twenty — not even the half! I have spoken to Mlle. Morel about it, and she will try to speak to one of my teachers about it. You know you said to stop it if Mlle. Morel thought best, and we are acting accordingly. Does this meet with approval? I have gotten to a point in the Algebra where it will be easy to stop. . . .

To his Children from W. C. S. [*Leysin, February* 3, 1917

. . . Janet, you and Mlle. Morel are to decide in regard to Algebra and do exactly what you think best. It is a great comfort to be able to rely so implicitly as we can on your judgment. Whether you drop the Algebra or continue it, we shall be absolutely serene in our confidence that you have done the right thing.

Ruth, dear, the Trocadéro is one of the famously bad buildings acoustically. It is supposed to have been once corrected. I have long been wanting just such an opportunity as you had, and I am more than glad to get your unbiased judgment of the auditorium, and your very vivid description of the phenomenon. If another occasion presents itself you must take me, and we shall sit as nearly as possible in the same part of the hall. . . .

From Janet Sabine to her Parents   [*Paris, February* 4, 1917

Today is Sunday, and I mean this to be a loving-time letter. I do a lot of thinking these days. I think I have grown years. Outside I am the same, and you will find me the same except in my way of thinking. We are not very talkative, except for Ruth, who keeps from thinking the way I do. All I do now is to listen, see, and watch every one, to study and do filet, which is only another way to think with my hands going. I begin to realize what war means, just a speck of a taste, but enough to make me feel for others more than I ever did before. Paris is opening my eyes to a lot of things, and I am being taught the best lesson of the world here. You may think from this letter that I am lonely. I am, but my mind has for the first time really begun to work, which makes me forget a little that I can't tell you all this on a father's knee or a mother's lap. . . .

To his Mother from W. C. S.   [*Leysin, February* 8, 1917

The glorious news has come that America is going to range itself on the side of liberty and civilization, and help overthrow the reign of barbarism with which the world was threatened. At last I am not ashamed! . . .

To Ruth from W. C. S.   [*Leysin, February* 14, 1917

This is a love-letter just to you alone — a Valentine, if you wish, but really more, very much more than that — an old-fashioned, homely love-letter, just a longing to gather you up in my arms and hold you close, close, close to my breast. My little girl — just to look down into your eyes, and back over the past ten years, and live over again each moment of the continual happiness you have given us.

Your letters, Ruth, have given us the greatest pleasure, every letter, and the very sweet story of The Fire Dream. We are distressed that you have not received an acknowledgment of it. Both mama and I thought we had written to you about it. Mama translated it into French as one of her lessons, and mama's teacher took it and read a translation of it, not mama's but one made by her sister, to her little children in the school at the foot of the hill. We are very, very sorry if we have been negligent.

Less than two weeks now, twelve days only, and we shall have you. We have just got word from Berne that our berths have been reserved for us on the evening of the twenty-fourth, so we shall now almost certainly arrive Sunday morning, the twenty-fifth.

To his Sister from W. C. S.   [*Berne, February 22*, 1917

, . . We are now here in Berne, getting our passports viséd, and making other preparations for our return to Paris and the little girls.

Of the recent developments I don't know which has given me the more satisfaction, the firmness which President Wilson has shown or the changed attitude of such papers as the " Vaterland " and the " Stadts Zeitung." It is splendid to see a United America on an American issue. It has made a profound impression throughout Europe. The last two months has seen the balance gradually equalize and then swing down on the opposite side, and now there is no longer any doubt as to the ultimate issue. After the War there will be an even greater call for help than before the War closes, for conditions will be at their worst, and it will take months to restore even a fraction of normal. There will then be both need and opportunity. I wish I could stay over here to help. The most I can do is to help prepare. . . .

To his Mother from W. C. S.   [*Paris, March* 30, 1917

. . . What a great kaleidescope we are tumbling around in. Just think, how the whole situation has changed since December! Oh! it is tremendous — simply tremendous. I can't write! But I can think, and think *with* you, even without a word between us. The initiative lost to Germany — its rejected offer of a victor's terms, its submarine madness, inflicted by the Gods, who would destroy it; its retreat — its isolated despotism. It only remains for Germany, like the tarantula within a circle of fire, to rush from side to side to pierce its burning barrier of shame, and then retreat to the centre and sting itself to death with its own fatal poison — with which it has threatened the world.

Oh, mother, this is a wonderful year in the world's history!

Sabine reached Paris only a few days before his postponed lectures at the Sorbonne were to be given. He felt his health to be restored, and he approached this return to work with an eagerness which evidenced a consciousness that these lectures, important as they were, formed only a stepping-stone to a greater work. The war bacillus was in Sabine's blood. New applications of the Science of Sound were essential in promoting the advantages of the Allied Forces. Who could devise the means so well as he!

SABINE's postponed Sorbonne Lectures, on the general subject of " Architectural Acoustics," began late in February, 1917, and ran into May. These presented in condensed form the mature results of his years of study and experimentation, and were illustrated with lantern slides. The subject matter of these lectures has been outlined in earlier chapters of this volume, except the following paragraphs, selected by his old pupil, Dr. Theodore Lyman, for publication in the " Collected Papers." These are given as illustrative of what Sabine himself felt was his contribution to Acoustics as an exact science — the consideration of " boundary conditions ":

" In no other domain have physicists disregarded the conditions introduced by the surrounding materials, but in Acoustics these do not seem to have received the least attention. If measurements are made in the open air, over a lawn, as was done by Lord Rayleigh in certain experiments, is due consideration given to the fact that the surface has an absorbing power for sound of from 40 to 60 per cent? Or, if inside a building, as in Wien's similar experiments, is allowance made for the fact that the walls reflect from 93 to 98 per cent of the sound? We need not be surprised if the results of such experiments differ from one another by a factor of more than a hundred.

" It would be no more absurd to carry out photometric measurements in a room where the walls, ceiling, and even the floor and tables consisted of highly polished mirrors, than to make measurements on the intensity, or on the quan-

titative analysis, of sound under the conditions in which
such experiments have almost invariably been executed. It
is not astonishing that we have been discouraged by the results, and that we may have despaired of seeing Acoustics
occupy the position to which it rightly belongs among the
exact sciences.

" The length of the waves of light is so small compared
with the dimensions of a photometer that we do not need to
concern ourselves with the phenomena of interference while
measuring the intensity of light. In the case of sound, however, it must be a quite different matter.

" In order to show this in a definite manner, I have measured the intensity of the sound in all parts of a certain laboratory room. For simplicity, a symmetrical room was selected, and the source, giving a very pure tone, was placed
in the centre. It was found that, near the source, even at the
source itself, the intensity was in reality less than at a distance of five feet from the source. And yet the clever experi-
menter Wien, and the no less skilful psychologists Wundt
and Münsterberg, have assumed under similar conditions
the law of variation of intensity with the inverse square of
the distance. It makes one wonder how they were able to
draw any conclusions from their measurements." [1]

Sabine's lectures at the Sorbonne started off with an attendance of twenty, an unusually large number in war-time,
and rose later to fifty — mainly professors and architects,
and students from the École des Beaux Arts. In addition to
the lectures, he was asked to speak before the Physical Society, and later before that most distinguished of bodies, the
French Academy of Science. He also gave a public lecture

---

[1] Sabine always insisted that an investigator should not permit himself to have
preconceived opinions, but rather should be led step by step to his final conclusions.
His great criticism of certain experimentors was that they did not take all things into
consideration, that they started out with something they wished to prove, and made
tests rather than investigations. This method, Sabine contended, made it obvious that
much of their work would have to be done over.

before the Society of Architects, and, subsequently, lectures before the architects alone. " I could not ask for a better reception than I am receiving," he wrote home. Just as his students at Harvard used to gather around him after his lectures, so did the French architects enthusiastically remain after the conclusion of the hour, to grasp his hand and to seek answers to specific questions. So successful were the lectures that the University of Paris invited Sabine to make his course an annual event, and the French Government asked him to train their architects so that in rebuilding the audience halls in the devastated areas proper acoustical conditions might be ensured. In 1922, when his daughter Janet offered herself for examination at the Sorbonne later than the announced date for enrolment, the authorities waived the technical *clôture* upon learning her identity, saying, " Is she not one of the family here? "

But, important as these lectures were, and in spite of the recognition they received, Sabine could not avoid feeling a sense of incongruity in lecturing or listening to lectures at a time when every one's thoughts were centered on the world cataclysm. " Lecturing at the Sorbonne," he wrote his Harvard colleague, Professor Edwin H. Hall, " while the world is being transformed into a totally different institution, and life, such as is left of it, is sobered for years to come, seems a thing apart. . . . The Society of Architects was so kind as to give me a medal [2] as a souvenir of my lecture — they find time and the heart to do things nicely in France, and kindly, even in the midst of death."

Opportunity for action was not long denied!

To Clifford M. Swan from W. C. S.   [*Paris, May* 8, 1917

I start tomorrow morning for the Front with the American Scientific Commission. They have asked me to work with them, as have also some of the French scientists engaged

[2] This medal was presented by Mrs. Sabine to Harvard University.

on war problems. Of course I am glad to do all I can. I was anxious to do what I could before America entered the War. I am more anxious now. My lectures are getting into such shape that I think I can do so very shortly, though just at the present moment I am pretty deeply involved.

The invitation Sabine refers to came from the French Government as a result of his supreme mastery of problems of Sound as shown in his Sorbonne Lectures; and the real purpose of the invitation, which Sabine was not at that time at liberty to explain, was to examine and report on the delicate telephonic and sound-testing instruments in use in the French army and navy. Out of this experience came his own invention of a highly successful sound-device for locating artillery, which was used to a large extent by the Allied Armies. The following letter tells as much of this experience as could pass the censor:

To Jessie and Emily Peirce from W. C. S.
                    [*Châlons sur Marne, May* 14, 1917
I have just had a most interesting trip along the whole Front from Reims to Verdun, and have seen everything, and have received courtesies and attentions beyond all possible expectation — beyond all reason. Now I am back at the headquarters of the Armies of the Centre.

Châlons, which was a great garrison and training town before the War, is of even more importance now as the centre of front from Reims to Verdun. For four days, with it as our centre, I was taken all over the whole of this portion of the Front, and shown everything — every process of locating the enemy batteries; of map-making; of aeroplanes for observation, for bombardment, for photographing, for chase and battle; of camouflage or concealment; of wireless; of anti-aircraft batteries; anti-aircraft guns against a visiting German aeroplane; the beginning of the attack by the heaviest guns on the French Front of the Moronvilliers battle; a long-

range, general bombardment all my own on the top of Fort
Douaumont in front of Verdun. I had the pleasure of lunch-
ing with General Fayeul, and later dining with General
Antoine, who prepared and conducted the attack on Moronvilliers, and later moved to another section where he has for
the last few weeks been conducting the brilliant French advance in Flanders. But the most interesting day of all was in
the Verdun region.

On the way to Verdun we passed through the village of
Charles le Roi, where a Bavarian regiment, in their retreat
after the battle of the Marne, set the houses on fire and shot
all the inhabitants when they rushed out. Every house destroyed. At Verdun I lunched with the Commander in the
Citadel, and then was taken out to Fort Douaumont. No pen
of Dante, no pencil of Doré, can describe Fort Douaumont
and Fort Vaux and the region for miles around them: not a
vestige of a tree trunk, not a twig of a bush, not a blade of
grass. All blown to atoms, and, as far as the eye can reach,
one continuous stretch of shell-holes — the little town of
Fleury completely disappeared, not even the color of brick
left, churned so deep into the ground. Unexploded shells
and hand-grenades and bombs everywhere, so that we had to
pick our steps; rifle-cartridges, German, Austrian, French,
everywhere, empty *soixante quinze* and *sieben und siebsich*
shells (am almost thankful I have forgotten how *sieben* is
spelled!) ; arms shrieking out of the powdered ground, and
legs and skulls; and over all the odor of decaying flesh.

But Fort Douaumont! The climax of it all! One mass of
powder so that one could not tell where the earth stopped
and the cement and rock began! And to think of human beings defending it to the last! They were digging it out, its
underground passages and the space inside the ramparts,
if it could be called a space, constantly pouring lime as they
dug.

It had been a quiet day, and the Commander of the Fort

said I might go up on the rampart and look off toward the German lines and to the left to Dead Man's Hill. I had hardly been up there a moment, stooping low, when I saw an observation balloon on the horizon rise rapidly. I was mildly interested, but thought nothing of it, when suddenly I heard the whistle of a shell, and fell flat. The next instant the shell buried itself in the powder not fifteen feet from me, and exploded. Another shell followed almost instantly. I rolled down into the Fort, and the bombardment was over for the day.

With characteristic avoidance of the dramatic, Sabine omits certain details of deep personal significance. He had come to Fort Douaumont especially to test new and delicate instruments of sound-detection, which he believed were powerful enough to intercept messages from the German High Command — supposed to be beyond the possibility of interception. Taking advantage of the lull in the hostilities, as referred to in his letter, Sabine strolled out on the rampart, and but for the keenness of his hearing would undoubtedly have lost his life. As it was, his clothes were torn by the shrapnel, and small pieces had to be extracted from his face and hands. On re-entering the Fort, he was greeted by his excited assistant with a message, intercepted through his newly invented instrument, giving instructions to train a gun upon " a civilian, who had appeared upon the rampart." Until then Sabine had no idea that the Germans had already discovered his supreme usefulness to the Allies. Not many men, in the history of the War, were honored by an attack made especially to destroy a single individual.

To his Mother from W. C. S.   [*Paris, July* 24, 1917

I have just been asked to stay over here for the next five years, in charge of one of the sections of the Red Cross work [3]

---

[3] It was a great temptation for Sabine to accept an invitation to take charge of the relief work in the Near East. Constantinople had always been one of the places

— civilian relief, one of their most important sections. I am not able to accept. Please do not mention this outside the family. There is so much exploiting of oneself over here that I do not wish to join in it.

I think I wrote you that I was asked to sit with the Committee of the French Academy of Science Commission against the Submarine. I am also serving with the Information Department of the American Navy here in Paris. This keeps me busy from morning to night, and I shall stay over here until September.

To Jessie and Emily Peirce from W. C. S.
[Paris, August 15, 1917

I took another trip to the Front with Mr. Elkins, the American Ambassador to Constantinople, this time through the devastated region between St. Quentin and Compiègne. This was awful in a totally different way — the ruthless, the utterly needless destruction: churches, public buildings, houses, all destroyed at such a distance from the Front which they meant to defend that they could have been no possible value in a military way — the fruit trees all cut down, not because they could conceal the advancing French, but because they were fruit trees, and would take fifteen to twenty years to replace. All other trees were left standing.

To Professor Edwin H. Hall from W. C. S.
[Paris, August 15, 1917

The Lectures had hardly stopped when I was asked to help in the Information Bureau of the United States Navy here in Paris on the submarine question — a week later by the French *Bureau des Inventions* on submarine and aeroplane questions; I am also definitely on the staff of the Bureau of Research of the Air Service of the American Expeditionary Force — a long title; and I have just received a

---

he had longed to see; but, owing to limited finances and also to his feeling that he would have to extend his absence from the College too long, he declined the post.

request from the British Munitions Inventions Bureau to come over to England for consultation on some problems in Acoustics.

The few remaining weeks will be full ones. In two or three days I shall go to Toulon, the Mediterranean base of the French fleet, for some direct experience in the submarine problem — then to Italy and the Italian Front — back to Paris, and three days later to England — back to the English Front, then to the French Front; again back to Paris to report, and then home. This programme is sufficiently active.

In the Air Service I cannot say that I have become a pilot, but I have become a good passenger, and this, the pilots say, is a very good thing to have along. I can also ride in a Paris taxicab without the slightest anxiety, but the other day I was taken by an American officer in a little Ford machine, and my heart was in my mouth all the time!

No assignment could have been more welcome to Sabine than that of assistant to Colonel E. S. Gorrell, Assistant Chief of Staff, Air Service, A.E.F., as his superior at once placed him in touch with the Allied Armies. During this service, his sincerity and his ability to make direct and practical application of his scientific knowledge so won the confidence of those high in authority that he became an uncommissioned confidential liaison agent between three great nations in military matters of paramount importance:

From Colonel E. S. Gorrell

Near the first of August, 1917, at a time when I was in charge of the Technical Section of the Air Service, A.E.F., I was extremely pressed for the assistance of educated men to aid in intelligently deciding upon the many technical features which were constantly arising concerning our work. Professor Sabine was secured to assist me in this work. He had a brilliant mind, but knew nothing of the subject of

Aviation.[4] To educate him in this subject, I sent him throughout France, Italy, and England, to observe and to learn all that he could possibly digest concerning the technical features of an air service in time of war. This occupied the months of August and September. At this time we were sorely in need of personnel capable of handling technical questions concerning aeronautics. Because of Professor Sabine's world-wide reputation, excellent intellect, knowledge he had gained of Aviation, and prestige, I then sent him to America to see if he could not personally convince the United States as to our needs in personnel capable of handling technical questions pertaining to aeronautics.

Sabine refers to the scientific assistance he rendered to the *Bureau des Inventions* in Paris. Here he worked with Commander Jean Perrin on a signaling device which was to be used for sound-signaling to troops during airplane attacks. The invention was completed, but the development of wireless telephony rendered its use unnecessary. At Toulon, he made a test trip in one of the French submarines, discussing with the high authorities the problem of detecting enemy submarines at a distance. At Spezia he continued his experiments in sound-detection — this time in an Italian submarine; and, at the request of the Italian authorities, he also made ascents in Italian bombing-planes over the Austrian lines in the Trentino, successfully demonstrating in the northern Alps the apparatus he had devised for locating and photographing enemy hangars. His associates marveled at his fearlessness in walking out on the stringers of the airplane to take his photographs, little realizing that under ordinary conditions he was abnormally sensitive to dizziness and vertigo when at an elevation. One of these photographs disclosed thirty-two hitherto unlocated enemy hangers! In

---

[4] Sabine at that time probably knew more concerning the subject of Aviation than any other civilian in Europe. The fact that he made no claim to knowledge was typical. For his earlier experiences in American aviation, see page 199.

War Photograph Taken by Wallace Sabine

from an Italian bombing plane over the Trentino, in 1917, with his war-invented camera, disclosing 32 hitherto unknown enemy hangars

Rome he experimented with Colonel Brocca in his celebrated wind-tunnel work — an experience which was later to prove of great value to America when Sabine became adviser to the engineers at McCook Field, and they began their wind-tunnel work.

From Dr. Robert B. Osgood

I met Sabine by chance one morning in September, 1917, in the store of Roberts, the chemist, on the rue de la Paix. The Red Cross had been kind enough to put an automobile at my disposal in connection with certain visits I had to make as a member of the Committee which was engaged in writing and having published a manual of splints for the medical officers. Professor Sabine said he had a little free time, and accompanied me on my visits in the automobile. I learned that he was then acting as adviser to the French Bureau of Inventions.

In discussing the war situation in general, he spoke in a deprecating way concerning the success which they had had in coping with the German submarine menace as far as any completely successful way of tackling the submarines themselves. He admitted, however, that the menace seemed to be diminishing in seriousness for two reasons, one of which was that the allied tonnage was increasing at a faster rate than the destruction of allied tonnage by the submarines. He also said it was proving a great help in lessening the number of allied vessels being sunk by the submarines to be able to furnish each morning, to allied shipping, bulletins giving very accurate information concerning the number of German submarines in the docks undergoing repairs, or held in harbor for some other reason; and I think he said there were only two German submarines that day seeking to destroy allied shipping. It, therefore, made it possible for many more ships to move with comparative safety than if a larger number of submarines were seeking their prey.

I was greatly impressed by the calm, judicial manner in which he discussed these important war problems, and by the optimistic view which he took of the eventual outcome of the War. It was obvious, although of course, as always, he was modesty itself concerning his own work, and talked very little about it, that he was performing a priceless service to the French, and, therefore, to the Allied cause.

By this time Sabine's military reputation had crossed over to England:

From Captain A. V. Hill to W. C. S.
[Munitions Inventions Dept., London
I have asked my Department to invite you to come to England to the Department, and elsewhere, to see things here, to meet our people, and to discuss with them any and every matter in which you and we are interested. During your visit here, if you can come, I will do my best to be at your disposal to take you anywhere you like, and to see any one you like. I am much looking forward to doing so, and very much hope you will come. I am forwarding the official invitation.

If there is any difficulty about getting the necessary authority to visit England now, I hope you will let us know what is needed and we will get it; but I imagine the American Embassy, or the British Embassy, or the British Naval or Military Attaché, will take the official invitation as a sufficient authority, and allow you to have the necessary permission.

Mr. Horace Darwin is particularly anxious for you to come. I saw his nephew, Charles Darwin, the other day, working his sound-ranging section at . . . , which is a much battered part of our line. I think there is no doubt that our sound-ranging is far better than the French, and I am sure your people ought to know about it. I hope your visit to Toulon has been a success.

From Major W. H. D. Clark, Assistant Comptroller, to W. C. S.   [Ministry of Munitions, London 8 August, 1917

I am desired by the Comptroller of Munitions Inventions, who is away for a short time on leave, to write you with reference to information received from Captain Hill, one of his officers, who has just returned from Paris, to the effect that you are at present in Paris, and might be able to pay a visit to this country.

I am to state that, if you can find time to come over here, the Comptroller will be very pleased to welcome you at this Department, in order that he and some of his technical advisers may have the advantage of discussing with you the application of Acoustics and other scientific knowledge to the solution of military problems.

The first problem which England asked Sabine to solve was how to correct the English anti-aircraft guns, which, when fired at enemy planes crossing the English Channel, failed to accomplish their purpose, but inflicted terrific damage along the coast. Sabine found the internal mechanism set at too high a rate of speed, and that the powder, being pressed between the seams, did not explode during the projection, but only by concussion with the ground. He was at once made an official part of the Aviation Section of the Signal Corps, part of the time serving on the Bolling Aircraft Commission.

But Sabine's most far-reaching service to England and Italy was his success in arranging conferences between the aeronautical departments of the two countries which facilitated a direct exchange of technical information and a mutual understanding of the complicated military problems involved.

Early in August, 1917, Doctor Joseph Blake's hospital, of which Mrs. Sabine had been appointed one of the six assistant surgeons, was taken over for the American wounded, and this seemed an opportune time for her to return to her children, to give them a mother's oversight. They had kept well, and had progressed rapidly in their studies at the *Cour Fénélon* under the faithful care of their governess; but both parents realized the importance of getting them away from Paris and the emotional atmosphere in which they had been forced to live. Speaking French like natives, and being thrown with French children in school, these girls were taking the daily tragedies of their companions too deeply into their own tender hearts. " We no longer chatter to ourselves as we go to school," Janet told her mother with unconscious pathos; " we just listen."

So Mrs. Sabine and the children went to Paramé, a seaside resort near St. Malo, while Sabine moved into a small hotel near the Sorbonne, where he could continue his experiments on original mechanical devices, making use of the University laboratory. Here his earlier habit of night work stood him in good stead, for there seemed no end to the demands made by the three governments, requiring frequent consultation and constant correspondence. Sabine's refusal to wear the uniform of any country left him unhampered in dealing with all, and greatly increased the value of his work through the unifications along mechanical and scientific lines which inevitably resulted. " The task of the Allies would have been simplified," wrote Robert Woods Bliss, of the American Embassy in Paris, " with more men like Sabine to direct their cause."

To his Sister from W. C. S.   [*Paris, August* 4, 1917

Jennie and the children have just gone to the seashore near St. Malo for the month of August. They need the change and the rest greatly, all three. Jennie has been working hard. Ruth is not as strong as we should like to have her, and Janet has been studying hard right up to the end of

July. The children have had to do two years' work in one —
the courses in the French schools and the American schools
do not correspond, and the children do not want to fall back
a year in their school program at home. This has fallen especially hard on Janet, who has had to make up a whole year
of Latin — to say nothing of Kittredge's English Grammar,
five plays of Shakespeare, and twenty compositions. It has
been great fun doing the Latin with Janet. It has given me a
chance to teach Latin as I think it should be taught — Latin
as Latin, not as bad English — Latin untranslated, and
Latin grammar and Latin phrasing as an expression of Latin
thought, not English.[5] We have enjoyed it hugely together,
but the little girl is tired. Ruth, who has a natural gift for
languages, has been half listening, and it is surprising how
much she has gathered in.

By September, Sabine's thoughts turned again toward his
Harvard work, and he planned to return to Cambridge in
time to resume his college responsibilities:

To his Sister from W. C. S.   [*Paris, August 4, 1917*
We shall be back toward the end of September, sailing
from Bordeaux about the middle, or a little after the middle
of September. It will be good to be home, only it will be hard
to leave quiet France for the turmoil of America. In France
everybody is simply and earnestly doing his duty, be it at
the Front, at the rear, or in civil life. In America, as far as I
can make out from the papers, everybody is getting into
khaki and then walking on each other's heels or backing
onto each other's toes. This is inevitable, of course, in the
beginning; but France has found herself. There is no hysteria here, but such courage, such quiet, sublime courage!
I love France as I never thought I could love a people, for
loving France is loving a people.

---

[5] For Janet's version of this experience, see page 96.

To Jessie and Emily Peirce from W. C. S.

[Paris, August 15, 1917

Four weeks now and we shall be starting back. How glad I shall be to see you all, and how strange America, with big cars and its funny green money, will seem. The University will have changed, the boys gone. Many of them I have already seen over here. The Laboratory will be overflowing with a new type of student. Yet my friends, my tried friends, will most of them still be there, and this is what makes home and country.

To his Mother from W. C. S.   *[Paris, September* 2, 1917

This summer has been wonderful. It *is* a pleasure to be wanted by the French, British, and Italian Governments as well as by our own. It *is* a pleasure to be of service. And along with it have come some wonderfully interesting experiences. I was in the last great Italian offensive on the Isonzo — the Carso — with the shells flying overhead in both directions. In a great bombarding aeroplane I was down over the Adriatic and Trieste, and later up over and into the Alps. Tomorrow I go out over the Mediterranean in a dirigible, Tuesday from Genoa in a hydro-aeroplane, and Wednesday from Toulon in a submarine. Everything has been opened to me.

But those were days when planning to leave France and actually getting away were entirely different stories. Passage was engaged for the family, and Mrs. Sabine left Paramé with the children, making a leisurely return to Paris in order to visit historical places of interest on the way. Instead of finding her husband awaiting her, as she had expected, she was advised that he had been hurriedly summoned to Italy for consultation. Then came the news that the steamer they planned to take would be held up for five days, to secure bigger guns as protection against submarines. Sabine joined his family to meet this date, but the sailing was further delayed, which enabled him to comply with an urgent appeal from the British Munitions Department to go to London. On his return to Paris, still another postponement was announced. Mrs. Sabine begged him to take advantage of this unexpected respite and secure a few days' relaxation, but, in spite of his exhausted condition, nothing could deter him from using this opportunity to have a final conference with the authorities at the " American Front." He affectionately reassured his wife, and departed for that carefully concealed objective, saying that he would surely rejoin her in time for the sailing.

The day before the final date arrived, with no signs of a returning husband. Mrs. Sabine packed whatever he had left in her hotel, but she knew that there was other clothing and a mass of important papers still stored in the room he had occupied near the Sorbonne. Noon came, and notice was officially served that no luggage would be received for the steamer after three o'clock that afternoon. Mrs. Sabine asked governmental assistance, and, in view of her husband's official position, was granted an extension until seven o'clock. The family trunks were delivered at the station at the last moment, still with no news of Sabine's whereabouts, and her anxiety was further increased by the delivery to her of official papers for her husband to take to Washington, which she was warned to guard carefully, as two attempts had already been made by German spies to secure them!

To connect with the steamer train, it was necessary to leave the hotel at seven o'clock the next morning. Mrs. Sabine retired at ten o'clock. At midnight a feeble knock on her door roused her, and her husband entered the room, more dead than alive. For eight hours he had been traveling in a dilapidated Ford car, bending forward most of the time to hold a hastily improvised contrivance to keep in place the motor, which had broken away from one of its rear supports. Stopping only long enough to exchange facts, Sabine rushed off to the little hotel near the Sorbonne, four miles away. Not knowing the urgency of time, he had not asked Colonel Bolling (a month later killed at the Front), who had brought him in, to wait for him. There was no taxi to be had, so he walked the entire distance. During the hours between that time and seven o'clock, when the train left, Sabine gathered together such papers and small things as he could carry with him, leaving the rest behind, and met his family at the railroad station.

Thus Sabine arrived in Bordeaux after seventeen months' service to the Allied cause, during which period, as Colonel A. D. Butterfield said, " he was the eyes and ears of the Technical Section of the Air Service." Thus did the man so ill before he left America that he fainted on the street, so nervously broken down from overwork with the Rockefeller War Relief Commission that only Nature's miracle saved him from death, show his utter disregard for personal safety in the face of plainly indicated danger signals.

" C'est la guerre! " He knew what he was doing, and he gloried in the opportunity for service. The greater the danger, the greater the service. If it meant the supreme sacrifice, he would have argued that other men had made it, and he was now a soldier, whose life belonged to his country. It was this exaltation which sustained him in the work he had done and in the valiant service he was yet to render. For when he returned to America that fall of 1917, although he would never have admitted it, Sabine knew that he knew more about the varied phases of warfare in the air than any other man.

XV. THE AMERICAN WAR DEPARTMENT DISCOVERS
SABINE · 1917–1918

S<small>ABINE</small>'s remarkable power of recuperation was a liability
as well as an asset, for it encouraged him to treat lightly the
many warnings of danger Nature continued to give him.
The joy of being again united with his family, and the complete relaxation on board ship, restored his depleted energy
and camouflaged the insidious disease which was making
steady headway. By the time New York was reached, Sabine's strength had returned with his enthusiasm, and he was
eager to put himself in contact with Washington.

On landing, Sabine's first indulgence was an ice-cream
soda, in which frivolity his family joined to celebrate the
home-coming! Then he placed them on board a train for
Boston; put himself in touch with the Johns-Manville Company to answer certain pressing questions in connection
with his acoustical affairs, the conduct of which had been
left in Mr. Swan's hands during his long absence; reported
for duty at Harvard the next morning, and then, the same
night, went on to Washington to deliver the official papers
entrusted to him by the Allied Governments, and to make
a first-hand report of conditions with which he had become
familiar. His reputation had preceded him, and he received
a prompt hearing from the American authorities. They saw
the great value of the information that he had brought
home, and at once referred him to the military department
having to do with airplane production and use. The following comment, made by the Chief of the Equipment Division

of the Aviation Section of the Signal Corps, gives a full history of Sabine's contact at Washington:

From Colonel Edward A. Deeds, A. S. A.

Wallace C. Sabine first became known personally to me on his return from overseas in the fall of 1917. I had known him previously by reputation. He had been abroad for one and a half years; was in close contact with the scientific development in connection with the War, especially as it related to aircraft, and had been actually at the Front. He was under shell fire, having on one occasion at least been covered with dirt thrown by a bursting shell. He saw the work of the bombing planes in Italy. He brought back many airplane photographs of the Italian Front. He was in great sympathy with the work of the Italians. The information he brought was accurate and trustworthy because it was not a first impression, he having been overseas long enough to gain the confidence of the scientific departments of our Allied Armies, and would get facts. His length of service also had given him a perspective which few men had.

During my first conference with him I was so impressed that I immediately made him one of my staff, giving him a desk in an adjoining office. All cablegrams regarding apparatus passed over his desk. He kept our Allies informed of our progress, and in turn interpreted their development to us. His judgment was considered so good that, within a few months, he was made the final authority to select, from the samples sent from overseas, instruments to be put in production — perhaps the most notable being the Wimporis Bomb Sight.

He possessed a wonderful power of analysis, a full portion of common sense, and an unusual knowledge of many broad fields of science. He possessed the rare combination seldom found in men — that of a highly technical knowledge combined with a sense of the practical. His logical thinking and clear expression gained for him the respect of all. His service was most valuable to the nation, and, because of his great unselfishness and self-effacement, will never be fully known and appreciated except by those who were immediately associated with him.

A further expression on the nature and value of Sabine's early work at Washington is made by the Chief of Staff to the various Directors of Aircraft Production:

From L. S. Horner
I was probably thrown in closer contact with Mr. Sabine than any other man in the Bureau. I became exceedingly fond of him, and did everything I could to have the Bureau take advantage of his splendid ability in the difficult problems which faced us. He was of the greatest value in assisting us in selecting types of apparatus which would best fill the exacting requirements of the Service, and we were exceedingly fortunate in the fact that he had spent many months abroad in active contact with the early development, and assisted us in differentiating the good from the bad, on the many recommendations which came to us from the Front. I know of no case where his recommendations did not prove to be the best for the Service, and we were exceedingly fortunate, towards the end, in getting him to accept entire charge of sifting and distributing the confidential, technical information which came to our Bureau from many sources, and sending it to those particularly interested.

Sabine was engaged in this work until after the separation of the Air Service from the Signal Corps in the spring of 1918, when, on June 21, John D. Ryan appointed him Director of the newly created Department of Technical Information in the Bureau of Aircraft Production. Sabine's work in his new position is given in detail in the official announcement of the establishment of this new Department:

1. Securing, collating, and distributing technical data received from abroad from the following sources:

(a) British Ministry of War and Munitions. The policy for transmittal of technical data between Great Britain and the United States has been outlined by Sabine, and an agreement drawn up between him and Sir Henry Fowler, of the Special British Aviation Mission.

(b) British, French, and Italian War and Aviation Missions.

(c) Scientific attachés accredited to the American Embassies in London, Paris, and Rome, by the National Research Council, Research Information Service.

(d) Special Mission headed by Henry Lockhart, Jr., sent by the Bureau of Aircraft Production, to make a personal survey of the situation in aviation matters abroad.

2. Coöperating closely with the Naval Aviation Information, from which it received and to whom it furnished important information.

3. Working jointly with the National Advisory Committee for Aeronautics.

The work of this Department was of the greatest importance, and the data received of the most confidential nature. Owing to the fact that technical information changed so rapidly, it was vital that it be kept up to date in order not to distribute data that would prove misleading.

In his official capacity in Washington, Sabine exercised the same ability, shown in so marked a degree in his administration of the Harvard Graduate School, of surrounding himself with able colleagues. Jay Downer, Engineer of the Bronx Parkway Commission, records the story of their association and his personal impressions:

From Jay Downer

 . . . I was very closely associated with Mr. Sabine from July, 1918, until after the signing of the Armistice, in connection with his work in the Air Service at Washington. Mr. Sabine had asked Mr. Alfred D. Flynn, Secretary, Engineering Council, to suggest some one to act as the Executive Officer of the Department of Technical Information, which he had been requested to organize in the Bureau of Aircraft Production. Mr. Flynn knew that I was available for war service, and suggested that I meet Mr. Sabine in Washington and discuss the proposed work with him. I wrote Mr. Sabine that I would come to Washington at his convenience, and he promptly called me on the long distance 'phone and asked me to breakfast with him at the Capitol Park Hotel.

At that time he explained the proposed work and the entire situation to me very carefully. During our conversation I asked him why he had not been given a commission as Colonel. He replied, " There are only two reasons that I know of why I should be a Colonel." I asked, " What are they? " He answered, " One is my daughter twelve years old; the other my daughter fifteen years old. I know of no other good reason why I should be a Colonel! "

As Director of the Department of Technical Information in the Bureau of Aircraft Production, Mr. Sabine set about to organize a Department which would provide the latest information about flying machines and accessories in this country and with the Allies. It was his plan to have a branch in Paris, one in London, and one at Turin, Italy, and to have representatives at the principal manufacturing points in this country. Information as to progress made by all of the Allies, and also information obtained as to development of enemy planes, was to be promptly forwarded to this country by special courier, compared, analyzed, digested, and made available for those who were charged with the responsibility of developing an air program and providing equipment in this country.

Before an actual organization on these broad lines had been built up, Mr. Sabine endeavored to effect an agreement with the Division of Military Aeronautics whereby one department of information could serve both the Bureau of Aircraft Production, the producing end of the Service, and the Division of Military Aeronautics, the operating end. His familiarity with conditions in Europe among the Allies, and on the various fighting Fronts, persuaded him to avoid, if at all possible, duplicating the work of another department, as was so commonly done during that stage of the War. Mr. Sabine told me that he knew personally of eight commissions, or special officers, who had been sent to Europe separately for the sole purpose of investigating bomb sights. These commissions, or groups of officers, unknown to each other, were roaming around France and Italy without direction, not knowing where to go, scarcely having any idea, themselves, of the instruments as to which they were seeking further information, and accomplishing little except to irritate and annoy the American and Allied officers in France, who were engaged in the actual business of fighting.

An agreement was effected with the officers in charge of information in the Division of Military Aeronautics, but subsequently the regular army officer of Military Aeronautics withdrew his consent to joining the Department, and started to build up an unwieldy organization, with complicated files, and with a laborious method of securing information, which, when received, would perhaps be too much out of date for the use of designing engineers.

I was very much impressed with Mr. Sabine's patience in handling this difficult situation. On several occasions I urged him to use the authority which had been given him, and proceed to organize along the lines which he had laid down. He declined to do this until the situation had been cleared up, for the reason that Military Aeronautics were developing along much the same lines, and he would not be a party to such a duplication of effort. His position was that if Military Aeronautics got the information, he would be well satisfied. He had no personal pride in the matter, and his only concern was for the good of the Service.

What he did, then, was to arrange quietly, through his personal acquaintances and friends among the Allies and in the A.E.F., to secure the latest information from all the Fronts, and regarding airplane development in England, France, and Italy. It was because of his extensive acquaintance among English, French, and Italian officers, and with nearly all of the leaders in the American Air Service, that practically all information of value was sent to him and distributed by him before it was received or heard of by the officers in Military Aeronautics, who had organized an exclusive service at very great expense to the Government. Copies of all plans, publications, and charts received by Mr. Sabine were invariably supplied to the Division of Military Aeronautics, and he insisted upon the fullest coöperation with them, to the end that every officer in the Air Service should have the information which he needed insofar as he was able to get it to him. This policy was carried out with the greatest tact and courtesy, with the net result that the purposes for which his Department had been created were fulfilled, but in a quiet way, by means of a small organization, and interference with, or duplication of the work of the Division of Military Aeronautics was avoided.

The work with Mr. Sabine was unusually interesting, owing to the large number of important matters which came before him which were not strictly related to the Department which he had organized. He had previously been appointed by the President as a member of the National Advisory Council on Aeronautics, and he was frequently asked to serve on important committees related to the Air Service. Mr. Sabine was generally considered as one of the best authorities on aero-dynamics, and he was consulted upon many questions involving abstruse problems, varied in character. It was astonishing how quickly and accurately he could analyze problems which, to the rest of us, were almost unsolvable. I can say, without hesitation, that he was one of the most respected and personally popular of all the men in the Air Service. His unfailing courtesy and kindness were appreciated by all, and, even under the greatest pressure of work, his temper was always genial. He eventually consented to divide his time between Washington and Dayton, where he was consulted as to specifications governing airplane construction.

From the time that I joined Mr. Sabine's Department in Washington until my family came down, late in September, he and I both lived at the Capitol Park Hotel, and had many of our meals together. Occasionally I used to telephone him late in the evening about some matter, and found that he was enjoying himself working over some difficult problem, in which he seemed to find real recreation. I considered it a privilege to be so closely associated with Mr. Sabine, for I have known few men possessed with such genial temper, such keen sense of humor, and such delightful old-fashioned courtesy.

Another of his co-workers, who served under him in the Department of Technical Information, refers to his attitude toward his subordinates and toward those outside his Department:

From Adelaide Hart

His unfailing kindness, courtesy, and sense of humor made work with him a pleasure. All through the Bureau was felt the same sentiment of regard and affection. In an atmosphere so unlike his college world, where of course he would be loved, to have won the love and esteem of every one is a proof of his charming personality.

His knowledge of French and Italian, and his associations abroad, enabled him to establish most excellent relations with the foreign missions sent to this country. The personal element and individuality in all his dealings with these foreign representatives, the language used in his correspondence, couched always in terms that they were accustomed to, all tended toward cordial relations. In the busy American atmosphere it was rare to encounter this old-world courtesy and polish, and it was appreciated.

His advice was sought in all directions, not only as to information on technical and scientific subjects, but also in regard to questions of policy, organization, coördination, etc., in other departments. Mr. Potter, Mr. Kellogg, Lieutenant Colonel Horner, and other executives, frequently requested his advice, and his recommendations on important matters bore weight.

Two personal friends of Sabine's saw him in action at Washington during that trying summer.

From Dr. H. S. Christian

. . . In an entirely different setting I see him again. This time in Washington, on a hot morning in the summer of 1918. I had arrived on the Federal Express, and gone to a hotel near the station for breakfast. Soon Sabine came in the dining room, looking a trifle sallow, distinctly worn, with a slight flush on each cheek. In a few minutes' conversation I had, came the advice from him that, if I were to do government work, it would be wise to keep out of uniform if possible, for he had found that, not being in uniform, he was in a position to do greatly more for his country. Then I did not know quite fully under what a handicap of poor health he had been working both hard and effectively, but I did appreciate how characteristic of Sabine was that remark; it meant his whole soul was in the work, and he cared not one whit for the outward trappings and insignia of office. His reward was in the knowledge of what he did, and he cared not for things that to others would mark him as a government worker.

From Eliot Wadsworth

In the first trying summer of great heat and great confusion, Sabine followed his line of service without deviation. We had occasional conferences about certain details of his work, in which he was of absolute single purpose — namely, to get results. Of his work abroad, of the risks he had taken in many expeditions in the air, and of his terrible illness, it was hard to get any word. That was all passed and not worth discussion. What he had to do was to get on with the immediate problems in hand. It was quite evident, in our last few meetings, that he was not at all well, and was overworking. That this was never mentioned and no complaint made, was typical of the man. Any suggestions of letting up and saving himself met with a silence and slightly disdainful smile, as much as to say, " That is not the part for a man to play in war times."

A prominent member of the Air Service remarked of Sabine, " He is the one man in the service who claims to know least, and who actually knows most about all phases of aircraft problems."

In September, 1918, in addition to his other work, Sabine was appointed by President Wilson a member of the National Advisory Committee for Aeronautics. The activities and functions of this new board are set forth in a statement issued in December, 1918, by C. D. Walcott, Chairman of its Executive Committee:

National Advisory Committee for Aeronautics

The functions of the National Advisory Committee for Aeronautics, as defined by Act of Congress, are " to supervise and direct the scientific study of the problems of flight, with a view to their practical solution, and to determine the problems which should be experimentally attacked, and to discuss their solution and their application to practical questions.

In carrying into effect these purposes, the Committee has regarded it as its duty to take active part in:

(a) Investigations in the Science of Aeronautics.

(b) The encouragement of research work in aeronautics at various universities and schools of technology.

(c) Stimulation of manufacturers and individuals to bring about the greatest possible development of aeronautics for all purposes, among other means by securing close coöperation between military authorities and manufacturers.

(d) The diffusion of knowledge and technical data concerning aeronautics, pure and applied.

(e) Initiation of suggestions regarding policy.

The program for the future is based largely upon the experience of the past four years, and may be discussed under the heads given above.

(a) *Scientific Investigations.* — The need of these is obvious, but a few special illustrations may be noted:

(1) Laws governing propeller design.

(2) Proper standards of performance of airplane instruments.

(3) Proper tests of airplane performance.
Continuous progress in design of airplanes and airplane accessories, progress which is required for military and commercial reasons, can be secured only by an active series of scientific investigations. Many of these may be performed in the existing military or civil laboratories of the country, but others require special installations such as the Committee expects to have.

(b) *Educational Work.* — The Committee has made itself familiar with the facilities and courses of instruction for aeronautics in various educational institutions, and it is its intention to stimulate a wider interest in this throughout all American universities. It should be possible to outline suitable courses, and to arrange for coöperation between the institutions and manufacturers, so that the students can have practical experience also. This development of aeronautical engineers is of the utmost importance.

(c) *Commercial Development.* — The Committee has endeavored to stimulate manufacturers to make use of the scientific and technical knowledge available, and in this way to contribute to the development of aeronautics, which is one of its most important duties.

The Committee proposes to formulate from time to time designs for new types of airplanes, and call the attention of manufacturers of aircraft and aircraft appliances to them.

(d) *Information Section.* — The Committee is a medium by which scientific and technical data are distributed among the military authorities, the various government laboratories and manufactories concerned. It has collected as complete a set of pamphlets, reports, etc., as possible from England, France, and Italy, and has made arrangements by which these may be added to. The library of the Committee should be an official depository of aeronautical papers of a scientific or experimental character, and the proper distribution of this material in response to outside inquiries should be increased.

(e) The Committee may report directly to the President upon all questions pertaining to Aeronautics and may suggest to the President of the United States or to the Secretaries of the various government departments important matters or problems that in the judgment of the Committee require their consideration.

During the winter of 1917–1918, Sabine found it necessary to make frequent official trips from Washington to the Wright Flying Field, in Dayton, Ohio, in connection with experiments on airplanes and aircraft equipment, occasionally stopping off at Columbus, Ohio, to visit his sister, Mrs. Siebert. After one of these experiences he wrote his mother in Cambridge: " Columbus seems more like home — change how it will. It was there that you made all the sacrifices that carried us through not a short, but a long, long period of years, and finally put us in the positions we are in."

In all this record of active war service at Washington, no mention has been made of the fact that, although his manifold responsibilities would seem far too heavy for one man to carry, Sabine steadfastly refused to give up his Harvard work, even during this emergency period. The only concession he asked was that his students adapt their hours to his necessities, and their cheerful acquiescence made it possible for him to condense a week of academic work into two days. He would arrive in Cambridge from Washington at eight o'clock on Tuesday morning, devoting all the time between then and the midnight train on Thursday to intensive collaboration with his classes. He even added a course on Aviation Ballistics, which he gave in the School of Aviation for new draftees.

The establishment of this course on Ballistics is an interesting example of Sabine's personality. Such a course primarily assumes knowledge on the part of the student of Advanced Mathematics. These draftees were scarcely familiar with even Elementary Mathematics, and there was no possibility of their acquiring it. Yet they needed some scientific knowledge regarding the effect of the density and the piling up of the atmosphere in front of a shell, or the flight of a shell after it leaves the muzzle of the gun, in order to make them efficient.

Sabine was convinced that such a course could be given, taking into account the limitations of the students, and he enlisted the assistance of a colleague:

From Professor William F. Osgood

Sabine's idea was to give these men knowledge of what lay behind the scientific formulas. Frankly, I didn't think this could be done with students who lacked a mathematical background. Except for the high regard I held for Sabine's ability to do constructive work, I should have flatly declined his request to coöperate with him. I have never known just how much I accomplished with my half of the course, but Sabine was convinced that the experiment was well worth while.

From Miss Macdonald, Secretary to John Goddard Hart

Do you remember, during those frightful days of 1918, when the S.A.T.C. was coming into being, how Professor Sabine went through the line, stretching from University 20 to Harvard Hall, sorting out those who had no right to be there? I have never forgotten his great desire to help us when he himself was in doubtful physical condition, and was also engaged in such important war work.

His family saw Sabine but twice during that summer, even during his weekly visits to Cambridge, for he slept in a hammock at the Laboratory. President Lowell finally persuaded him to engage a permanent room in Washington to prevent the extra strain of going to Baltimore to sleep during the hectic, crowded conditions in the Washington hotels.

Neither family nor friends could influence him to respect the increasing evidence of the alarming return of his kidney trouble, and to submit himself for the surgical operation. " Not while the War is on and other lives are in danger," was his stubborn response. Only one war demand did he refuse, and that only because he considered the alternative more important. A plan was considered of sending him back to France to become the head of a bureau of technical information, which should serve as a clearing house for the aeronautical service of the United States and of the associated governments; but he had resumed his duties at Harvard in a Department where all his younger colleagues were in governmental service. He therefore felt it necessary to remain at his post, continuing and combining his teaching at Cambridge and his duties as general adviser, information expert, and adjuster of personal relations in Washington until the Armistice, on November 11, 1918, relieved him of a part of the necessity.

By November 30, 1918, Sabine had completed his work at Washington, and on that date he sent in his formal resignation, which the Secretary of War accepted:

From Newton D. Baker, Secretary of War

I have the honor to acknowledge receipt of your letter of November 30, 1918, tendering your resignation as one of the representatives of the War Department on the National Advisory Committee for Aeronautics. In view of the fact that your official relations with the Bureau of Aircraft Production have been terminated, I regret there is no other course but to accept your resignation as a member of that Committee.

I desire to express to you the official thanks of the Nation, and particularly of the War Department, for the very valuable services which you have, in time of need, rendered with gratifying zeal and patriotism.

At the time of his resignation, Sabine was Editor-in-Chief of the Specification Section of the Experimental Engineering Department. His important duties here charged him with the responsibility of recording all development of engineering work in the Bureau of Aircraft Production. He was further required to secure the same data in practical form for the confidential information of officers and engineers, both here and overseas.

Sabine's last official act in his relation with Washington is described by a fellow-member of the Committee:

From Captain Adelbert Ames, Jr.

. . . Mr. Sabine had charge of the collection and distribution of technical information for the Bureau of Aircraft Production while I was helping reorganize the Aeronautical Information Section of the Department of Military Aeronautics, which had a similar function. After the Armistice, I was with him on the Committee of Science and Research and Aeronautical Development, which was a sub-committee of the Board for the Organization of the Air Service on a peace basis.

Mr. Sabine was personally responsible for the Report,[1] which outlined the steps and organization for the proper development of Aeronautics and its stimulation for commercial purposes. He had a very clear and true vision of it all, and I hope the Government will have the wisdom to follow his recommendations.

It was always a pleasure to see him. With his sincerity, quiet directness, and beautiful, old-school manners, he stood out most markedly in the hectic, driving, scolding throng that was trying to carry on the business of the Air Service. He seemed almost of another age and civilization. We would have accomplished so infinitely much more if we had only had a few more men like him.

---

[1] See Appendix C.

XVI. In the Shadows · 1918–1919

Sabine's home life practically came to an end when he went abroad in June, 1916, expecting to give his Sorbonne Lectures that fall. His serious breakdown, and the enforced convalescence at Leysin; the giving of the Sorbonne Lectures from February to May, 1917; his active war work with the French, Italian, and British armies, had kept him in Europe until October, 1917. His family was with him, but they were rarely together. On his return to America, he had plunged into war work in Washington, and although in Cambridge two days every week, he scarcely saw his wife and children, who were spending the summer at Woods Hole. In November, 1918, after the Armistice, he had expected an opportunity to resume the home ties he loved so much; but within a month he went to the hospital for a preliminary operation, and two weeks later the end came.

As we have seen, his two great passions were his family and his profession; his obsession was the Great War. Up to the moment when he returned from Europe that last time, he had been able to indulge himself in both his devotions without sacrifice to either; after his return, both were denied him. So he had thrown himself, regardless of the consequences, with the zealous fanaticism of a Crusader, into the struggle to save the world from a cataclysm he knew was still to come; and, as a soldier engaged in a hazardous undertaking at the Front, the intensity of his love for those nearest and dearest, and the full consciousness of their reciprocal loyalty and affection, gave him the courage to face and accept the inevitable.

During those last years Sabine clearly showed the results of his disregard of overwork and the ravages of his disease, and it irritated him to have his wife even refer to his condition. The long period of abnormal hours had formed a habit which prevented him from sleeping even when opportunity offered. Mrs. Sabine never woke after midnight without finding him awake, and usually in his study at work. He would never take a sedative.

Few of his students were aware of the night vigils or of the strain under which he worked for so many years. Occasionally some one, more discerning than most undergraduates, would discover the fatigue he so bravely fought to conceal:

From F. A. Eustis

. . . I recall noting the tired look that so often betrayed his long hours of labor. I used to wish that he could regulate his work so as to cut out some of the nights of constant effort, that he might be fresher and more able to enjoy himself as he enabled us to enjoy our work with him. I do not mean that this operated against his work with his students; but, looking back, I am sure that during this year he was often overtired, although never would he allow bodily fatigue to alter his charming manner or his universal kindness of address.

One bright spot in this last year, 1918, was the culmination of the offer made Sabine by a wealthy Chicago business man, who was enthusiastically interested in the development of sound problems, to build for him a laboratory after his own plans, and fully equipped for definitive experimentation in his contemplated study of Sound Transmission. After so many years of labor made difficult by inadequate facilities, Sabine had welcomed the proposition with satisfaction. Out of this came the Wallace Clement Sabine Laboratory at Geneva, Illinois; but its completion was too late to afford him the opportunity he so greatly anticipated. His final illness prevented him from ever using it.

During these last months, Sabine's exhaustion made him absent-minded. He would take a second bath, only becoming aware of the repetition when he found the towel moist from previous use; he was constantly losing suit-cases on his trips to and from Washington, because he could not recall where he had left them, or locate the checks; he frequently rose from the table, believing that he had completed his meal, when he had actually eaten nothing.

No one will ever know the extent of his actual suffering, for he was a Stoic in his attitude toward pain. This characteristic came largely from his mother, who, at times in her life, endured excruciating suffering without a murmur. His inheritance of her wiry vigor, endurance, and vitality led him to disregard flagrantly the danger signals by which Nature tried to warn him.

It was natural that the odds against which Sabine was fighting should at times have made him moody, and cause his wife untold anxiety. His stubborn refusal to care for himself until too late was a continuing trial to a sympathetic and understanding woman. They rarely discussed at home the professional side of either's life. Once, when Mrs. Sabine read in the daily press that he had supervised the plans for the great auditorium at the Pan-American Exposition, she expressed surprise that he had not spoken of it. " I don't like to speak of my work while it is in progress," he replied; " and when it is done, I forget it."

Sabine's resignation from the War Department in Washington was no admission on his part that the War was over, but rather a declaration that Cambridge and Harvard University now offered him greater opportunity to continue his war services. In 1909 he had forecast the War — years before any government discerned the threatening clouds on the horizon; in January, 1917, he had written his mother from Leysin, " No worse calamity could befall the world — no more ominous event could occur in history — than peace at this moment." His experiences and observations at the Front had confirmed his convictions, and he later knew that the ill-advised Armistice, forced too soon upon the unwilling Allies by President Wilson, left dangerous embers still smouldering from which — sometime, unless checked — would blaze forth a world holocaust even more devastating. He knew that for a lasting peace and a prompt readjustment of the wounded nations it was absolutely essential that the Treaty should have been signed in Berlin.

The frenzied shouts of joy with which the war-tired people greeted the Armistice left Sabine cold. November 11, 1918, was to him the most tragic date in all history. Knowing the Germans as few Americans did, he recognized the relentlessness of Prussianism, and realized that before the German people would admit or accept defeat,[1] they must be dealt an overwhelming blow that would forever destroy their military arrogance and their unholy lust for world power. Even at the time the Armistice was signed, Sabine was about to propose to the Government at Washington a titanic scheme he had conceived for ending the War.

By Colonel Edward A. Deeds, A. S. A.

He had in mind, as I know from a hint he let fall, some desperate enterprise, which I took to be an airplane expedition on a great scale, for dropping immense quantities of high explosives in a place where they would be most likely to end the War. In 1922 I told his mother of this surmise of mine, and she appeared almost shocked, saying gently, " I should think he would have wanted to prevent that."

---

[1] While the author was billeted in Coblenz, in March, 1919, with the Second Army of Occupation, A. E. F., he conversed with many of the German people. Not one believed that Germany had received a military defeat. " Our statesmen in Berlin have blundered," they admitted; " but when did our armies ever lose a battle? "

A few days later she said to me, in the same gentle way, " I would have opened the earth and let the Germans down." Verily, the militant Quaker is a formidable figure!

Her son would have substituted the word " Prussians " for " Germans."

The creation of the Student Army Training Corps at Harvard appealed to Sabine's imagination. Here was enlisted the generation upon which the burden of reconstruction must fall as a result of what had already happened; here was the material from which the defense of the country would be drawn if his prognostications became verified. These boys required the best that he could give them of himself to fit them intellectually for what lay before them; and they also needed a first-hand picture of past, present, and future military conditions which he was so well qualified to contribute. Sabine returned to Cambridge not only as a teacher of Science but as a zealous Crusader, determined to continue his own war work in spite of what official Washington had done in accepting a return to peace conditions which he was convinced rested upon false hypotheses.

He knew himself to be a seriously sick man, but this knowledge encouraged his fanatical enthusiasm, which completely disregarded personal danger. If his time was now limited, then was the demand that much the greater that he devote such measure of his life as still remained to the great cause he served. His friends, who noticed his physical decline, urged him to think now of himself; his wife, seriously alarmed, reminded him again of Doctor Tuffier's warning that, at the slightest reappearance of the symptoms of the condition from which he had so miraculously escaped in 1916, he should submit himself to a surgical operation; his physician and devoted friend, Dr. David Cheever, wrote him (July 12, 1918) : " You are in bad shape and going down hill. I cheerfully acknowledge that you know your own affairs better than I do, but, from a purely medical or surgical point of view, I think it is only fair to say that you may be riding for a fall if you don't have this septic process attended to. I know that you are doing valuable work, and I feel that the probability of your continuing to do it for a long period would be vastly improved by your taking a few weeks now to get straightened out."

To all these pleadings, his invariable answer was, " The War is still on. There are still lives in danger." He resented the fact that he had not been of age to fight — he welcomed the thought of danger to himself.

With the opening of the college year 1918–1919, Sabine threw himself desperately into the work he had allotted to himself. He assumed again the full schedule of the college curriculum, to which he added his contributions to the military courses. It was Sabine who urged the continuance of this military education; it was Sabine who worked overtime to impress upon the students the vital importance of military knowledge; it was Sabine who drew up the Basis of Personnel on which this Student Army should be permanently organized.[2]

By Professor Edwin H. Hall

Into the work of teaching — teaching for war — he plunged with a crusading enthusiasm, quite prepared to give his life, if need be, in the effort. I tried to make him see that failure to meet a class, when he had, let us say, a temperature of 102°, was not quite so base conduct as deserting the Front in the crisis of a battle; but I made little impression on him. So long as he could stand, he would do his work. It is a pleasure to reflect that his students, if they did not prove themselves altogether worthy of his efforts in their behalf, at least did give him their admiring attention and their love.

---

[2] See Appendix D.

Any time, looking upon his spiritual, still youthful face, and noting the smiling obstinacy with which he followed a course of toil that must end his life too soon, one might be tempted to think of him as some elfin being that had taken human form in benevolent caprice, but was now planning departure and adventures new. Not that he ever, save in the very ecstasy of pain and weakness, showed any symptom of world-weariness. He was full of affection, full of the zest of life, full of plans for future years. He told me that he never enjoyed his work of teaching more than during this past fall, so trying to most of those who remained in academic life, and he had been looking forward joyfully to the prospect of resuming his work of research.

In December, 1918, Sabine consented to devote the Christmas vacation to " getting himself patched up," expressing the firm conviction that these college holidays would be sufficient to put himself in condition to go on with his work when the winter term opened. A preliminary operation was performed at the Peter Bent Brigham Hospital, in Boston, which afforded temporary relief, and he returned to his Marlborough Street home; but the college term opened without him, as he appeared to have contracted influenza — an epidemic which was raging at that time. His inability to meet his classes worried him.

From Roger Pierce

He telephoned to me in the absence of President Lowell to apologize (I can use no other word) for not being on hand for his teaching engagements. He stated in detail what the trouble with him was, and just why he was not then at Cambridge as he had expected to be. I expressed some surprise that he had recovered so quickly from the operation, to which he replied that he was not over-rugged, but was doing well enough. Afterwards I found that at the time he telephoned he was in bed with a temperature of 103°.

At the end of the conversation he made inquiries about Milton Academy, and begged that the pupils be not worked too strenuously in the attempt to make up the work that was lost by closing the school on account of the influenza. He hoped that the vacation would not be curtailed, that they would not have to work longer than the regular hours on week days or on Saturdays. I now think of this conversation in the light of his own life. He never spared himself, over-worked immorally, and was wishing for others comforts which he denied himself.

Hearing of his serious illness, Professor Hall telephoned his house for further particulars:

By Professor Edwin H. Hall

Sabine at once answered me, in a voice so cheerful and strong that my fears might have been dissipated if I had not remembered that on a previous occasion, after going home from the Laboratory unmistakably ill, he had answered my inquiries in the same way. This was, in fact, his method of censoring health bulletins relating to himself.

A day or two later, not venturing to use the telephone again, I called at his door and asked for Mrs. Sabine. Being told that I could not see her, I left my name and was turning away when I was called from within the house, and Sabine, who had heard me at the door, came halfway down the stair-way from the second story to meet me. Finding that he really wished to have a talk with me, I went to his room. He must have known his condition to be one of great danger, but evidently he was not submissive to the ordinary rules of the sick-chamber. Most of the time while I was with him he re-clined, half-sitting, on a couch, apparently taking whatever position was most tolerable, and I knew it would be useless to offer advice. In his care, or lack of care, for his own health he was now, as he had been during all the thirty years of my

MR. AND MRS. WALLACE C. SABINE IN 1918

acquaintance with him, a defier of precept, a law unto himself.

But Sabine had reached a point where he could defy the law of Nature no further. The septic condition had been allowed to run too long, and a major operation became imperative. On January 5, 1919, he returned to the Peter Bent Brigham Hospital, and two days later Doctor Cheever made the final desperate but hopeless effort to save his life.

During his last hours he remained fully conscious. He urged his wife not to call the children, who were waiting in the corridor, saying that he preferred to have their memory of him rest upon happier conditions. His chief concern seemed to be lest the nurse, who was fanning him, should become fatigued, and his final words were to urge her against overexertion.

The eulogies which followed the passing of Wallace Clement Sabine on January 10, 1919, would form a volume in themselves. From them I have selected only those which serve to summarize the broad horizon of his work, the transcendent beauty of his character, and the enduring impression made upon the world by the part he so valiantly played. The greatest difficulty the biographer has found has been to discover contrasting incidents and characteristics against which to bring out in greater clearness the amazing accomplishments, the unbelievable capacity for endurance, the extraordinary versatility of this man, whose entire life seems to have been devoted to concealing rather than revealing his capacities and achievements:

By Professor Edwin H. Hall

From his ancestry Sabine should have had long life, and he probably counted too much on this inheritance. He had lived through more than one tremendous crisis of illness, and he seemed to feel that he could brave off any attack of disease. But even if he had seen death unmistakable in his path, he would not have halted or turned aside so long as the War lasted. With all his high courage and resolution, however, and a clearness of head likely to take him in safety through difficult passes, he was no seeker of danger for its own sake, no sportsman, in the ordinary sense, no player of rough games.

We say of such a man, it is a pity he died so young. If he had taken care of himself, had been regular in his meals and in his hours of sleep, he would have had a long as well as a useful life. Yes; but a man must work according to his nature, and Sabine's temperament was not that of the ordinary man, not that of the ordinary scientific investigator. Some of the high things he did could not have been done by a man who must be regular at his meals and regular in his hours of sleep. When we remember how long the plagues he grappled with had baffled the efforts of others, and with what intensity of labor he finally exorcised them, it seems not irreverent or unfitting to recall the words: " This kind goeth not out but by prayer and fasting."

From Robert D. Andrews

There was something choice and unusual in Sabine's make-up, resembling what is admirable in fine women — a sort of spiritual rank, indefinable, yet very definite in impression. I never discovered when his capacities found their bounds. His talk and statements were of concrete facts, things within the range of ready comprehension. His feet were on the ground; his position close to that of the inquirer. The absence of any pretension to knowledge greater than his hearer's had the effect of making their relations impersonal. Because he laid aside professional authority, he exercised it the more profoundly. This explains the singular hold he had on the confidence of those with whom he worked.

From Doctor Theodore Lyman

When I passed from the classroom to the problems of my own particular research, I came to look upon Sabine as an inexhaustible spring of knowledge, and a never failing source of inspiration. He possessed one of the clearest minds that I have ever known, and he added to the power of exact thinking a most remarkable gift of clear exposition. He visualized the inter-relations of the phenomena which he discussed, and he impressed the picture on the minds of his hearers. It was, in fact, this process of visualization, this insistence on maintaining the physical reality of every step in a piece of reasoning, that chiefly characterized Sabine's methods in teaching and in research. He could never be wholly satisfied with methods which relied solely on the setting up of differential equations, and which rested content with their solutions.

No one came in contact with him without being impressed by his genius. Unfortunately, the number of such contacts embraced relatively few of his colleagues outside his own University. Modest and retiring, he never pushed himself forward at meetings of learned societies, and, toward the end of his life, he seldom even attended scientific gatherings. He persisted in affirming that his classic work in Acoustics was not Physics, and he often refused to communicate his results to those publications most read by physicists. Thus it came about that the real greatness of the man, rarely exhibited in public, was never fully nor sufficiently appreciated.

Outside the field of Acoustics, the considerable influence which he exercised on the progress of Science in this country was communicated through the high standards of the Jefferson Physical Laboratory which he helped to establish, and by the researches of his students which he inspired. His was one of the leading scientific minds of this country.

From Byron S. Hurlbert

I wish that I could give you an idea of his genuineness, his staunchness, the flash of his just wrath at anything unjust, his humor, his fun, the joy of his laughter — the things that made him so rare a man and so good a friend.

From Professor Dayton C. Miller

Four great men stand out prominently from the large group which tremendously developed the Science of Sound in the last half of the Nineteenth Century — Tyndall, Helmholtz, Koenig and Rayleigh. If we may call these men the four great pillars of the modern temple of Sound, I would add a pediment over the pillars, dedicated to Wallace Clement Sabine, whose epoch-making work on Reverberation was presented in the final year of the century. Sir J. J. Thomson said of Lord Rayleigh that he found the theory of sound bricks and left it marble. We may say of Sabine that he left the temple of Architectural Acoustics in marble, but he did not find it brick. He may have found a few pieces of rough, loose material here and there, but for the most part he had to blast his building blocks out of the solid earth.

From Barrett Wendell

His life was beautifully complete; true to the core, suffused with the modest simplicity of personal greatness, supremely conscientious, inestimably intelligent, measurelessly useful, and cloudlessly happy to remember.

From Dr. Alexis Carrel

When one realizes that it was Sabine's entire thoughtlessness of self and devotion to his country in her time of need which brought on his last illness, and prevented his undergoing the operation which would have spared him for years of further usefulness, the magnitude of his sacrifice almost overwhelms.

From LeBaron R. Briggs

There are persons in whom we believe at first sight and forever. Sabine was one of these: meeting all kinds of men, he instantly commanded their confidence; severely simply in his own life, he was admired no more warmly by the scholars in his laboratory than by men of fortune and wealth. For, quite apart from his reputation in Science, he exercised the charm of all charms — the charm of unmistakable truth. Not naturally a good speaker, he was among the best lecturers in his Department; though no lover of " society," he was a delightful companion. We hear of plain living and high thinking; rarely, if ever, do we see it more clearly than in Wallace Sabine.

From the " Harvard Crimson," January 15, 1919

It is rare for a research worker of the first rank to be also a real teacher of his subject. It is even rarer for such a man to prove that he is not a mere cultured ornament of a practical world, but a strong support in time of need. Professor Sabine was all three. Science remembers him for his studies in Acoustics. The men of the University hold him dear for those hours in Jefferson when notes and books were forgotten as " sound ghosts," and electric discharges were made real by a man who had explored all their wonders and yet had a sympathetic interest in the misunderstandings of young undergraduates. The country honors and thanks him for the lives of many soldiers saved from German batteries, located by his sound-stations.

From T. W. Richards

Our honorary classmate,[3] Wallace Sabine, was a hero. His life was sacrificed in the Great War quite as definitely as though he had been killed in the trenches. He literally gave his life for his country.

---

[3] Sabine, a graduate of Ohio State University, in the Class of 1886, was " adopted " by the Class of 1886 of Harvard University.

Devotion to a high cause was not a new factor in his life. His preëminence in Acoustics was attained by patient work in the small hours of the morning, when the complete quiet, so essential to his delicate instruments on sounds and their echoes, was attainable. The next morning, after such a night of persistent endeavor, he would always meet his students as usual with a gentle, kindly smile, giving no hint of the time of vigil. To his academic work he devoted the same conscientious and faithful attention as to scientific investigation and war work; if he ever abandoned a proposed lecture when it was within his power to be present, I have never heard of such an occurrence.

One can hardly grasp now the meaning and value of a life so full of high endeavor and rich attainment. Not only his direct contributions to Science and to the cause of the Allies, not only his long, patient, and fruitful instruction of students in the facts and principles of Physics, are destined to carry his influence far into the coming years; but also the memory of his high character, of his devoted unselfishness, and of his bravery and noble ideals, will help those who knew him to make their lives, too, truly worth while.

From Minutes of the American Physical Society

Viewed both by the scientific and practical man, there are certain outstanding features of Professor Sabine's work that mark it as of the highest order. He succeeded in solving problems which had baffled all investigators for hundreds of years; he had a peculiarly clear vision for the right kind of experimental investigation and of the best way of attacking it; when he had thought out a method, he then proceeded, with untiring energy and unending patience, to accomplish practical results of benefit.

To his colleagues, his work appeals as being constructive in the highest degree: definiteness of purpose, directness of attack, simplicity of method, and thoroughness and complete reliability of results distinguishes it throughout. To the architect, it appeals strongly because his results were always presented in a form immediately applicable to concrete and very troublesome problems.

While he held himself most rigorously to the highest standards of scientific research, and while he drove himself to the utmost of human endurance in the accomplishment of the results, yet to his associates and to his family he was the gentlest and kindest of men. He was generous to a fault. He was modest with regard to his own work, and most appreciative of that of others. He gave most freely of time and effort, which were so precious to him for study, to help all others who asked his advice. We honor him for his work and we revere him for his personal character.

From Minutes of the Harvard Faculty

Was it, then, so easy and simple a thing to do? Did Sabine merely happen to find the solution of a difficulty thousands of years old? No. He succeeded by reason of a combination of qualities, among which were unending patience and untiring energy. . . . He must work with the most scrupulous regard for conditions that to another might seem trivial. Such was the difficulty of his undertaking, on the mere physical side, and such the rigor of his devotion to it. . . . In the faithful performance of his duties he was too busy for the surgical operation which his physical condition demanded. He refused military rank, declaring, with that severity of judgment which sometimes verged upon intolerance, that the uniform should be worn only by those who were subject to the dangers and labors of the Front. But he risked his life constantly, and at last fatally, in the service of the country and the University.

From President Abbott Lawrence Lowell

Personally Sabine was ever sympathetic, kindly, and lovable, completely devoid of any selfish thought — too much so for his own interest. In fact, his neglect of himself helped to cause the malady that brought his work to an untimely end; but not until he had made contributions of enduring value to Physics and to scientific progress. His eyes were always on the great objects he cared for, and hence he was ever ready to yield in non-essentials, a quality that made it a pleasure for any one to deal with him. His was a rare nature, intent only on fulfilling a lofty purpose, and combining therewith the clarity of insight to perceive the means to its attainment.

So long as buildings continue to be built freed from haunting echoes and obedient to the will of the Master who conquered them, the name of Wallace Sabine will be remembered. So long as the War Records of four great nations remain available, the part he played in the great struggle will be found recorded. But the most enduring monument of all is that which Wallace Sabine himself unconsciously erected out of the affection and devotion of hundreds of students, whose life-work, compositely, perpetuates and continues the high principles and dynamic force he instilled in their souls.

HE CARED *not, when the call of duty came,*
To reckon how, by husbanding his power
He might make life the longer by an hour,
But rather made its quality his aim.
To Science true, indifferent to Fame,
Of manhood brave and fine the perfect flower,
Of rectitude and strength a very tower,
*   He left a priceless heritage — his name.*
O Prodigal of gifts so great and rare!
Your mind attuned to catch the sound of Truth
And make it audible to listening youth,
*   No gain you counted that you could not share.*

Thus having lived, how else could he have died
Who loved his fellow-men all else beside!

[JEROME D. GREENE]

APPENDIX A (*page* 165)

SABINE's plans for organization of the Harvard Graduate School of Applied Science, published in the " Harvard Graduates' Magazine " (June, 1906) :

For a long time it has been the wish of many that the technical scientific work of the University should be organized in a Graduate School, and raised to the level of the work in the Law and Medical Schools. This was frequently expressed during the recent discussion of the merger with Technology, and such ultimate destiny for the Lawrence Scientific School was particularly urged by those who were opposed to the merger. Since the failure of the negotiations, the plan has commended itself generally. It has, however, come more quickly than many believed possible.

For four years at least the present organization and programs of the Lawrence Scientific School will be continued, if for no other reason than to provide the instruction and degrees offered, practically promised, by the University to the students now in attendance. But, as Dean Shaler wrote in one of the last circular letters that he prepared, " Although students who so desire may continue to follow the present four-year programs leading to the degree of B.S. in a designated field of study, it is expected that the usual course of the student who wishes to prepare himself for a scientific profession will be to spend three, three and a half, or four years in Harvard College as a candidate for the degree of Bachelor of Arts or of Bachelor of Science, adopting his choice of courses to his projected studies in the Graduate School of Applied Science, where he will obtain his specialized professional training."

As in the Law and Medical Schools, the sole requirement for admission to the Graduate School of Applied Science will be a bachelor's degree from a college or scientific school of good standing. But at this point the simplicity in the conditions under which the Law and Medical Schools proceed cease in the Graduate School of Applied Science. The latter is embarrassed by two circumstances. In the Schools of Law and Medicine, practically none of the entering students has anticipated any of the work of the schools, and the requirement of a degree is intended rather to insure capacity and breadth of training than specific attainments. The student-bodies in these two schools are thus comparatively homogeneous. In the Graduate School of Applied Science, on the other hand, it is inevitable that the students should vary greatly in their preparation. This arises from the fact that the work in Applied Science is more closely dependent on the subjects ordinarily taught in undergraduate departments. Work in Engineering is closely dependent on courses in Mathematics; Mining, Metallurgy, Forestry, and Applied Chemistry, Biology, and Geology are dependent on courses in Pure Science; while Architecture depends on courses in the Fine Arts. It follows that the entering students will vary and vary greatly in their scientific preparation to pursue the graduate work. This more or less embarrassing situation is still further increased by the fact that many really technical courses will probably be open to the undergraduates in Harvard College.

The several departments in the Graduate School have prepared statements of the specific preparation necessary for doing the work regularly outlined for the two years in the Graduate School. Any holder of the bachelor's degree may enter the Graduate School, but if seriously deficient in this special preparation it will take him longer than two years to secure the degree. The opportunity to secure this preparation will be supplied by courses in Harvard College, the student in the meantime, however, being registered in the Graduate School. On the other hand, a student, who, because of excessive specialization as an undergraduate in some technical school or college, has not only fulfilled the expected preparation but has in part anticipated the work of the Graduate School, may secure the degree in less than two years of study.

Indeed, this is the weakness of the whole scheme. The central idea in placing the technical work of the University in a graduate school was to combine the breadth of an ordinary college education with a concentrated technical training. In the required programs in the Lawrence Scientific School and in other scientific schools, a certain amount of collateral work is prescribed in Mathematics beyond that absolutely necessary for the technical work in Modern Languages, in Economics, and in the Pure Sciences. None of this work being here forescribed, it may happen that a graduate of this school may be a much more narrowly trained man than a graduate of almost any other technical school. Of course, it is hoped that this will not occur, and some of the departments of the Graduate School have placed such restrictions around their courses as to discourage, if not prevent it, but this is not generally the case.

It is proposed to offer in the Graduate School the following degrees: Bachelor in Civil Engineering, Bachelor in Mechanical Engineering, Bachelor in Electrical Engineering, Mining Engineering, Metallurgical Engineering, Bachelor in Architecture, Bachelor in Landscape Architecture, Master in Forestry, Master of Science in Chemistry, Master of Science in Biology, and Master of Science in Geology. Recommendations for the several degrees will originate with the several departments, each department determining its own method of testing the candidates' qualifications.

Finally, it may be added that it is intended that departmental organization shall be particularly strong in the Graduate School. The nature of the central organization has not yet been determined. The administration for the present is in the hands of a committee which was formerly the Committee on Studies in the Lawrence Scientific School, its functions and title having been enlarged. The Chairman of this Committee, when the administration of the Graduate School was referred to it, was, of course, Dean Shaler. Its present Chairman is Professor H. L. Warren.

The vote establishing the Graduate School also established in Harvard College the degree of Bachelor of Science, to be given on terms as liberal with regard to choice of studies as those governing the degree of Bachelor of Arts. The number of courses which will be required for the two degrees will be the same, and there will be the same restrictions in regard to the maximum and minimum number of courses that may be taken in one year. The two degrees may thus be obtained in the same length of time, in three, three and a half, or four years. The essential difference between the two degrees will be in the terms of admission. A knowledge of elementary Latin will not be required for admission to the freshman class of students intending to be candidates for the degree of Bachelor of Science, and their choice of electives in the admission examinations will be from a little greater list than the list available to students intending to be candidates for the degree of Bachelor of Arts. The admission requirements for students intending to become candidates for the degree of Bachelor of Science more nearly fit the usual high school curriculum, and make it possible for a much larger number of high schools to prepare their pupils for admission to regular standing in Harvard College than when such admission was open only to candidates for the degree of Bachelor of Arts.

APPENDIX B (*page 271*)

Extracts from Sabine's Report to the Rockefeller Foundation on the tuberculosis situation in France:

In considering the advisability of the Rockefeller Foundation aiding in the fight on tuberculosis in France, only incidental consideration need be given to the gravity of the problem, always and everywhere great, or as to whether the undertaking is appropriate to the Rockefeller Foundation, for obviously it is in line with some of the best work that the Foundation has done. The question is rather as to whether the conditions in France are such that especially large results may be expected in the country at a critical moment, and as to whether there is here the possibility of general results by enlarging the knowledge, if not of the disease itself, then of its therapeutic treatment and of the best methods of disseminating this knowledge and of persuading to or enforcing its mandates. The following report will therefore lay emphasis on certain features of the situation which would otherwise be of minor importance. . . .

All the hospitals and sanatoria in and near Paris, in which tuberculosis patients are treated, were visited under the guidance of Dr. Letulle and Monsieur Maurice Lazard, the solicitor for Baron de Rothschild, and the very extensive sanatorium and École du Soleil of Dr. Rollier at Leysin, in Switzerland, under Dr. Rollier's escort.

The statistics in regard to tuberculosis in France are admittedly far from satisfactory. The best figures available are those prepared recently for presentation to the Chamber of Deputies. They show that, in 1912, out of a general mortality in France of 692,768, the number of deaths due to tuberculosis was 83,783, and that of these the number due to pulmonary tuberculosis was 69,731. The deaths due to pulmonary tuberculosis were thus a little over 10% of the total number of deaths, the corresponding figures for other countries being: Germany, 8.3%, England, 7.2%, and Belgium, 6.2%. The number of deaths by pulmonary tuberculosis per 1000 inhabitants was 1.30% against 1.04% in England. This report also stated that the percentage of deaths due to tuberculosis of persons aged between 20 and 39 was in the same year 44.

No similar figures are available for the conditions since the war began, but there can be no doubt that the deaths by tuberculosis have greatly increased. In the absence of systematically collected statistics one must rely on the impression formed by the medical, governmental, and military authorities, and on the logic of the situation. Governmental and military opinions may be eliminated as unreliable. To both of these groups of officials the problem of tuberculosis is presented practically for the first time, and comparisons of conditions before and during the war are therefore out of the question. Moreover, the financial burden and the loss in military efficiency naturally exaggerate the problem, the one to one, the other to the other group of officials. Medical opinion, however, is clear and strong that there has been a very great increase in tuberculosis.

The logic of the situation bears this out. The sudden call to national defense has brought into the service and has put under conditions of strain and exposure men whose physique is not able to stand the strain, and who in consequence contract a new or develop an incipient or quite recent infection. Many of these men, broken in health, have been rejected into civil life from the preliminary training. Others, standing the strain longer, have been sent back in advanced stages of tuberculosis from active service.

It is further to be noted that modern trench warfare, with its life in underground, close, and crowded, bomb-proof dugouts, is very unlike open air campaigns, and favorable in the extreme for the propagation of this contagion. The statement, made over and over again, that 90% of the *reformés* (mustered out) are dangerously tuberculous, seems at first incredible, but may be true.

In 1903 there was established a *Commission Permanente de Preservation contre la Tuberculose* under the presidency of M. Leon Bourgeois. By the statement of its officers, this commission was able to accomplish little or nothing, because of the indifference and inertia of the people. The committee endeavored to make the reporting of cases of tuberculosis obligatory, but this was resisted by a portion of the medical profession in a manner not unfamiliar in America with certain types of disease, although readily accepted in others. Through the efforts of this commission a few sanatoria were established, but probably its own measure of its success may be accepted as just. The secretary of this committee gives the total number of sanatoria in France open to tuberculosis as 12, against 1500 similar institutions in Germany.

Shortly after the outbreak of the war the problem of tuberculosis rapidly changed from being while grave yet met with indifference, to one which still more grave was met in an equally dangerous manner, with panic and alarm. The direct problems of the war were so great that France was hardly in a position to cope with this literally, decimating menace. The Government first thought to cope with it directly. In the spring of 1915 it called on the departments and communes to turn over to the military authorities all hospitals and sanatoriums available for tuberculosis, to be used entirely for the treatment of soldiers. The number of beds thus available, 6000, was hopelessly inadequate, and the time given to any one tuberculous soldier was reduced to three months. The following fall the Government appropriated the sum of two million francs for the assistance of the *militaires tuberculeux.*

Now, almost in despair, the Government has turned the whole problem over to a privately organized but officially recognized committee, the *Comité Central d'Assistance aux Militaires Tuberculeux.* This committee, of which also M. Leon Bourgeois is president, has for the time being practically succeeded the *Commission Permanente de Preservation contre la Tuberculose.* Under this organization the tuberculous are distributed as a burden on their respective departments and communes. The *Comité Central* is endeavoring to organize in the several departments and communes committees which in general are for the care and financial relief of the dependent military *reformés.* The *Comité Central* acts in an advisory capacity to the *Comités Departmentaux,* distributes among them the very slender resources which it may have at its command, and in general seeks to distribute, equalize, and alleviate where possible the burden.

One aspect of recent developments should not be lost sight of. Incomprehensible as it may seem, absolutely the whole effort in France at the present moment is devoted to *militaires tuberculeux.* This is shown in many ways. The old *Commission Permanente de Preservation contre la Tuberculose* is practically extinct, and has been supplanted by the *Comité Central d'Assistance aux Militaires Tuberculeux.* The few beds in the City Hospital for tuberculous patients are occupied wholly by soldiers. The only sanatorium in the neighborhood of Paris, that at Bligny, with two large buildings, originally one for men and one for women, is occupied, both buildings, wholly by soldiers. The departmental committees, which are being organized throughout France under the *Comité Central,* have taken over the local hospitals and sanatoria, and concern themselves also wholly with the *militaires tuberculeux.* Of course the private enterprises in Paris by the Americans and others are wholly directed to the soldiers and *reformés,* for in France this is the only road at the present moment to attention and recognition. Finally, all the applications for aid by the Rockefeller Foundation are related to the *militaires tuberculeux,* and efforts to give to the question its true proportions meet with but momentary attention and but partial comprehension.

This military aspect of the problem took an extreme form in an argument advanced in behalf of aid from the Rockefeller Foundation in the statement that soldiers being still under army discipline, could be subjected to any desired treatment. It is at least open to question, if indeed the negative is not clear, whether the Rockefeller Foundation can with propriety concern itself with soldiers until after their discharge. The restoration of a soldier to military service is a questionable neutrality — and also a questionable charity. But, altogether aside from this, the treatment merely of the *militaires tuberculeux,* without reference to the great civil reservoir of infection, to say nothing of the fact that women and children are at least worthy of equal attention and help, would be, to characterize it mildly, ineffective. It is a terrible statement to make, that at the present time there are no hospitals or sanatoria in France open to women and children for a disease that accounts for one-tenth of the deaths. This is not the form in which the French ordinarily state the situation, but it is a fact. . . .

As indicated by the high death-rate of tuberculosis, the methods of living in France are favorable to its spread. The closed windows by night and day, and the general avoidance of fresh air, are well known. The remedy of this will be extremely difficult, for it is based not merely on the habit and temperament of the people, but on the construction of their buildings and the methods of heating.

The medical profession professes familiarity with the literature of other countries in regard to tuberculosis treatment. If so, it is unique among the sciences of France, for French science is peculiarly independent of others. Dr. Letulle at least is very frank in saying that, while they may possess the literature, they have no first-hand knowledge of American practice. Their hospitals and sanatoriums bear this out. For example, the sanatorium at Bligny is placed in the midst of a grove of trees, and while its beds are well exposed to the southern sun on open porches, the patients who are able to walk wander all day long under dense and damp foliage. The larger sanatorium at Angicourt is even worse placed. Neither is maintained in a sanitary condition according to standards elsewhere. It is a common remark that none of the French hospitals is clean in the American sense.

Your Commission has investigated the very great work now going on at Leysin in Switzerland. This important cure is high on the southern slope of a mountain, forming one side of a small valley that runs off from the valley of the Rhone a few miles above, where it empties into the Lake of Geneva. The conditions here of sun and air are very unusual. Some fifteen years ago a number of hotels were established at Leysin as sanatoria for the air-cure of tuberculosis in the American sense. Twelve years ago Dr. Rollier, of Lausanne, established a clinic for the treatment of tuberculosis by exposure to the sun. Since then his work has grown to enormous proportions, and is well and most favorably known to the whole German medical profession. At the present time he has fifteen hundred patients, many of them, indeed most of them, in free or nearly free clinics. The cures which he has accomplished, not merely in children but in adult cases and in cases of long standing, are remarkable.

On this visit to the various clinics of Dr. Rollier there were seen probably over a thousand cases of tuberculosis, including all its very varied forms, and in all stages of cure by the sun-treatment alone, wholly without operation — extreme cases of Potts disease, made quite straight without operation or jackets, coxalgie, tuberculous fistules and ulcers, peritoneal tuberculosis, glandular tuberculosis in all forms, all making remarkable progress or approaching remarkable cures.

There is much for America to learn from this work of Dr. Rollier, and if it were possible to find in America a place offering conditions similar, or sufficiently similar to those at Leysin, it would be a tremendous contribution to American medical practice to establish such an institution. Certain it is that the message from American practice to France in regard to the treatment of tuberculosis, while very necessary and of more general applicability, would nevertheless be but partial if the Foundation were to ignore this work of Dr. Rollier.

American practice, varying of course with conditions, is generally available, and involves large principles of hygiene which must gradually enter into the daily life of a people. It is thus the larger problem. But the work of Dr. Rollier is of tremendous significance, not merely in the result which it accomplishes, but in the very searching insight which it affords into the essential nature of the therapy of tuberculosis.

For the Foundation to widen the scope of its undertaking, and to include with American practice this distinctly Swiss practice — and not merely to make its endeavor international, but to make its source of medical intelligence also international, would not only be of wider ultimate value, but would have many peculiar advantages in the present case.

The French wish — the Government, the medical profession, and the men of public affairs wish the financial aid of the Rockefeller

Foundation. In a vague way they believe that America has some standards of practice to offer. On the other hand, they are scientifically a self-contained and a sensitive people. As countrymen of Pasteur, they are not unnaturally peculiarly sensitive under suggestions of hygiene. The sting of this would be removed if the Foundation were to send not a representative of American practice, but an international commission, very small — only so large that it might be regarded and possibly be called international. This commission might, in addition to serving France, undertake to investigate the best method for any national endeavor against tuberculosis. For such a problem France would be an admirable laboratory. Two years ago tuberculosis in France was greater than in any other country of western Europe; since then it has greatly increased. It is practically without institutions to prejudice the undertaking; and the country includes within its limits almost the whole gamut of conditions from the low, cold, and damp conditions of the north, to the high, dry, and clear atmosphere to be found at places in the Haute Savoie or perhaps even better in the Pyrenees.

Such a commission should have at least three medical representations, one from France, as a matter of course, one from America, and one from some other country, and should include one layman. It should be directly responsible to the Foundation. If it were to be given affiliation in France, it should be with the *Commission Permanente de Preservation contre la Tuberculose*. It should not be concerned with the *militaires tuberculeux* especially, but with the problem as a whole, thus also for women and children, and the equal balance of its endeavor should be clearly defined in the beginning. It should be made clear and public that the recommendation of the Commission will be followed if possible by the financial support of model institutions. It should also be made clear that an important factor in any equipment is the element of cost, and that the measure of its value is in part at least the ratio of cost to the results obtained. . . .

APPENDIX C (*page 322*)

Sabine's Report outlining the steps and organization for the proper development of Aeronautics and its stimulation for commercial purposes:

[*November 30, 1918*]

MEMORANDUM for the Chairman of the Board on Organization
  Subject: Report of the Committee on Invention and Research

The Committee appointed " to study and recommend a permanent organization for peace times on matters of invention, research, and so forth, in connection with the work of the Air Service," begs to report as follows:

The Committee in presenting its recommendations can not do better than quote from the instructions given it: " It is important that the American Air Service should lead the world in progress. A strong and comprehensive plan of organization is therefore necessary. The Scope " of the work of this Committee " is wide, and includes everything that could help in creating an organization along these lines."

The report is presented in two parts:

1. Existing organizations, as materials out of which a new organization may be constructed.

2. A suggested plan of organization.

I. Existing Organizations for Inventions and Research

The National Advisory Committee for Aeronautics

The National Advisory Committee for Aeronautics was established by Act of Congress, No. 271, 63d Congress, approved March 3, 1915:

" An Advisory Committee for Aeronautics is hereby established, and the President is authorized to appoint not to exceed twelve members, to consist of two members from the War Department, from the office in charge of military aeronautics; two members from the Navy Department, from the office in charge of naval aeronautics; a representative each of the Smithsonian Institution, of the United States

Weather Bureau, and of the United States Bureau of Standards; together with not more than five additional persons who shall be acquainted with the needs of Aeronautical Science, either civil or military, or skilled in aeronautical engineering or its allied sciences: Provided, That the members of the Advisory Committee for Aeronautics, as such, shall serve without compensation: Provided further, That it shall be the duty of the Advisory Committee for Aeronautics to supervise and direct the scientific study of the problems of flight, with a view to their practical solution, and to determine the problems which should be experimentally attacked, and to discuss their solution and their application to practical questions. In the event of a laboratory or laboratories, either in whole or in part, being placed under the direction of the committee, the committee may direct and conduct research and experiment in aeronautics and such laboratory or laboratories: And Provided further, That rules and regulations for the conduct of the work of the committee shall be formulated by the committee and approved by the President."

The National Advisory Committee has fostered research work in aeronautical problems before America entered the war, and has continued these at the Bureau of Standards, and in its own laboratories at Langley Field, as well as at Leland Stanford University. It has passed on all aeronautical inventions referred to it by the Board at the War College, having primary survey, by the Bureau of Standards, by the Aircraft Board, and by the Navy Department, in all some seven thousand inventions.

BUREAU OF STANDARDS

The Bureau of Standards serves the same purpose in America as the Reichenstalt in Germany, and the National Physical Laboratory in England. The present equipment of the Reichenstalt is not known, but the National Physical Laboratory has eight wind tunnels, all actively engaged in aeronautical problems. The Bureau of Standards has but one wind tunnel, and that a small one. It has, however, an almost unique institution in its high altitude laboratory for the testing of motors under conditions of temperature and barometric pressure, corresponding to the high altitudes of modern aviation. Indeed, it has appropriations from the Bureau of Aircraft Production for the construction of two more such laboratories. It also has unexcelled equipment for the testing of aeronautical instruments, and has placed its general facilities freely at the disposal of the Air Service.

SCIENCE AND RESEARCH

The Division of Science and Research was created shortly after America entered the war, first in the Signal Corps, and later in the

Bureau of Aircraft Production. It has suffered from not having had at any time a clearly defined relationship to either of these organizations, or a clear definition of its powers and responsibilities. It has suffered, also, from the fact that it has had no laboratories of its own, and only such facilities for work in the way of space and apparatus as it could, from time to time, arrange at Langley Field, at the Bureau of Standards, at the laboratories of the Carnegie Institute in Pittsburgh, and in college and university laboratories.

Of even greater importance are the institutions outside of Washington:

MC COOK FIELD AT DAYTON, OHIO

The work accomplished by the Experimental Department at McCook Field in plane and engine design, in the synchronizing of guns, and in other problems of a similar nature has been greater than in all other American organizations together. In this organization there will be much to be retained, both in form and personnel.

LANGLEY FIELD AT HAMPTON, VIRGINIA

In the summer of 1917, it was the intention that Langley Field should be the great research institution for the Bureau of Aircraft Production. To this end it is only partially developed. It has many natural advantages, arising from its great area, and nearness to the water. It is, however, inconvenient to reach. This is a considerable disadvantage; however, from a military standpoint there is a certain compensation arising from its privacy and possible secrecy. On this field a large sum of money has already been spent, looking toward a permanent aviation post, with special reference to experimental engineering, and technical and scientific research.

TECHNICAL SECTIONS

There are two Technical Sections belonging to the Division of Military Aeronautics, the Technical Section at Dayton, and the Technical Section with the American Expeditionary Forces in France.

THE TECHNICAL SECTION AT DAYTON

This section is the acceptance section for designs, sample planes and instruments, and the planes and instruments in production. It also has charge of the files of technical data. Its headquarters are in Dayton; its acceptance park is at the Wilbur Wright Field.

THE TECHNICAL SECTION, A.E.F., FRANCE

This section is a well developed organization operating with Production Center No. 2 and with the active American Expeditionary Forces. It is in very close touch, not merely with all the aeronautical problems of the front as they develop under actual fighting conditions, but with the Technical Sections of England, France, and Italy. It is probably in closer touch with the problems and accomplishments of each of these sections than they are with each other. It has its own laboratories and its own experts.

The above are the governmental organizations now engaged in handling inventions and scientific and technical research. Besides these there are the great technical and scientific laboratories of the country whose efforts and whose facilities were by no means adequately developed or called upon in the emergency just passed, where many problems properly placed could have been quickly solved; one of our great mistakes has been the failure to properly inspire and utilize these facilities.

II. RECOMMENDATIONS IN REGARD TO ORGANIZATION

It is the belief of the Committee that general aeronautical development could be best furthered by a centralized control of all aeronautics, both military and non-military. In view of the lack of such control, and in consideration of the existing governmental organizations, the Committee begs to submit the following general recommendations:

1. That there be established a permanent Technical Section of the Air Service, to which will be submitted all inventions for judgment in regard to their military value, which shall have charge of research relating to scientific and technical problems of a military nature in aircraft engine and plane designs, armament, instruments and accessories; that this Section shall be liberally equipped with personnel, laboratories, machine shops and testing fields. Attached hereto, marked "Appendix A" is a plan showing the organization and activities of the Technical Section. The personnel required would be as follows: 100 officers, 100 enlisted men, 300 civilians. These figures do not include the military organizations necessary for the proper running of the Post where the laboratories and testing fields are to be established.

2. That the Air Service look to the National Advisory Committee for Aeronautics for the solution of problems relating to scientific and technical research other than military, also for the commercial development of aeronautics, the continual output by universities and technical schools of scientifically and technically trained specialists, and the reference to research laboratories connected with industrial institutions of special aeronautical problems. That the National Advisory Committee for Aeronautics be continued in its laboratories, with even increased facilities, on the fields which are

under the jurisdiction of the Technical Section, and in close connection with it. Attached hereto marked " Appendix B " is a brief statement of the activities and functions of the National Advisory Committee for Aeronautics drawn up by said Committee for the purpose of being attached to this report.

3. The Bureau of Standards, a permanent Government organization, will by its very nature continue to serve in the future as it has in the past.

4. The Division of Science and Research should disappear with the close of the war, but in its personnel, valuable officers may be found for the Technical Section. Officers should be retained for the completion of a number of the problems on which they are at present engaged.

The following more specific recommendations are submitted:

5. That the Chief of the Air Service and the Chief of the Technical Section should be the Army representatives on the National Advisory Committee for Aeronautics.

6. That there be Aeronautical attachés connected with the American Embassies and Ministries in Europe.

7. That from the technical data now in the various departments and from that received in the future from the aeronautical attachés should such be created, there be formed at least three libraries of technical aeronautical information: One connected with the Technical Section, one with the Smithsonian Institution and one with the National Advisory Committee for Aeronautics; that at least one of these libraries be so organized as to care for the proper distribution of its material in response to outside inquiries, and to encourage to the greatest possible degree the commercial development of aeronautics. It is desirable that all these libraries should be supplied with original documents.

8. That the Bulletin of the Engineering Department, which has already reached several numbers, should be continued by the Technical Section, as far as possible under its present organization and personnel. It has established an excellent practice of publishing the work of the department and re-editing foreign material. With the cessation of war conditions, this Bulletin should be given a greatly increased circulation.

9. That in the organization of the Technical Section careful consideration should be given to the present personnel of McCook Field, of the American Technical Section, and the Technical Section with the American Expeditionary Forces in France, to the end that the best officers in each should be persuaded to remain in the service. Each of the three has had its unique experience, and this occasion of demobilization and re-organization permits a choice of personnel which should not be lost, and which may not again recur.

Finally, this Committee desires to place itself on record as believing that the officers of the Technical Section of the Air Service in France should take part in planning the organization of the permanent Technical Section. This Committee, not recently conversant with the work of the Technical Sections of France, should not attempt to make further recommendations than the above, which look to the immediate necessities.

APPENDIX D (*page 328*)

Sabine's Basis of Personnel for the permanent organization of the Student Army:

The personnel of this service should be of three classes, officers, mechanics, and enlisted men as laborers.

The service demanded of the mechanics and of the enlisted men will be such as to call for no special training in advance, or at least only such training as must be given on the specific machinery. Only the training of officers is here considered.

These cadet candidates for training as officers should all be of some collegiate training.

So far as possible they should be selected from those who have had the R.O.T.C. training. For the past year or two there have been maintained in a number of American colleges and technical schools, at the present moment to the number of seventy-three, intensive instruction in military science and drill. In some of these institutions this work has been admirably given. These students have had military drill, including target practice, and three weeks of trench work; they have had experience in map reading and map making, in meteorology and in military science and tactics. This is, of course, not sufficient for the purpose in hand, but it is an excellent foundation on which to build. Aside from its value as training and consequent shortening of the preparation of an efficient corps of men, it has for the present purpose some value as a guarantee of the earnestness of the young men and of their sincere desire to serve the country. It will have the advantage of protecting this service from those who seek to enter it from curiosity.

In order to test this out thoroughly, a single R.O.T.C. corps, the largest in the country, has been analyzed with great care with the aid of the commanding officers. Of the 950 members of this Reserve Officers Training Corps, 88 stood out as preëminently qualified for this service on the basis of their work in the field under instruction and under examination. Of these 88, 60 were twenty years of age and over, that is, between twenty and twenty-one; practically all over twenty-one in the university had enlisted. The commanding officers were clearly of the opinion that to get any considerable proportion of these 88 they would have to be assured of active service at the front. As it is, they all may look forward with reasonable certainty to be acceptable candidates for officers' commissions in the infantry service on reaching the age of twenty-one. No attempt has been made, of course, to sound the members of the Corps themselves. But the officers are of the opinion that if it could be made clear that this would be a quick route to active service at the front, three quarters of these 88 men would thereby be persuaded to enter this service. Only the promise of an immediate service, say in five or six months, can counter-balance the necessary lack of precision as to the nature of that service. This is a difficulty in the organization of the personnel which I did not fully realize in advance.

While admission to this service should be in the main from the Reserve Officers' Training Corps, it should not be strictly so limited. But in the beginning at least, the drawing from men from without this Corps should be the exception rather than the rule, and should be justified by some obvious qualification. For example, in the institution having the above Officers' Training Corps, there can be found some ten or twelve men who for the past year, instead of being in the Corps, have been doing ambulance service at the front. It is the opinion even of the officers, that the year's experiences in the trenches of these men would be of great value as a stimulus to the others. Moreover, there are certain men doing scientific and engineering work in the university who, while they have not been in the R.O.T.C., nevertheless wish to enter the active service, and while perhaps lacking military training, nevertheless have other qualifications especially fitting them for the service.

Finally, even after the application of these general requirements, the men should be selected for the service on the basis of a personal interview and examination.

In view of all this, some leeway should be allowed in the physical examination, if the best men are always to be obtained.

The good men in the R.O.T.C. are practically sure of a commission on entering the service. To attract them into this special Service it will be necessary to give them similar assurance.

APPENDIX E. MEMBERSHIPS AND HONORARY DEGREES

AMERICAN PHYSICAL SOCIETY
(Council, 1908–1911, Board of Editors " The Physical Review,"
1916–1918, Vice President, 1918)
AMERICAN ASSOCIATION FOR THE ADVANCEMENT OF SCIENCE
(Chairman Section of Physics, 1906, Vice President, 1907)
AMERICAN ACADEMY OF ARTS AND SCIENCES
(Fellow)
NATIONAL ACADEMY OF SCIENCE
AMERICAN INSTITUTE OF ARCHITECTS
(Corresponding Member)
WASHINGTON ACADEMY OF SCIENCES

Doctor of Science, Brown University, 1907
Doctor of Science, Harvard University, 1914

[In conferring the degree at the Harvard Commencement in 1914,
President Lowell said: " Wallace Clement Sabine, physicist and
administrator; a generous spirit, solicitous only for the public good;
who has traced in Science the waves of sound, with a mind attuned
to nature and a soul in harmony with men."]

APPENDIX F. PUBLICATIONS

" Sabine's publications are not extensive, as compared with those of many others. This is partly due to the fact that he could not spare time from his experimental work, but largely due to his most severe standard of what a research paper should be. ' It should describe some piece of work so well and completely done that no one would ever have to investigate this particular matter again.' To this standard he held true, with the result that his published papers were remarkably few and remarkably significant." (From the Minutes of the American Physical Society.)

WAVE LENGTHS OF METALLIC SPECTRA IN THE ULTRA-VIOLET. (With John Trowbridge.) (Proc. Amer. Acad. of Arts and Sciences, vol. xxiii, 1887–1888, pp. 288–296.)

SELECTIVE ABSORPTION OF METALS FOR ULTRA-VIOLET LIGHT. (With John Trowbridge.) (Proc. Amer. Acad. of Arts and Sciences, vol. xxiii, 1887–1888, pp. 299–300.)

ON THE USE OF STEAM IN SPECTRUM ANALYSIS. (With John Trowbridge.) (Amer. Jour. of Science, 1888.)

ELECTRICAL OSCILLATIONS IN AIR. (With John Trowbridge.) (Proc. Amer. Acad. of Arts and Sciences, vol. xxv, 1889–1890, pp. 109–123.)

A STUDENT'S MANUAL OF A LABORATORY COURSE IN PHYSICAL MEASUREMENTS. (Ginn & Company, 1893.)

ACOUSTICS, REFLECTOR, RESONANCE, SOUND, SOUNDING BOARD, WHISPERING GALLERIES. (In Sturgis' ' Dictionary of Architecture and Building,' and the ' International Encyclopedia.')

ABSORBING POWER OF WALL SURFACES. (Proc. Amer. Inst. of Architects, 1898.)

ARCHITECTURAL ACOUSTICS. (Amer. Arch. and Bldg. News, 1900.)

REVERBERATION. (The Amer. Architect, 1900. Copied in French in the Journal de Physique, and in German in Winkelmann's Handbook der Physik.)

THE ACCURACY OF MUSICAL TASTE IN REGARD TO ARCHITECTURAL ACOUSTICS. THE VARIATION IN REVERBERATION WITH VARIATION IN PITCH. (Proc. Amer. Acad. of Arts and Sciences, vol. xlii, No. 2, June, 1906.)

THE OPTICAL ADVANTAGES OF THE ULTRA-VIOLET MICROSCOPE. (Jour. of Med. Research, 1906.)

MELODY AND ORIGIN OF THE MUSICAL SCALE. (Vice-presidential address, Section B, Amer. Association for the Advancement of Science, Chicago, 1907.)

EFFECTS OF AIR CURRENTS AND OF TEMPERATURE. (Engineering Record, June, 1910.)

SENSE OF LOUDNESS. (Contributions from the Jefferson Physical Laboratory, vol. viii, 1910.)

THE CORRECTION OF ACOUSTICAL DIFFICULTIES. (The Architectural Quarterly of Harvard University, March, 1912.)

THEATRE ACOUSTICS. (The American Architect, vol. civ, December 31, 1913.)

BUILDING MATERIAL AND MUSICAL PITCH. (The Brickbuilder, vol. xxiii, No. 1, January, 1914.)

ARCHITECTURAL ACOUSTICS. (Journal of the Franklin Institute, January, 1915.)

INSULATION OF SOUND. (The Brickbuilder, vol. xxiv, No. 2, February, 1915.)

WHISPERING GALLERIES. (Collected Papers on Acoustics, Harvard University Press, 1922.)

NOTE ON MEASUREMENTS OF THE INTENSITY OF SOUND AND ON THE REACTION OF THE ROOM UPON THE SOUND. (Appendix to Collected Papers on Acoustics.)

Note. The " Collected Papers on Acoustics," published by the Harvard University Press in 1922, contains most of Sabine's writings on Architectural Acoustics enumerated above.

INDEX

INDEX

ABSORPTION, 104, 106, 112, 113; tests made by W. C. S. in, 117–124, 173; coefficients of, 178

Absorptive coefficients, 249, 250

Abstemiousness, attitude of W. C. S. toward, 92

Academy of Music, the, Philadelphia, 140

Acoustical Science and Engineering, birth of, 44. *See* Architectural Acoustics

"Acoustics," paper written by W. C. S. on, 128

Acoustics, theoretical, 105. *See* also Architectural Acoustics

Adams, Charles Francis, 2d, 155

Adams, Henry, 51

Advisor, attitude of W. C. S. toward position of, 56

Aero-dynamics, W. C. S. one of best authorities on, 313

Aeronautics, early interest of W. C. S. in, 199; war-work of W. C. S. in, 297–299, 307–322; report of W. C. S. on proper development of, 350. *See* also Airplanes, Aircraft

Africa, development of musical scale in, 176

Agadir settlement, the, 198

Agassiz, Louis, 8

Aircraft problems, W. C. S. "claims least, knows most about," 316

Airplane, Wilbur Wright's, 199

Airplane construction, W. C. S. and, 314

Airplanes, interest of W. C. S. in, 199; experiences of W. C. S. in, 304. *See* also Bombing Planes

Air Service, the, A. E. F., W. C. S. serves with Bureau of Research of, 296; W. C. S. appointed assistant to Col. Gorrell, 296

Air space, 182

Airy, Sir George Biddell, 36

"Akousticos Felt," 193, 243

"Akoustolith," 208

Albert Hall, London, 246, 249

Alcyone Literary Society, the, 21

Allen and Collens, 183; letter from W. C. S. to, 237

Allied Armies, the, W. C. S. in touch with, 297, 308, 313

America, development of musical scale in, 176; attitude in the War of, 286, 288, 303

American Academy of Arts and Sciences, the, W. C. S. elected to, 69; 177, 180

"American Architect and Building News," the, quoted, 105, 107, 109, 112, 113, 115, 116, 118, 119, 122, 211, 248

American Association for the Advancement of Science, the, 3, 174, 175

American College of Surgeons, the, 252

American Institute of Architects, the, W. C. S. speaks before, 128

American Navy, the, information department of, W. C. S. serves with, 296

American Physical Society, the, Minutes of, quoted, 336

American Scientific Commission, the, in the War, 292

Ames, Capt. Adelbert, Jr., quoted, 322

Ames, Winthrop, 192; quoted, 224, 225, 226

Amherst Agricultural College, 169

Anderson, Newton M., 16; influence on W. C. S. of, 18; 38; letter to W. C. S. from, 164

Andrews, Robert D., quoted, 332

Animal vision, interest of W. C. S. in, 212

Anti-aircraft guns, English, work of W. C. S. with, 301

Antioch College, 7

Apparatus, designed by W. C. S., 43, 44, 50; extreme simplicity of, 116; 220, 222, 236, 255, 308, 309

Architects, work of W. C. S. with, 148, 149, 183, 222, 224, 233, 235, 240, 242